THE UTOPIA

OF

SIR THOMAS MORE

𝕷𝖔𝖓𝖉𝖔𝖓

HENRY FROWDE

OXFORD UNIVERSITY PRESS WAREHOUSE
AMEN CORNER, E.C.

𝕹𝖊𝖜 𝖄𝖔𝖗𝖐

MACMILLAN & CO., 66 FIFTH AVENUE

THE

UTOPIA

OF

SIR THOMAS MORE

IN LATIN FROM THE EDITION OF MARCH 1518, AND IN
ENGLISH FROM THE FIRST EDITION OF RALPH
ROBYNSON'S TRANSLATION IN 1551

WITH

ADDITIONAL TRANSLATIONS, INTRODUCTION AND NOTES

BY

J. H. LUPTON, B.D.

SURMASTER OF ST. PAUL'S SCHOOL, AND PREACHER OF GRAY'S INN
FORMERLY FELLOW OF ST. JOHN'S COLLEGE, CAMBRIDGE

WITH FACSIMILES

Oxford

AT THE CLARENDON PRESS

M.DCCC.XCV

Oxford

PRINTED AT THE CLARENDON PRESS

BY HORACE HART, PRINTER TO THE UNIVERSITY

TO

FREDERIC SEEBOHM

AUTHOR OF 'THE OXFORD REFORMERS'

AND TO

FREDERICK W. WALKER, M.A.

HIGH MASTER OF ST. PAUL'S SCHOOL

THIS EDITION OF THE 'UTOPIA'

IS DEDICATED WITH GRATITUDE AND ESTEEM

PREFACE

---◦◦---

AN attempt has been made, in this edition of Sir Thomas
More's work, to treat it with something of the same
exact care that is looked for, as a matter of course, in
editing a classical author. The text has been revised, the
variations made in it by the author himself noted, and the
readings of different editions compared. The allusions
to persons and events, real or imaginary, have also, as far
as possible, been traced out.

How much remained, and I fear still remains, to be
done in this respect, a single example will show. More's
narrator, Hythloday, is made to speak in one place of
having with him on board ship a companion, whom he
calls Tricius Apinatus. No commentator hitherto, so far
as I am aware, has taken the trouble to ascertain what the
author meant by this name, or to recall the   *apina*

'Sunt *apinae tricaeque* et si quid vilius istis'   *trica*

of Martial. In endeavouring to discover the origin of
other names of More's invention I may very probably
have gone too far; but it seemed proper at any rate to
make the attempt.

I have endeavoured to illustrate the bearing of the

Utopia on some of the great questions of the day, by
studying the circumstances amidst which it was composed.
It is now the fashion, in some quarters, to try to detach
More as far as possible from the great movement known
as the Humanist. And certainly, if the only accredited
representatives of that movement were such men as
Poggio and Filelfo, or even as Politian and Valla, More
could have had but small sympathy with it. But that
great tide of reawakening thought and energy flowed in
many channels. Many others besides those mentioned
drank of its streams, and found them not Circean. And if
it is fair to cite More's later writings to prove that he
never could have really held some of the opinions which
he seems to advocate in the *Utopia*, it is at least as fair to
lay stress on the time and circumstances of its origin. It
was written—the greater part of it, at least—at Antwerp,
a city than which no other in the Netherlands, according
to Ullmann, was more deeply imbued with the spirit of the
Reformation. If it was not a true child of the Renais-
sance, it was ushered into the world with all the creden-
tials of such a birth. It had commendatory verses hung s
about it by Cornelius Schreiber of Alst, who five years
later was in prison at Brussels for heresy; and by Gerhard
Geldenhaur of Nimeguen, who had already published
what More calls biting satires upon the religious orders,
and who, after being himself a monk, embraced the reformed faith, and died a married layman. On its second
appearance, the *Utopia* was prefaced by a long letter from
Budé, the restorer of Greek learning in France; who, as
such, was suspected by many of a leaning to heretical
opinions; and who had at any rate inserted, in a work
preceding More's by a year or two, a very bitter, and not
very generous, invective on the lately deceased Pontiff,
Julius II.

That this *setting*, so to call it, of the *Utopia* may be

brought into due prominence, I have translated the letter
of Budé, as well as some other pieces not included by
Robynson. There is no need to specify which these are.
The style of the older translator speaks for itself. Whatever is not his, is mine.

The reader will find in the present edition everything
comprised in the original one of 1516, excepting the letter
and verses of Joannes Paludanus. These were deliberately
omitted from the second edition, probably as having no
intrinsic merit, and so are properly omitted here. Nothing
is here left out which was in the second edition of the
Latin, or in the first edition of the English translation.
The reason for adopting different editions of the Latin
and English is simply this. In the Latin, the later one
was more complete and accurate than its predecessor, and
evidently more what the author designed to make it. His
wish is entitled to respect. On the other hand, our interest
in Robynson's translation is chiefly due to its representing
an early period of English; and for this purpose the
earlier edition is the better. Moreover, while the second
edition of Robynson has been often reprinted, the first
has never been so, and it thus has the advantage of freshness. It will be seen from the various readings, which are
all carefully noted, that, except in matters of spelling, the
differences between the two are not really important.

In obtaining texts suitable to print from not a little
difficulty was experienced. It was not thought advisable
to reproduce the contractions, with which the old typo-
graphy abounds. And so, after losing some time in
trying expedients, I wrote out the whole of the Latin,
from a copy of the edition of March, 1518, kindly lent
me by Mr. Seebohm. A transcript of the first edition
of Robynson's translation was also made for me, by the
obliging permission of Dr. Sinker, from a copy in the
Library of Trinity College, Cambridge. In making both

Paludanus letter.

these transcripts, the only alteration permitted has been expanding the contractions, and occasionally readjusting the division of sentences.

No student of the period of English history in which More lived can fail to own his obligations to the Calendars of Letters and Papers of Henry the Eighth's reign made by the late Professor Brewer, and to the valuable Introductions prefixed to them. For my special subject I have, besides these, found great assistance in Dr. Lumby's excellent edition of the *Utopia*, and in the bibliographical Introduction to Professor Arber's reprint. Both of these, however, deal only with the English translation. To Mr. Seebohm's *Oxford Reformers* I am much indebted, not now for the first time. The edition I have used of it is the second. I have also derived much benefit from Father Bridgett's recently published *Life and Writings of Sir Thomas More*. It is the work of one well acquainted with his subject, and is pervaded by a candid spirit. I could wish that the chapter on the *Utopia* had been fuller.

For the loan of scarce books my thanks are due in several quarters. The use of a copy of the rare folio edition of More's English Works has been allowed me by the kindness of the Master of the Library of Gray's Inn, John Archibald Russell, Esq., Q.C. For the like use of a copy of Robynson's second edition, and of the Paris edition of 1517, I am indebted to the kindness of Professor John E. B. Mayor, and the Librarian of my own College, Mr. J. Bass Mullinger. Through the courtesy of the late Dr. Sieber and his assistants, I had the privilege, in the autumn of 1891, of inspecting some early copies of the *Utopia* in the University Library at Basle; among them being one that had belonged to Froben's old masters in his craft, the Amerbachs, bearing their autographs and a few annotations. I have to thank Bodley's Librarian

for allowing the three facsimiles given in this volume to
be made from a copy of the edition of March, 1518, in
his charge. To Dr. F. J. Furnivall, who has contributed
to our knowledge of More's time by his editions of its
ballad literature ; to Mr. R. W. Douthwaite, the Librarian of Gray's Inn ; and lastly to my son, Mr. J. M.
Lupton, assistant master in Marlborough College, my
acknowledgements are due for kind help in various ways,
which has greatly lightened my task.

J. H. L.

St. Paul's School :
Easter, 1895.

CONTENTS

INTRODUCTION.

CONTENTS.

THE UTOPIA.

INTRODUCTION

INTRODUCTION.

§ 1.—Early Life of the Author.

The latter part of the life of Sir Thomas More is so closely interwoven with the general history of his country, that it need not be re-told here. But the reader may be better able to appreciate the ensuing work, if he has presented to him a brief outline of the earlier portion, especially in so far as it bears on the production of the *Utopia*.

Thomas More was the second child, and eldest son, of John More, gentleman, afterwards a judge in the Court of King's Bench, and Agnes, daughter of Thomas Graunger. He was born, February 7, 1478, in Milk Street, in the City of London, 'the brightest star,' as Fuller has it, 'that ever shined in that *Via Lactea*.'

His family, 'non celebris, sed honesta,' was well descended. His father, and also his grandfather before him, appear to have filled successively the offices, then accounted honourable, of butler and steward at Lincoln's Inn, and thence to have become, as students, members of the society[1]. Judge More received the coif, and in consequence left the Inn, in 1503; was made one of the Judges of Common Pleas in 1518; was thence transferred to the King's Bench in 1520; and died in 1530.

More's connexion with Lincoln's Inn, of which he himself afterwards became a member, and, not being made a Serjeant,

[1] See a paper by Mr. E. W. Brabrook, printed in the *Transactions of* the *London and Middlesex Archaeological Society* (1875), iv. pp. 434–5.

never left, was thus hereditary. And the circumstance helps to account for the attachment which he always manifested for his Inn. Coming down to 'Lincoln's Inn diet, where many right-worshipful and of good years do live full well,' was the first step of the descent in his broken fortunes that he playfully discussed with his family in later years. And the arrangements for dining at the public tables, in the communal life of the Utopians, would seem to have been suggested by the dining in Hall of the Benchers and other members of his Inn [1].

The school to which young More was sent is said to have been St. Anthony's, attached to the hospital of that name in Threadneedle Street. The foundation was due originally to Henry III, but had been increased and endowed by Henry VI and Edward IV; and, just about the time when More would enter, had been annexed to the Collegiate Church of St. George at Windsor, which proved the beginning of its dissolution [2]. Colet is said to have been at the same school; but, if so, he would have left before More's entry, being twelve years older. The master was Nicholas Holt, a scholar of some eminence [3]. Here More laid the foundation of a knowledge of Latin, which was both copious and accurate. St Anthony's school was, by its constitution, designed to be a feeder of Eton College, its scholars having exhibitions provided to take them afterwards to Oxford. Whether More was ever at Eton does not appear. Probably he was not, as his school-days were shortened by his entrance into the household of Cardinal Morton. Here he would have the advantage of being trained in a school of manners under one of the leading men of his time. And, like Bentley long afterwards at the table of Bishop Stillingfleet, he seems to have impressed his patron

[1] See below, p. 164. A statue of More was erected in 1889 by George Arnold, Esq., at the corner of Carey Street, Lincoln's Inn. Father Bridgett speaks of this as being the first statue of him erected in London. But there is one outside the new building of the City of London School, on the Victoria Embankment, which had been placed there some years before.

[2] Stow's *Survey*, ed. 1720, i. p. 120.
[3] According to Johnson, in his *Life of Linacre*, 1835, p. 20 n., this Holt was himself the author of an Accidence, but he is not to be confounded with the John Holt, author of the *Lac Puerorum*, for whom see Bloxam's *Register . . . of Magdalen College*, iii. p. 15.

with a conviction of his own future greatness. 'This child here waiting at the table,' Morton is reported to have said, 'whoever shall live to see it, will prove a marvellous man[1].' More's own opinion of the Cardinal, in the language of affectionate recollection, is put into the mouth of his speaker, Hythloday[2].

Morton united again the broken thread of More's education by sending him to Oxford. We are, unfortunately, unable to ascertain at what college he entered, or whether he remained long enough to take any degree. His father seems to have looked with a jealous eye on the attractions of literature as a rival of the law, and to have given him but a stinted allowance[3]. But More secured the great object of his residence at the University. He perfected his acquaintance with the Latin tongue, practising the art of composition in it, as Erasmus tells us, in every form ; and, above all, entering on the then new and enthralling study of Greek. For this, he had the great advantage of Grocyn's instruction, as well as that of Grocyn's younger friend Linacre[4]. According to his own testimony, he attended Linacre's lectures on a work of Aristotle's in Greek[5]. Could it have been the *Politics*? More

[1] *Life* by Roper, ed. 1822, p. 4.

[2] *Infr.* pp. 41-43. Lord Campbell's opinion of Morton is not so favourable. It is on a judgement of his as Lord Chancellor, that he makes the caustic remark: 'Equity decisions, at this time, depended upon each Chancellor's peculiar notions of the law of God, and the manner in which Heaven would visit the defendant for the acts complained of in the bill.'—*Lives of the Lord Chancellors*, 1845, 1. p. 425.

[3] See the passage from Stapleton, quoted by Seebohm, p. 26 n. For the hardness of the life at Oxford, at this period, and the general poverty of students, see Boase's *Register of the University of Oxford* 1885, Pref. p. xii., and the same writer's *Register . . . of Exeter College*, 1879, p. x. There is, unfortunately, a gap in the University

Register between 1463 and 1505.

[4] 'Recens tunc [c. 1492] ex Italia venerat Grocinus, qui primus ea aetate Graecas literas in Angliam invexerat, Oxoniique publice professus fuerat; a cujus sodali Tho. Linacro [Morus] Graecas literas Oxonii didicit.'— Stapleton : *Tres Thomae* (*Thomae Mori Vita*, c. 1).

[5] In his letter to Dorpius, 1515, More refers to his attendance on these lectures, and adds that a translation of Aristotle might soon be expected from Linacre's pen, which had only been delayed by the claims of Galen.— See Th. Mori *Lucubrationes*, 1563, pp. 416-7 It is worth noticing that the first lecture delivered in the newly opened University of Alcala was upon Aristotle. Prescott : *Ferdinand and Isabella*, ed. 1886, p. 660.

was undoubtedly familiar with the *Republic* of Plato. His knowledge of Greek enabled him to bear Lily equal company in translating epigrams from the *Anthologia*; and the fictitious names in the *Utopia* are almost all, as it will be observed, of Greek formation. But, in fact, his proficiency in Greek became an influence that modified all his future life, making him at one with Erasmus, and Lily, and Colet, and other like-minded men of the New Learning.

We must hasten quickly over the period of More's stay at New Inn—an Inn of Chancery, affiliated to Lincoln's Inn— which he entered after leaving Oxford. In the 'mootings' there, to which he alludes long afterwards in his controversy with Tindal, his vigorous intellect would be still further whetted and strengthened. On February 12, 1496, being then just eighteen, he was admitted a student of Lincoln's Inn. His life there would naturally be uneventful, and we do not know even the date of his call to the Bar. But it is worth while to pause a moment, and recall the stirring scenes which were then being exhibited in the great drama of the outer world.

Just four years before More went into residence at Lincoln's Inn, the last Caliph of the Moors in Spain had signed a capitulation, by which the banner of Castile waved over the highest tower of the Alhambra. The same year that saw the expulsion of the Moors from Granada, witnessed the discovery of the new world by Columbus. The bounds of Christendom were being enlarged. Commerce felt her fetters loosed, and the *Intercursus magnus* of 1496 was but one sign of the reviving energies of peace. In 1497 John Cabot sailed from Bristol and discovered Newfoundland.

With what eager interest the mind of the young law-student would follow these events, it needs no stretch of imagination to conceive. His perusal of the narratives of Vespucci is in itself sufficient evidence. But we may possibly find, in the excitement of those eventful years, an explanation of one proceeding on More's part which has generally been thought singular. That is, his delivering a course of lectures on Augustine's *De Civitate Dei*, in the church of St. Lawrence,

Jewry. The subject and the place alike (though his old tutor, *Lectures on St. Augustine* [margin note] Grocyn, was rector of the parish) have seemed unusual for a young student of an Inn of Court to choose. If we connect it with More's former studies at Oxford, and with the tidings ever pouring in of discoveries in a new world, we may perhaps discern more reasons for the choice. The subject of an ideal commonwealth was doubtless working in More's mind years before the *Utopia* took form.

After his call to the Bar, More was made 'reader' at Furnivall's Inn for three years or longer; and it must have been about this time that he passed through a period of suspense and inward struggle, as to his ultimate choice of a profession. His success in legal studies, no less than his father's strong wish, might seem to have already decided this for him. But it is no uncommon experience for a season of doubt and unsettlement to ensue, when the excitement is over of working for a high degree at the University, or surmounting the first barriers of a learned profession. At any rate, More was now strongly drawn to the priesthood, and for 'about four years,' Roper tells us, lived as a sort of unprofessed brother *Roper* [margin note] of the London Charterhouse. He had thoughts of being ordained, Stapleton tells us, along with his friend Lily[1]. What diverted both the friends from this course, we can only conjecture. Colet, we are expressly told, advised More to marry. His own feelings, Erasmus tells us, prompted him to that as the wiser and safer, though not the ideally loftier, course. And so in 1505 he married Jane Colt, of Newhall, in Essex. *1505* [margin note] Lily also married, probably before his friend[2].

More's home was now in Bucklersbury, where for a time he passed what must have been a happy and prosperous life. Children were born to him in rapid succession: his beloved Margaret at the end of 1505, Elizabeth in 1506, Cicely in 1507, and John in 1509. He was a rising barrister, much employed in commercial cases. Moreover, in the spring of 1504[3], when

[1] 'Meditabatur sacerdotium cum Lilio suo.'

[2] Lily's wife, Agnes, died before him, having been married, as her epitaph tells us, seventeen years. He died in 1522.

[3] Bishop Stubbs, *Lectures on . . . Medieval and Modern History*, 1887,

M.P.
1504

only twenty-six, he had been summoned as a burgess to parliament. In that capacity, indeed, he incurred some danger, by the boldness with which he resisted the unconstitutional demands of the ministers of Henry VII. Roper tells us that the king, to show his displeasure, imprisoned his father in the Tower, till he should pay a fine of £100. And it has been conjectured[1] that a visit to Louvain and Paris, in the year

1508

1508, was only a prudent retirement, for a short time, from political life.

Erasmus

But these events did not seriously disturb More's happiness, which centred in his home. There, at the latter end of 1505— his marriage year—he had Erasmus for a guest. The converse of two such spirits may be imagined better than described. The tangible form it took was the composition of epigrams, and the translation of some dialogues of Lucian from the Greek into Latin[2]. As far as Erasmus was concerned, this may have been only so much literary work, of a kind likely to be read, which promised to bring him in much-needed remuneration. But More's selection from the old Greek satirist was probably made with a deeper object. The very titles of two of the three dialogues chosen are suggestive: *Cynicus* and *Philopseudes*.

Lucian

His attraction to the first of these he justifies by the example of St. Chrysostom, who had incorporated a large portion of it in a homily on St. John. The second he commends as specially useful for his own generation. 'This profit, at any rate,' he says in his dedicatory letter to Ruthall, afterwards Bishop of Durham[3], 'the Dialogue will bring us, that we shall

---

p. 416, points out that no parliament was held in 1502, the year in which More is sometimes said to have opposed the demand in question. As the grant was actually made in 1504, he thinks that More 'probably was instrumental in limiting the sum.'

[1] See Bridgett's *Life*, p. 44.

[2] These were printed at Paris, 'in aedibus Ascensianis,' in the following year, 1506, under the title of *Luciani compluria opuscula*, &c. See the

Bibliotheca Erasmiana, now being compiled by M. Vander Haeghen, Librarian of the University of Ghent. They were reprinted in 1512 and 1516. The first edition of Erasmus's *Epigrammata* was also in 1506, at Strasbourg.

[3] The letter is included in the *Lucubrationes*, 1563, pp. 273-7. Bishop Ruthall was the founder of Cirencester school.

not put faith in impostures (*magicis praestigiis*), and that we *Lucian used against superstition:* shall be free from the superstition which is everywhere creeping over us under the guise of religion. Moreover [it will make us] spend a less solicitous life ; I mean, one less terrified by gloomy and superstitious falsehoods '— the confident and authoritative assertion of which he goes on to denounce. ' Cease to wonder,' he continues, ' if the minds of the un- educated multitude are impressed by these fictions.   The men they come from only think they have achieved a success, or won the lasting favour of Christ, if they have invented an untrue story about some saint, or a tragic tale of those in hell (*de inferis tragoediam*), for poor old women to cry hysterically over, or shudder at in terror.   There is hardly any life of a martyr, or of a virgin, that they have passed by, without inserting some lies of this description—piously, of course ; for otherwise there would have been a danger of truth not being self sufficient, unless propped up by falsehoods !   They have not shrunk from polluting with figments a religion founded by Him who was the very Truth ; whose will it was that it should stand in naked truth.   They have not perceived that fables of this description, so far from being of service to it, are of all things the most dangerous obstacle.'

I have given these extracts at some length, as being ex- pressive of More's feelings then and long after.   In these first- fruits of his studies in Greek, as he calls his productions later on in the same letter, we have the spirit of the New Learning in its better and purer aspect.   When Étienne Dolet, on reaching the word 'Literae ' in his great *Thesaurus*, paused to take a review of contemporary men of letters, it was not without reason that he cited More, with Linacre, as repre- sentatives of English enlightenment.   As he viewed in thought the long procession sweeping past, with Bembo and Sadolet to carry the banner of Italy, Erasmus that of Holland, and the rest, he could well exclaim : ' Quels hommes, et de quel cœur ils combattent pour la cause de la liberté [1].'

---

[1] Buisson : *Répertoire des Ouvrages Pédagogiques du xvi͏ᵉ siècle*, 1886, Préf. p. viii.

Animated as he was with such a spirit as his early epigrams and translations show, the accession of Henry VIII in April, 1509, must have seemed to More the earnest of a new and brighter era. In a long congratulatory ode which he wrote on the coronation, he calls the day that witnessed the ceremony 'the end of bondage, the beginning of freedom.' 'Now the magistracies and public offices, that were wont to be sold to bad men, were freely bestowed on the good.' And, quoting Plato's thought of the recurrence of aeons, he avers that now at length, after an iron age, the age of gold has come back again [1].

In the following year, however, sorrow came. His young wife, the 'Ioanna uxorcula Mori' of his tender epitaph, died in 1510, and the happy household in Bucklersbury passed through their first great trial together. If More seems to have been comforted full soon, marrying a second wife before the year had run out, it is not for us to judge him. He was absorbed in professional and other work. He had just been made Under-Sheriff [2] of London, an office which would bring him much labour of a judicial kind. His young children must have needed a mother's care. And so he married Alice Myddelton, a widow with one daughter of the same name, who thus became added to the household. The stepmother did her duty by the children, and her husband trained her assiduously, as he had done his first young wife, in literature and music. But one trace of the sorrow of his heart may perhaps be found in the publication about this time of a *Life of Johan Picus, Erle of Myrandula*, which he had before drawn up, with a selection from his Letters, and a translation of his touching Prayer [3].

The next few years of More's life must have been years of

---

[1] *Lucubrationes*, pp. 182-9.

[2] On the title-page of the *Utopia* More is called *Vicecomes*, as if Sheriff, for which that is the recognized Latin term. This perplexed Burnet, who could not find More's name in the lists of Sheriffs. See the Preface to his Translation, 1753, p. ix.

[3] The book was printed by Wynkyn de Worde, in small quarto, without date. A barrister of More's Inn, Mr. J. M. Rigg, lately reprinted it with a valuable Introduction and notes, Lond. 1890.

incessant activity. He was made a Bencher of his Inn, and in
1511 was called upon to 'read' there. His practice at the Bar
had so increased that he made 'without grief,' as Roper tells
us, from it and from his appointments together, an income of
more than £400 a year, equivalent to at least ten times as much
now. In the letter to Peter Giles, prefixed to the *Utopia*, he
has drawn a picture of this busy life[1]. And yet, in the midst
of it all, he found time to write, or translate[2], the *History of
Richard III*, and thus earn a title to be considered the first
writer of English prose, properly so called.

It should have been mentioned that in 1508 he had been
made free of the Mercers' Company[3], and would thus be drawn
into the current of that communal life, as it existed in this
foremost of the city guilds, which in those days had something
of reality about it, and may have suggested some of the features
of his communistic romance. In the council-chamber of that
Company he would meet his friend Colet, now Dean of St.
Paul's, a Mercer and the son of a Mercer, and with him would
often talk over the foundation of his great school, the walls of
which were rising at the east end of the cathedral. That
school of St. Paul's, the first in this country in which Greek
was publicly taught, was an embodiment of the principles of
Humanism at its best[4]. For it Erasmus wrote text-books, and
for it, when sharing the obloquy to which its founder was
exposed, More stood forth as a champion. His words in its
defence have been prophetic. The enemies of good learning

[handwritten marginal notes: 1511; Hist. of. R III; 1508; Mercers; Communism; St. Paul's school]

---

[1] See below, p. 3.

[2] Mr. Archbold, the author of the
article on Cardinal Morton in the
Dict. of National Biography, comes to
the conclusion that Morton probably
wrote the history in Latin, and More
translated it into English.

[3] *Account of the Hospital of St. Thomas
of Acons* by Mr. John Watney
(privately printed), 1892, p. 87. The
evidence, though not absolutely certain, seems to leave no reasonable
doubt that the Thomas More then

made free of the Company was the
future Chancellor.

[4] It is worthy of note that the late
Dr. Karl Hartfelder, of Heidelberg,
whose works entitle him to speak with
high authority on such a subject,
singled out St. Paul's as the type of
a Humanist school—'das Ideal einer
Humanistenschule'; and read a paper
on it, under this title, before a conference of professors at Munich, in
May, 1891. See the *Zeitschrift für das
Gymnasialwesen*. Berlin, 1891, p. 711.

perceive, he wrote to Colet[1], that 'just as there came forth from
the Trojan horse Greeks, who laid waste barbarian Troy, so
from your school are coming forth scholars, who refute and
overthrow their ignorance.' It was but the length of Chepe
that separated St. Paul's School, at one end, from More's house
at the other. And not often has that busy thoroughfare borne
a greater share in the history of learning than when, in 1510,
Lily began to teach under the shadow of the cathedral, and
Erasmus wrote his *Praise of Folly* under More's roof[2].

Whether it be true, or not, that between the date of his
leaving Bucklersbury, and that of his forming a larger household
at Chelsea, he resided for a while at Crosby Place, Bishopsgate[3],
More's life was in the fullest sense that of a citizen. His
reputation as a lawyer, his office of under-sheriff, and his
connexion with the guild of the Mercers, combined to point
him out as a fit person to defend the legal rights and privileges
of his fellow-citizens.

And so when, in 1514, disputes were becoming acute between
the London merchants and their foreign competitors, who
were quartered among them, and a commission was talked of for
settling these disputes, it was earnestly desired that More might
be a member of it. In Roper's words, he was, 'at the suit and
instaunce of the English Merchauntes,' sent as an ambassador
'in certaine great causes betweene them and the Merchauntes
of the Stilliard.' But the matters in dispute were not merely
the rival interests of the English and Hanseatic merchants in
London, but the interests of all English exporters of wool, then
the staple commodity of our trade. As far back as the thirteenth
century, it had been asserted that 'all the world was clothed
from English wool wrought in Flanders[4].' Henry III had

---

[1] Stapleton: *Tres Thomae*, ed. 1612,
p. 166, quoted by Seebohm, p. 251.

[2] The earliest edition of the *Encomium Moriae* yet discovered by
M. Vander Haeghen (see the *Bibliotheca*
before mentioned) is that of Strasbourg, 'mense Augusto,' 1511. An
'édition douteuse,' of the same year,
at Antwerp, is also mentioned. This
seems to point to 1510, or the early
part of 1511, as the date of the composition of the piece.

[3] Bridgett's *Life*, p. 139; Besant's
London, 1892, p. 138.

[4] See Hallam's *Middle Ages*, ch. ix.
pt. ii.

Embassy

given the Hanse traders a guildhall or factory in London ; and
their successors enjoyed many privileges, in what Hallam calls
'the capricious vacillations of our mercantile policy.' It was
doubly important, therefore, that if cloths of Flemish manufacture
were freely introduced into England, Flemish ports should not
be closed against the admission of English wool. This untoward
event had now come about. The breaking-off of the proposed
marriage between Prince Charles, the son of Philip, Archduke
of Austria (afterwards Charles V), and the Princess Mary, sister
of Henry VIII, had caused the English government, as a mark
of displeasure, to forbid the exportation of wool to Holland and
Zealand. This was soon felt to be as injurious to the native as
to the foreigner, and so a legation, of which More was junior
member, was sent to the Low Countries in May, 1515, to re-
adjust the commercial relations. It was evidently a case in
which great tact would be necessary. Hence so able a man as
Tunstall was chosen for the chief of the embassy. It is sufficient
here to add, that the objects of the mission were attained, and
More returned to London towards the end of the year [1]. It was
during the enforced leisure of the months spent in the Low
Countries in 1515, that More composed the Second Book (the
one first written) of his *Utopia*. The First Book, meant to be
a setting to the other, was written in the spring or summer of
1516, when Wolsey was trying hard to draw its author into the
immediate service of the court.

May 1515

Utopia

1516

Wolsey & Court

cf. Hexter

Now that we have reached this point, there is no necessity
for following out the life of More in detail. Our object was
merely to show from what antecedents the *Utopia* sprung. The
immediate causes of its appearance will be discussed more
particularly in the next section. The dates of a few succeeding
events may be just indicated in conclusion.

On Evil May-day, 1517, More was requested by the Privy
Council to use his influence with the excited mob, who had

May-day 1517

---

[1] The progress of the embassy may
be followed in Brewer: *Letters and
Papers*, vol. ii. pt. i. See the Introduction, p. lvi. and n. for More's
mission ; p. cxiii. for Tunstall's character (he was not made Master of
the Rolls till May 12, 1516, *ib*. no.
1882) ; and no. 1551 for More's arrival
home.

attacked the houses of the foreign merchants. In this arduous task, for one moment, it seemed as if he would have succeeded, and become an illustration of the fine simile of the poet :—

> Ac veluti magno in populo cum saepe coorta est
> Seditio, &c.

But popular passions were too strong.

In 1518, if not before, he was made Master of Requests, and sworn of the Privy Council; in 1520 he attended the King to the Field of the Cloth of Gold[1], where he would have abundant opportunity for recalling some of the sentiments expressed in his romance; in 1521 he was knighted[2] and made Under-Treasurer; in 1523 he removed to his final home at Chelsea, where he lived the almost Utopian life that Erasmus has so charmingly described[3]; the same year he was made Speaker of the House of Commons; in 1529 (Oct. 29) he was made Lord High Chancellor, an office which he resigned in 1532 (May 6); in 1534 came his refusal of the Oath of Supremacy, and committal to the Tower; and in 1535 his trial and execution (July 6)[4], an act which will ever be a stain on the memory of Henry VIII.

[margin note: April 17 1534]

[1] See the *Rutland Papers* (Camden Society's Publications), 1842, p. 33, where More's name comes among the Esquires. On June 6, 1522 (*ib.* p. 95 n.), he is 'one Sir Thomas More, *Knight*, and well learned.'

[2] For the date, which has often been incorrectly given, see the correspondence in *Notes and Queries*, July 18, 1891, p. 46; and also the preceding note.

[3] The date of Erasmus's letter to Budé, in which this description occurs, is given as 1521 (Jortin, i. 260; iii. 68). This, if correct, would make the letter too early to refer to Chelsea. But a date two years later would remove the difficulty caused by calling young John More a boy of 'about thirteen.'—See Bridgett's *Life*, p. 114 n. The description of Judge More as 'non minorem annis octoginta,' while in any case an exaggeration, would suit the later date better than the earlier.

For the subsequent history of More's house, see Beaver's *Memorials of Old Chelsea*, 1892, pp. 118-140, and Mr. Sidney Lee's article in the *Dictionary of National Biography*. The grounds extended across the line of the present Beaufort Street, formerly Beaufort Row.

[4] I do not remember to have seen quoted, on this subject, a letter of Tielman Gravius, *or* a Fossa, dated 16 Cal. Sep. (August 17), 1535. It is at p. xxiii. of Burscher's *Spicilegia*, 1784-1802. After giving some particulars of the death of Fisher and More, the writer adds : 'Nec tutum est percontari in toto regno quam ob causam boni illi Viri capitis supplicio affecti sunt.' His informant was Arnold Birckmann, who was in England at the time, and in part an eye-witness.

§ 2. CIRCUMSTANCES THAT GAVE RISE TO THE UTOPIA.

The events that led to More's embassy into Flanders, where the greater portion of the *Utopia* was written, have been partly related in the last section. With regard to this embassy, he tells us himself that he and his fellow envoys first met with the deputies of the Flemish government at Bruges ; that, after due conference, when they could not agree on all points, these deputies withdrew to Brussels, 'to know their Prince's pleasure'; and that he himself, 'for so his business lay,' went on to Antwerp. As it is in Antwerp that he lays the scene of his meeting with Hythloday, we need not speculate further as to his movements in the Low Countries.

Though this was not More's first visit to the continent[1], there would be much to excite his curiosity in the busy towns of Flanders. We have seen that his thoughts had long been turned to the subject of civil communities ; and here he would find the tide of social life flowing vigorously, and in new channels. Bruges was famous for the splendour of its buildings, and the extent of its foreign trade, in which it had surpassed Ghent. It contained, if Guicciardini's statement be not incredible[2], 35,000 houses. Though Antwerp, its younger rival, had begun to draw much of its trade away from it, it was still one of the four depôts of the Hanseatic league, London being another. We can thus easily imagine that More, who had, besides the general business of the embassy, matters to settle with which he had been individually charged by the London merchants, would find much to occupy him both at Bruges and Antwerp. He would be inevitably led to compare the methods of business, the forms of municipal government, the manners and customs, of these flourishing towns with those of his own city. Even such details as the width and cleanliness of the streets were evidently carefully studied by him ; and the results, as he idealized them, were shadowed forth in his City of Amaurote.

---

[1] See note above, p. xxii.
[2] Quoted by Hallam : *Middle Ages*, ed. 1869, p. 616.

The circuit of the walls of Bruges is said to have been more than 15,000 yards, or nearly nine miles[1]. If so, it must have had much open space within it, and so have presented a great contrast to the closely-built city of London, with its narrow, ill-paved, unsavoury streets, at times little better than open sewers[2]. More had, no doubt, often compared those noisome alleys with the fair dwellings of the nobility along the Strand, with their gardens stretching down to the shining Thames, and their open view across the river on to the Surrey hills. And as he mentally compared them now with the broad wharves of the 'city of many bridges,' the thought came into his mind of what should be in his ideal Amaurote. And so it is ordained that in that city all the streets shall be of ample width[3]. In the rear of every house is to be a garden, with 'all maner of fruites, herbes and flowers'; so that every street there must have been as sweet-smelling as his own Bucklersbury in 'simple-time.'

But municipal life, at least in these its outer forms, was not the only thing then forcing itself upon More's thoughts. As he had once before had to choose, after a severe mental struggle, between the clerical life and the lay, so now he must decide whether to abide by the profession he had chosen, or be drawn into the vortex of a court. His being sent at a youthful age

---

[1] Guicciardini, as before.

[2] Writers who have studied the subject seem at a loss for language uncomplimentary enough to describe the state of the streets in London during this period. Even after the middle of the century they are said to have been 'little better than narrow lanes, undrained, often unpaved, and the nightly receptacle of filth of all kinds.'—Select Works of Robert Crowley, ed. by J. M. Cowper, 1872, Introd. p. xiv. See also Brewer: Reign of Henry VIII, i. p. 266 n. What Prof. Brewer there says of the beauty of the situation of the noblemen's houses on the north bank of the Thames,

must be understood of the view in front. The Strand which flanked them was in such a bad state that 'in 1522-3 an act was passed for the paving of that "very noyous, foul, and jeopardous" highway, the Strand, by the owners of houses and lands along its course.' Eccleston: English Antiquities, 1847, p. 287.

[3] Twenty feet, which is what More allows (infr. p. 130), may seem to us now a very modest width. But it may be remembered that the upper end of Ludgate Hill, one of the busiest thoroughfares in London, was, until a few years ago, only about a third wider.

as a burgess to parliament, his being chosen to serve on the
present commission, and now the urgent solicitations of Wolsey,   *Wolsey*
must all have appealed to the spirit of vanity or ambition, if
there were any such within him.   In his desire to escape from
service at court, More was perfectly sincere.   'No one,' writes ⎫
Erasmus, 'ever strove more eagerly to gain admission there ⎬
than More did to avoid it.'   But it would be idle to suppose ⎭
that such a decision would not cost him anxious thought.   And,
as he turned over in his mind the ways of kings and courts, as
they must then have presented themselves to a close observer,
what were likely to be his reflections?

The two princes he was most nearly concerned with, at the   *Hen. VIII*
moment, were those betwixt whom he was going as an ambassador, his own sovereign and Prince Charles.   What had   *French*
been Henry's exploits during the past two or three years?   *ventures*
There had been an expedition against France, in the summer   *1512*
of 1512, conjointly with Ferdinand of Spain, in which the
English contingent had miserably failed.   A second expedition,
to retrieve the disgrace, had been organized at great cost the
following year, but with so little approval on the part of
thoughtful men, that Dean Colet, who preached the Lent   *1513*
sermons before the court in 1513, was denounced by the war
party as damping the spirits of the soldiery.   The result gained
by this was the capture of Tournay and Terouenne, an empty
success; while the Scots, under James IV, had tried to serve ⎫ *Flodden*
England as England was serving France, and some of the best ⎬
blood of both countries had reddened the field of Flodden. ⎭

'The right highe and mightye Kyng of Castell,' as More
styles him, was, at the time of his writing the words, a youth
of fifteen.   He had been proclaimed King of Castile when   *Charles*
a mere child.   On the death of his father, the archduke Philip,   *1506*
in September, 1506, he was left, the heir of splendid prospects,
with a mother, deranged in mind, as her grandmother had been
before her, unable to bring herself to sign a state paper, or
take any interest in public affairs[1].   A few years later, an
absolute jealousy of the boy prince took possession of the mind

---

[1] Prescott: *Ferdinand and Isabella*, ed. 1886, p. 642.

of his grandfather Ferdinand, who looked on him as a rival rather than as an heir [1]. So that, when the English embassy reached the Low Countries in the spring of 1515, instead of being able to address themselves to a responsible sovereign, they had to deal with a regency, swayed by many conflicting interests.

If he extended his survey beyond the concerns of England and Castile, a keen observer like More would find presented to him, in the aspect of Europe at large, a political chess-board, affording ever fresh matter for satirical, if not sardonic, reflec-

The League tion. In 1508, by the League of Cambray, some of the chief pieces on the board—the Emperor, the Pope, King Ferdinand and King Louis—had been combined together against the unhappy republic of Venice. When the victory of the French at Agnadello had satisfied the ambition of Julius II, he was

Julius II disposed to rest content with his gains, and made it his object, in turn, to keep the power of France from growing too high. If this meant a dissolution of existing treaties, what were treaties made for, but to be broken? 'A Prince that is wise and prudent,' writes Machiavelli, 'cannot nor ought not to keep his parole, when the keeping of it is to his prejudice, and the causes for which he promised, removed [2].' Unfortunately, while the chief players, like Xerxes in Atossa's dream, retained their thrones, whether successful or unsuccessful, the pawns, their subjects, were swept away unpitied. Their cries could not yet make themselves heard. 'Regi dissentit nemo,' wrote More [3], 'malum hoc gravius.'

The domestic life, no less than the public policy, of the reigning sovereigns would in many cases have afforded equal matter for sarcastic comments. In particular, the selfish and

[1] Prescott: *Ferdinand and Isabella*, ed. 1886, p. 685. By her will, dated Oct. 12, 1504, Queen Isabella had left the regency of the kingdom of Castile, during the minority of her grandson, and the mental incapacity of his mother, to her husband Ferdinand. He died in January, 1516, leaving Cardinal Ximenes regent, who at once had Charles proclaimed afresh in Madrid.

[2] *Works* (English translation), 1675, p. 223.

[3] Epigram on 'Quis optimus reipublicae status?' The similarity of this title to that of the *Utopia* should be noticed. They stand in the relation of question and answer.

unscrupulous arrangements often made for the marriage of
their children, the utter disregard of human affections, the
matrimonial bartering of mere infants, may have roused the
spirit of Democritus in More, and suggested to him, in
a mocking humour, the custom by which the intending bride
and bridegroom in Utopia might at least enter into their contract with eyes open.

Arthur, Prince of Wales, 'could hardly have been more than
a twelvemonth old, when a proposal was made by Henry to
Ferdinand and Isabella of Spain for his marriage, as soon as he
should reach a suitable age, to their infant daughter Katherine,
who was just nine months older[1].'   At the beginning of 1502
the marriage actually took place, and in April, four months
after, the boy-bridegroom died.   Prince Charles of Castile
was barely out of his cradle, when he was betrothed to the
little daughter of Louis XII of France.   But this project,
though ratified at least twice afterwards by formal treaties,
never came to anything.   When the Duke of Brittany died in
1488, he left two daughters, of whom the elder, Anne, was not
quite twelve.   She had for suitors Charles VIII of France,
and the Emperor Maximilian, whose own daughter, by the
treaty of Arras, was betrothed to this same Charles.   After
being married by proxy to Maximilian, whom she had never
seen, and assuming, as his consort, the title of Queen of the
Romans, she was persuaded to repudiate the unreal union,
and in 1491, a girl of fourteen, became the queen of Charles[2].
To find a suitable bride for James IV of Scotland, a man of
thirty, a treaty was made for the hand of Margaret of England,
then a child of eleven.   This was on January 24, 1502.   Being
still of such tender years, it was stipulated that 'her father
should not be obliged to send her to Scotland before the first
of September, 1503[3].'   But her dowry was carefully provided
for, whatever contingencies might arise.   The year before

---

[1] Gairdner : *Henry the Seventh*,
pp. 88–9.
[2] *Ib.*, p. 86.   Compare also Stubbs :
Lectures on Medieval and Modern
History, 1887, pp. 387, 418.
[3] Tytler : *History of Scotland*, 1864,
ii. p. 269, quoting Rymer.

c

More wrote, her sister Mary, whose early affections had been won by Charles Brandon, Duke of Suffolk, was sold, at the age of sixteen, to be a bride to the old King of France, as one of the conditions of a treaty for peace. She was 'consigned to age and decrepitude, instead of to the most gallant of English knights.' But nature avenged herself in this case also. On November 5, 1514, she was crowned Queen of France. On the New Year's day following, Louis XII was dead; and Mary, after this humiliation, became the wife of Brandon.

As More called to mind such instances, and reflected on the disappointments and misery thus caused, he may well have felt impelled to raise a protest for the personal liberty of the human being in this important act of his life, and his freedom, if but his animal freedom, to choose or refuse his mate.

But a thing of far more importance in his eyes than the ways of kings or emperors must have been the condition of the people. At home, in his earlier years, he had witnessed the extortions of Empson and Dudley. In his *Epigrammata*, which are the chips from his workshop, we may see how actively his thoughts had been employed on the subject of greed, public or private; on the difference between a good ruler and a bad, between a lawful king and a tyrant[1]. More's own sentiments are perhaps most tersely summed up in the lines:

'Tutus erit, populum qui sic regit, utiliorem
Ut populus nullum censeat esse sibi[2].'

In his own country he had seen but too many instances in which the interests of king and people did not seem to coincide, where the people must have doubled the *utility* of their rulers. The sight of the prosperous weavers of Bruges and Antwerp must have increased his compassion for the farm-labourers at home, ever more and more dispossessed of their homesteads,

[1] Epigrams 'In Avarum' begin the *Progymnasmata*, and such titles as 'Dives avarus pauper est sibi' occur among the *Epigrammata*. The number of those on 'Tyranni,' 'Prin- cipes,' &c. is considerable.

[2] End of the epigram headed 'Re- gem non satellitium sed virtus reddit tutum.'

that fresh land might be turned into pasture, and wool produced for the consumption of the foreign looms. The subject is so familiar, that I am ashamed to quote authorities that to many of my readers must be commonplace. A very few shall suffice.

Enclosures

The preamble of an Act passed almost while More was writing (7 Hen. VIII, cap. 1),[1] recites that 'greate ynconvenyentes be and dayly encrease by desolacyon, pollyng downe, & destruccion of houses & townes wythin this realme, and leyng to pasture londes which customably have been manured[2] & occupyed wyth tyllage and husbandry, wherby Idelnes doth encrease.' Examples are then cited of the extent to which this depopulation had gone on. Townships of 200 people had been minished and decreased; husbandry greatly decayed, churches destroyed, and the service of God withdrawn. In the temperate Dialogue, which Starkey, a chaplain of Henry VIII, composed as appropriate to be put into the mouths of Pole and Lupset as interlocutors, there are many references to the disorders from which the country was suffering. And this decay, writes the editor, summing up the spirit of their colloquy, 'is generally attributed to sheep-farming and the enclosure of lands. Wherever the finest wool was grown, there noblemen and abbots enclosed all the land for pasture. They levelled houses and towns, and left nothing standing except the church, which they converted into a sheep-house[3].'

T. Starkey, Dialogue

These evictions, as we should now call them, could only lead to one of three endings. Men must either starve, or steal, or beg. The severity of the laws against vagabondage was powerless, as More points out below[4], to remove or even extenuate the evil. 'Thys multytude of beggarys here in our countrey,'

[1] Quoted in *Ballads from Manuscripts*, ed. by F. J. Furnivall, 1868–72, i. p. 6.

[2] That is, *manœuvred*, or tilled by hand.

[3] See J. M. Cowper's Introduction to the *Dialogue* (Early English Text Society's publications), p. cvi. This is almost a quotation from More's own description below, pp. 51–56. Much more to the same effect may be seen in the various *Supplicacyons*, edited in the same series by Mr. Cowper, 1871, pp. xvii, 95 sqq., and in the Introduction to Gascoigne's *Loci* by Prof. James E. Thorold Rogers, 1881, pp. xxiv–v.

[4] Page 44.

Pole is made to say in the *Dialogue*[1], 'schowyth much pouerty, ye, and, as you say, also much idulnes and yl pollycy.' The cry was no mere factious cry, raised by reformers like Simon Fish. But it gathered strength and bitterness as the Reformation went on, because the dissolution of so many religious houses at one and the same time dried up springs of charity, and increased the number of those dependent on them.

Hence Lever, preaching before Edward VI in 1550[2], could exclaim: 'O mercyfull Lorde, what a numbre of Poore, Feble, Haulte, Blynde, Lame, sycklye, yea, with idle vacaboundes, and dissemblyng kaityffes mixt among them, lye and creepe, beggyng in the myrie streates of London and Westminster.'

So far as remedies could be provided by law, More, through his spokesman Hythloday, is at one with the Parliament of 1516. 'Make a lawe,' says he[3], 'that they whiche plucked downe fermes and townes of husbandrie, shal re-edifie them, or els yelde and uprender the possession therof to suche as wil go to the cost of buylding them anewe.' This was almost identical with the language of the Act (7 Hen. VIII, cap. 1) already quoted. It is there ordained that 'all suche townes, villages, etc. shalbe by the said owner or owners . . . within oon yeare next after suche wylfull decaie, re-edified & made ageyn mete & convenyent for people to dwelle.' But the evil was too deep and far-reaching, being, to some degree, one inseparable from a period of transition, to be cured by Acts of Parliament.

---

[1] *Dialogue*, as before, p. 91. See also the ballad *Nowe-a-Dayes*, ed. by F. J. Furnivall, lines 157 sqq.

[2] *Sermons* by Thomas Lever, ed. by Arber, 1870, p. 77.

[3] Page 57. The writer of an able article on the *Utopia* in *The Month and Catholic Review*, 1874, p. 168, has some sensible remarks on the subject. 'There is no denying,' he says, 'the accuracy of More's description of pampered abundance and helpless destitution, those two plague-spots on the face of society. But it is one thing to identify a disease, another thing to devise a remedy that shall be adapted to the strength of the patient. Human nature is too sickly to be taken for change of air to Plato's city of Mansoul, or More's island of Utopia. Some people are fond of the text: *they had all things in common*. But they forget the beginning of it: *the multitude of believers had one heart and one soul* (Acts iv. 32). Union of faith and charity preceded the union of property. And still through faith and charity lies the only road to a salutary and practical communism, that of the city of God on earth.'

And so More, whose sagacious eye foresaw the rapid approach of that state of things which we find Starkey and others lamenting, a few years later on, as having actually come to pass, could devise no more effectual remedy than the spread of a wide spirit of communism. He professes, indeed, to argue against this opinion, which he puts into the mouth of Hythloday. But, as desperate diseases require desperate remedies, it is pretty certain that he wished these doctrines to work in the minds of the thinkers of his age, if only as an antidote to the policy, as blind as it was selfish, which turned adrift farm-labourers and discarded serving-men to steal or beg, and then hanged them, by twenty on a gallows, for stealing.

§ 3.—FRAMEWORK OF THE STORY.

There can be no doubt that for the groundplan of his story More was indebted to the *Voyages* of Amerigo Vespucci. He himself says of his imaginary narrator, Hythloday, that 'for the desire he had to see and knowe the farre countreyes of the worlde, he joyned himselfe in company with Americke Vespuce, and in the iii. last voyages of those iiii. that be nowe in printe and abrode in every mannes handes, he continued styll in his company, savyng that in the last voyage he came not home agayne with him. For he made suche meanes and shift . . . that he gotte licence of mayster Americke (though it were sore against his wyll) to be one of the xxiiii. whiche in the ende of the last voyage were left in the countrey of Gulike [1].' After the departure of Vespucci from this last-mentioned settlement, Hythloday is represented as starting, with five Gulikian natives, in quest of fresh adventures. He roams through many countries, and at last, 'by merveylous chaunce,' reaches Taprobane (Cyprus), whence he gets to Caliquit on the Malabar coast, and at last, meeting with a Portuguese vessel, reaches home, contrary to every one's expectation.

It is in these wanderings through many countries that the imaginary traveller is supposed to discover and visit Utopia.

[1] For the origin of the name Gulike, see the note below, p. 28.

But besides the general suggestion thus derived, a slight inspection of those four *Voyages*, 'that be nowe in printe and abrode in every mannes handes,' will show how attentively More had studied them, and how many accessories for his picture he had borrowed from them.

Vespucci   In a little tract of four leaves, without date or place of publication, but simply entitled *Mundus nouus*[1], Vespucci gives an account of his second voyage, on which he started from Lisbon, May 14, 1501. He wrote it originally in Italian, as a letter to Lorenzo de' Medici, and this has been turned by a 'iocundus interpres' into Latin. The voyage was past the Canary islands to Cape Verde. In those regions—the voyager names them very vaguely—'the people live according to nature, and may be called Epicureans rather than Stoics . . . Property they have none, but all things are in common. They live without a king, without any sovereignty, and every one is his own master.' And a little later on : ' No kinds of metals are known there except gold, in which those regions abound. This fact was told us by the inhabitants, who asserted that in the inland parts was a great quantity of gold, and that it was not prized or held of any account there[2].' This account was repeated, and expanded in some particulars, in the later treatise referred to by More, in which an account is given of the first *four* voyages of Vespucci[3]. 'Gold, pearls, jewels,' the traveller relates, 'and all other such like things, which in this Europe of ours we count riches, they think nothing of; nay, they utterly despise them, and care not to have them[4].' Compare with this what More says of the Utopians[5] :—'And these metalles [gold and silver], which other nations do as grevously and sorowefully forgo, as in a manner their owne lives, if they should altogethers at ones be taken from the Utopians, no man there would thinke that he had lost the

---

[1] The press-mark of the copy I have seen in the British Museum is G. 6534.
[2] Leaf iii. ' Nulla ibi metallorum,' &c.
[3] *Qvattvor Americi Vespvtii Navigationes*, appended to *Cosmographiae*

Introdvctio, 4°., printed at St. Dié in the Vosges, iiij. Kal. Sept. 1507. A copy in the British Museum is press-marked C. 20 b. 39.
[4] Leaf A. viii.   [5] *Infra*, p. 176.

worth of one farthing. They gather also pearles by the sea-side, and diamondes and carbuncles upon certen rockes, and yet they seke not for them; but by chaunce finding them they cut and polish them. And therwith thei deck their yonge infauntes.'

It is in the account of the fourth voyage that the incident occurs, which more than anything else suggested the historical setting for the *Utopia*. A few words about this voyage may therefore be fitly premised.

According to his own account, Vespucci started on the 10th of May, 1503; but Varnhagen has shown good reasons for regarding this as a slip for the 10th of June[1]. After reaching the Cape Verde islands, where they stayed a month, the consort ships struck out SW., in search of Serra Leoa (Sierra Leone). They crossed the line, and on Aug. 10, when now in lat. 3° south, they sighted an island, which may be identified as Fernando de Noronha. Here the chief vessel, of 300 tons, struck on a reef, and was wrecked. Vespucci, who was in command of a ship four leagues off, was ordered to go in search of a harbour. In this quest he got permanently separated from his consorts, with the exception of one vessel, which waited with him a considerable time at Bahia in hopes of news of the rest. The two captains then determined to go on exploring the coast southwards, and at length reached a harbour, which, according to Varnhagen, could be no other than that of Cape Frio. Here they took in a quantity of brazil wood for dyeing, and determined to leave on the spot a small garrison, or factory, of twenty-four men, with arms and provisions; which done, they sailed away, and finally reached Lisbon on June 28, 1504[2].

[1] *Amerigo Vespucci, son caractère, ses écrits, etc.*, par F. A. de Varnhagen, ministre du Brésil . . . Lima, 1865, p. 114. M. de Varnhagen remarks that the voyager's name was accented Amerígo, as still at Florence, and not Amérigo. Dibdin has the odd notion that he was called Americanus, from being the first writer who gave an account of America. See p. 27 n. of his edition of the *Utopia*, 1808.

[2] As the passage is important, from its bearing on More's conception, it may be worth while to give it in the original:—'Relictis igitur in castello prefato Christicolis xxiiij. et cum illis xij. machinis ac aliis pluribus armis, vna cum prouisione pro sex mensibus

On this suggestive hint the imagination of More had fastened, and out of it he constructed the first framework of his romance. Vespucci had described their penetrating some forty leagues inland, before leaving for home, and ascertaining the disposition of the inhabitants to be friendly. Hythloday is made to relate how the settlers dwelt among the natives 'not only harmlesse, but also occupying (trafficking) with them verye familiarly.' He adds, that in the course of lengthy journeys, like Vespucci's of forty leagues, they found 'townes and cities and weale publiques, full of people, governed by good and holsome lawes.'

One of these 'weal publiques' was Utopia, and it is need-less to attempt to define its situation more closely. More places it between Brazil and India, 'beyond the line equi-noctial'; but to give its latitude and longitude would require the genius of a Ptolemy, who could discover a Siatutanda in his Tacitus, and then assign to it a local habitation.

Utopia, and its eponymic King Utopus, bore names expres-sive of the nonentity of the imaginary islanders. By-and-by it became an obvious play on the Latin form of the word to make U- represent Eu-, and so convert this *Nusquamia* into a sort of Island of the Blest[1]. Hence the poet laureate of the islanders is made to say:

> Utopia priscis dicta ob infrequentiam,
> Nunc civitatis aemula Platonicae ...
> *Eutopia* merito sum vocanda nomine;

while Budé, in his letter to Lupset, chooses to call it *Udepotia*, as if *Nunquamia*, not *Nusquamia*.

Having thus found a stage sufficiently removed in Cloudland,

sufficiente, nec non pacata nobiscum telluris illius gente . . . introiuimus.' Leaf F. iii. vers. of the *Qvattvor Navi-gationes.* In 1511 the factory was found still stationed on an island in the harbour. — See Major's *Life of Prince Henry of Portugal*, 1868, p. 379.

[1] The subject was re-discussed in *Notes and Queries*, Seventh Series, v. pp. 101, 229, 371. Sir James Mackin-tosh sums up the matter rightly, in saying that 'all the names which he invented for men or places were in-timations of their being unreal, and were perhaps, by treating with raillery his own notions, intended to silence gainsayers.' — *Miscellaneous Works*, 1851, p. 197. He adds the remark of Joseph Scaliger that Οὐτοπία is a word not formed according to analogy.

More brings his actors upon it. But the dramatic element in his romance is of the simplest. In the portion of the work first composed—the Second Book—there is none at all. It is merely a series of essays, under some eight or nine headings, in which, under the thin disguise of a fictitious narrative, he gives utterance to his own views on various social, political, or religious questions. That these views are all alike seriously propounded, as held by himself, it would be preposterous to maintain. Such a notion would be to crystallize what More purposely left in a state of solution. Much more sensible is the view of Sir James Mackintosh, that the writer regarded the theories he started 'with almost every possible degree of approbation and shade of assent ; from the frontiers of serious and entire belief, through gradations of descending plausibility, where the lowest are scarcely more than the exercises of the ingenuity, and to which some wild paradoxes are appended, either as a vehicle, or as an easy means, if necessary, of disavowing the serious intention of the whole of the Platonic fiction.' If the reader should complain that, on this showing, it is impossible to be sure what More really meant, the remark would have been equally true of much of his conversation, when it was often hard to make out whether he spoke in jest or in earnest. Socrates and More would have understood each other[1]. Much of what he committed to writing in his enforced

---

[1] Through want of perception of this, writers have been found to draw the most opposite conclusions as to the real nature and purport of the *Utopia*. The late Dean Hook held that the Second Book was intended ' to expose the impracticability of those proposed reformations which lollardism had advanced, all founded on communism' . . . ' He showed that he was satirizing the lollards by the very title that he gave to his work, and to his chief speaker' (*Lives of the Archbishops*, v. p. 482 n.). A Roman-catholic writer, on the other hand, Reinhold Baumstark, can see nothing in the theological part of the *Utopia*, but what is plainly anti-Christian, for which the author must be held up as a warning : — ' Allein abgesehen von dieser socialistischen Grundlage, ist der hochwichtige, das Religionswesen betreffende Theil des Buches, dessen Bedeutung abzuschwächen man sich vergebens bemüht hat, geradezu *wider-christlich*.' As for More, he was ' in Leben und Wandel ein unverbrüchlich treuer Anhänger der katholischen Kirche,' but for ordinary mortals ' ein warnendes Beispiel ' to keep them from being lured away by force of imagination from the right path.— *Thomas Morus*, Freiburg, 1879, p. 108.

leisure at Antwerp had probably been in his thoughts for years; may even have found partial expression in his Lectures on the *Civitas Dei* of Augustine. Its now taking definite form may have been hastened, as before suggested, by the life he saw about him in the Flemish towns, by the news from Spanish and other foreign merchants he would meet in the factory at Bruges, by the conversation he would have with Tunstall on the matters of State policy ever coming under that statesman's eye[1], by the letters that would reach him from home.

It only remained, when More had thus embodied his theories in the practice of an imaginary people, to give an air of *vraisemblance* to the whole; which he did by a fiction not unworthy of his favourite Lucian, of Rabelais or of Swift. He had met at Antwerp with a citizen of that town named Petrus Aegidius, or Giles. More's description of him might almost have served for one of himself. One day, after hearing mass at St. Mary's Cathedral, he espied his friend in conversation with a stranger, by his appearance a seafaring man[2]. Being introduced to him by Giles, More had some talk with the new-comer; whom he found so interesting a companion, that he took him, with Giles, to his own house. There, in a garden at the back, seated on a grassy bank, the conversation was resumed. The stranger's name was Raphael Hythloday[3]; he was one of the twenty-four left by Vespucci, as above related, in the fort on the Brazil coast. Moreover he had sojourned in other days in England; he had sat at the table of More's friend and patron, Cardinal Morton, and had many anecdotes to tell of him. This led on the conversation to subjects dear to More's heart, the causes of destitution and crime, the administration of laws, the merits of various forms of civil government. In many of these respects, things were far better managed by the Utopians, whose institutions Hythloday had seen at work, than they were by the nations of Europe. More pressed him to

---

[1] Much State correspondence was at this time constantly passing through Tunstall's hands. See Brewer: *Letters and Papers*, ii. pt. i. p. cclxix.

[2] The incident is told in a most life-like manner below, p. 25.

[3] For the name, see the note below, p. 27.

describe this strange country and its ways minutely to them ; and to this Hythloday consented.   But as it was now midday, they would adjourn to dinner, and after that the relation should begin.

This relation forms the Second Book, already written.   The setting to it, just described, forms the First Book, probably composed by More, when back again in London, in the spring or summer of 1516.   In the mystification which his Swift-like verisimilitude produced, More was well assisted by two or three friends.   Chief of these was Giles, who, as he tells us himself[1], contributed, besides a commendatory letter to Busleyden, the Utopian alphabet, the 'meter of iiii. verses in the Utopian tongue,' and some of the marginal notes which appeared in the second edition.   In fact, Giles's account[2] of the accident which prevented him from catching what Hythloday said about the exact situation of Utopia, is conceived in the same spirit, though not so artistically worked up, as the masterly touches of More himself, where he professes to want settled a point in dispute with John Clement, as to the exact width of the bridge over the Anyder.   Other helpers in the first edition were Gerhard of Nimeguen, and Cornelius Grapheus, or Schrelber, of Alst ; an account of whom will be found in its proper place below[3].

§ 4.—Comparison of the Utopia with Other Ideal Systems.

The constitution of the Utopians, according to the description given, dated back to the conquest of the country by Utopus, 1760 years before the time of Hythloday's visit.   Its name was then Abraxa, and it was not an island but a peninsula.   Utopus made it an island by cutting through an isthmus of fifteen miles. Since that time the prosperity of the community had steadily increased ; so that instead of cottages with mud walls and roofs of thatch, and a people weakened by religious dissension,

---

[1] *Infra*, p. xcviii.   [2] Page xcix.   [3] Pp. 320, 322.

nothing was now to be seen but 'houses curiously builded, after a gorgeous and gallant sort,' with a happy and united population.

Their polity was a confederation of free states, each sending representatives to the general council of the central city, Amaurotc, which thus ranked as the capital. There were in the island, including Amaurote, fifty-four of these states, each consisting of a city with its shire, or adjacent territory. No two cities were less than twenty-four miles apart, nor more than a day's journey on foot. In each were six thousand 'families,' besides an indefinite number of persons living in farmsteads out in the shire. The households in these farm- steads consisted of forty persons each, with two bondmen, under the rule of the goodman and his wife; the members coming in rotation from the number of the townspeople, in such a way that every one of them got two years of country life in turn. The city families were composed of members usually of the same kindred, but not all the children of two parents. Each family was to have not fewer than ten, nor more than sixteen, children of the age of fourteen or there- abouts allotted to it. Should the numbers in any one family become excessive, the superabundance was to be transferred to another that might be deficient. So with the total in one city as compared with another. If it should chance that the population in the whole island became excessive, unoccupied lands in adjacent countries were to be colonized; war being made on any people that resisted such an arrangement. 'For they count this the most just cause of war, when any people holdeth a piece of ground voyd and vacant, to no good nor profitable use.'

For their government, every thirty families are under a 'head bailiff,' anciently called a Syphograunt, but now a Phylarch. Every ten Syphograunts are under a superior officer, once called a Tranibore, but now in like manner a Chief Phylarch. All these are subject to annual election, but the Tranibores are not changed lightly. As there are six thousand families in each city, it follows that there will be in each two hundred

Syphograunts. These elect the Prince [1], anciently called *princeps = mayor?*
Barzanes, now Ademus, out of four candidates sent up to
them, one from each of the four quarters or wards, by the
inhabitants at large. The election is secret, and the office is
held for life, 'unless he be deposed or put down for suspicion }
of tyranny.' The municipal council of each city is formed of
the Tranibores, with the ' Prince ' or mayor ; two Syphograunts
(fresh ones at each meeting) being summoned to their delibera-
tions. These municipal councils are held every third day, or
oftener if need be. The national council of the island meets }
once a year at Amaurote, and consists of representatives, three }
in number, from each of the cities.

The great principle on which the life of the Utopians is based, *Communism*
is community of goods. There is no private property ; no use
of money, except as a means of commercial intercourse with
other nations. In this, More seems to have taken his idea }
from what he had read of Solon or Lycurgus. At intervals } *Lycurgus (Plutarch?)*
along each street the traveller would come to a 'great hall,'
in which dwelt the Syphograunt and his wife. Hither, for
the daily meals, would resort the members of the thirty
families attached to each, as the members of the City Companies in London might have resorted to their Halls. More
draws the picture of the social gathering, as it might often have
presented itself to his eye in the Hall of his own Guild, or in
that of Lincoln's Inn. There is the high table 'overthwart
the over end of the hall.' At every table they sit 'four in
a mess.' The Syphograunt and his wife—for there the women
attend as well as the men—are in the place of honour, supported on either side by two of the 'auncientest and eldest.'
Due provision is made for the young people, for children, for

---

[1] The use of the word Prince by
the translators, for the Latin *princeps*,
seems to have led to the notion that
the government in Utopia was mon-
archical; that there was a king over
the whole island. Thus Morris speaks
of there being ' bondslaves and a king '
(*Reprint of Robynson's Translation,*
1893, pref., p. vi). But Utopia is
expressly called a Republic. Its epo- *Republic*
nymic king, Utopus, vanished, like
Lycurgus, after giving it a constitution,
and left no successor. The *princeps* }
(mayor?) is the head of each city }
alone.

infants and their nurses. The food, which is plain but ample, has been fetched from the common market earlier in the day by stewards, but with a reservation of the very best for the hospitals, one of which, outside the walls, is provided for each of the four wards of the city.

To provide the necessary supplies for maintaining this course of life, but very moderate labour is needed. And this for two reasons. First, there is no object in hoarding, or in super-fluous expense, when all eat and dress alike; and secondly, the number of those excused from active labour is very small. Scarce five hundred in each city with its shire, not counting the aged and impotent, are so exempt. These form the learned class, from which are to be chosen ambassadors, the various public officers, and the priests. The privilege of admission to it comes from the people, 'persuaded by the commendation of the priests, and secret election of the Syphograunts.' If any one so privileged grows idle, he is 'plucked back,' and put to manual labour again. Contrariwise, if any artisan, by good employment of his leisure hours, has made profit in learning, he may be admitted among the *scholares*; not to have an easier life, but to have the opportunity of cultivating better his own proper talent.

Under these conditions, six hours' work a day is found to be sufficient, or even more than sufficient. Three hours are so devoted before dinner; after that comes a rest of two hours; and then another short spell of three hours brings them to supper-time. At eight o'clock all go to bed, to rise (two hours later than More is said himself to have done) at four. Lectures, and music, and honest games fill up the intervals of the day. For in the institution of that weal public 'this end is only and chiefly pretended and minded, that what time may possibly be spared from the necessary occupations and affairs of the commonwealth, all that the citizens should withdraw from the bodily service to the free liberty of the mind, and garnishing of the same.'

In their foreign policy the Utopians are not chivalrous. War they detest. With them *bellum*, whatever philologists

may say, is *res belluina*. The abhorrence of bloodshed, which
at home makes them class the hunter with the slaughterman,
and leave both occupations to their serfs, prompts them, when
forced to enter on a campaign, to resort to almost any means
sooner than have recourse to a pitched battle. It is not that
they are unprepared. They train themselves to martial exercises, and not their men only, but their women. If money be
the sinews of war, of that, as spending none upon themselves,
they have always plenty. But they prefer fighting with brain
to fighting with muscle. And so, if driven to take the field,
which is more often to help an oppressed neighbouring country
than for their own interest, they try every expedient to save
shedding the blood of their own people. They have no objection to let the Zapoletes shed their own in their cause ; for
of those objectionable mercenaries the more killed the better ;
and so they hire them in great numbers. But chiefly they
endeavour to make away with the leaders of the nation they
are at war with. And so they incite, by offers of immense
rewards, any of their own subjects to compass their assassination. They are even ready to lure an invading fleet to its
destruction by 'translating' the marks and signs which pilots
have to guide their ships through the dangerous channels
leading to their great harbour.

If some of these practices are repellent to us, we may be
sure that they would seem not less so in the age of Bayard.
More's plea might have been that, as the world then was, it
was ever the old story: *delirant reges, plectuntur Achivi*. He
would now turn the tables, and let it be seen whether there
would be the same reckless eagerness for war, if the crowned
head were sure to be the one first struck at.

More's last, and one of his longest chapters, is headed ' Of
the religions in Utopia.' The space given to this subject is
what we might have expected from one in whom the theologian
predominated over the statesman. As the Utopians have very
few laws, and of them the interpretation is so plain that every
man is a cunning lawyer, so have they very few priests. These
are men 'of exceeding holiness'; 'and therefore,' says the author

religion

somewhat sardonically, 'exceeding few.' The religion, or rather religions—for 'there be divers kinds' in the island— are described as various forms of nature-worship, culminating in a kind of deism, in which the more part worship 'one chief and principal God, the maker and ruler of the whole world, whom they all commonly in their country's language call Mithras.' Before the coming of Utopus they had been torn by religious dissensions. It was chiefly that which had weakened their resistance, and given him the victory over them. He, consulting more wisely for them, than they had done for themselves, ordained that 'it should be lawful for every man to favour and follow what religion he would, and that he might do the best he could to bring others to his opinion, so that he did it peaceably, gently, quietly, and soberly, without hasty and contentious rebuking and inveighing against others.' The only exception to this toleration was that, in case any denied the immortality of the soul, or the existence of a controlling providence, he should be 'deprived of all honours, excluded from all offices, and rejected from all common administrations in the weal public.' This, of course, was punishment; but no direct penalty, in the way of death or fine, was inflicted.

For the curious and instructive details of their public worship, with its prayers 'so made that every man may privately apply to himself that which is commonly spoken of all'; its priesthood, to which women of due age were admissible; and its music, 'for the most part of other fashions than these that we use in this part of the world'; the reader must be referred to the work itself.

In comparing the ideal thus briefly sketched with others that have preceded or followed it, our object must be, not to set these out in any detail, but simply to notice any points in which they markedly resemble, or differ from, the *Utopia*.

Of these, there is one that will attract us in the first place, not from its presenting any close parallel, but because More is known to have lectured upon it; I mean, the *De Civitate Dei* of St. Augustine. What line More took, in his discourses on this work, we can only conjecture[1], as unfortunately no record of them has been preserved.

St. Augustine

But a short study of the *De Civitate* will disclose some features, common to it and the *Utopia*; on which, therefore, we may suppose that More would have dwelt, when lecturing to his City audience in the Church of St. Lawrence, Jewry.

The origin of Augustine's great work is too well known to need any preface. In 410 Rome was taken and sacked by the western barbarians[2]. This appalling event, which no human language seemed adequate to describe, save by similitudes drawn from the Day of Judgement itself, was ascribed by numbers to the wrath of the older gods. Christianity had drawn men away from their worship; therefore Christianity was the guilty cause. To learn what answer could be made to this charge, a soldier, Marcellinus, applied to Augustine. His bishop's reply was expanded in time into the *De Civitate Dei*, in which both the accusations of the heathen were refuted, and the beginning and growth of that City of God described, which was to flourish and endure when every earthly Rome should have been destroyed. As this heavenly City has a dual existence, its citizens being at once the saints who have passed from human sight, and those who are still treading the earth; and as, moreover, this mundane side of it has always coexisted with an earthly rival, the City of the World[3], it has not in itself such a local and separate habitation as would make it easy to be compared with More's ideal republic. In the conception, however, of a perfect order, as it prevailed in the City of God; in the due subordination of every member of the society, each being glad to do his own work and fall into his own place; in the community of goods, and in the

---

[1] See above, p. xxi.

[2] It was strange that More should himself live to relate another capture and sack of Rome. But this was so. The Imperialist forces took it in 1527. Their excesses, which More ascribes as much as he can to Lutherans, were such, at least in his description, as to make the blood run cold to hear of. See the *English Works*, pp. 258–9.

[3] 'Quas in hoc interim saeculo perplexas quodam modo diximus invicemque permixtas.' Lib. xi. cap. 1.

use and limitation of bond-service, we may perhaps trace a derivation of ideas from the *De Civitate* to the *Utopia*.

'Peace in the household,' says St. Augustine, 'springs from
an agreement among the dwellers therein as to rule and
obedience. They who provide for the welfare of others, bear
rule ; as husband over wife, parents over children, masters
over servants. They who are thus provided for, obey . . . .
And yet even those who rule are the servants of those over
whom they seem to rule[1].'

These principles are reproduced and expanded in the *Utopia*.
There every 'family' is under the rule of the oldest member,
unless he be too infirm ; if so, then under the next in age.
Before divine worship, wives confess to their husbands what
faults they have committed, children to their parents. In
church, and at the daily meals, the younger sit or stand before
the eyes of their elders, that decorum may be ever observed.
The principle of order, in short, is rigid and all-pervading.
So with the idea of membership of the body politic. In Utopia,
if any one is found best fitted for the pursuit of learning, he
passes into the class of those so occupied ; not to be idle, but
to work in the sphere that suits him best. If any others, not
being fitted by nature for the contemplative life, desire the
practical, the course is open to them. They enter it, and are
happy and contented in their work. So it was in the polity
drawn by Augustine, after the pattern traced out for him by
St. Paul. No inferior, there, felt jealous of a superior[2]. The
hand complained not that it was not an eye. Whatever gift
a member was endowed with, that he prized, and coveted not
the gift of another.

On the community of goods, which indeed More may have
taken directly from Plato, rather than from Augustine, something will be said further on[3]. A few words may be added on
the subject of bondage, before we leave the Christian Father.
Bondage, says St. Augustine, came in with sin. No bond-slave

Plato

[1] Lib. xix. cap. 14.
[2] Lib. xxii. cap. 30 'Nulli superiori inferior invidebit,' &c.
[3] See below, p. 105.

bondage

is mentioned in Scripture, till Noah pronounced serfdom to be the future doom of his undutiful son. *To whom ye yield your-selves servants to obey, his servants (bond-slaves) ye are to whom ye obey*[1]. Hence sin is the primal cause of servitude. Men chose the service of sin. Now they suffer the penal servitude which is its consequence. Being penal, and working reforma-tion of character, let those under the yoke bear it patiently[2].

Now it is noticeable that, in the *Utopia*, the slaves are not people of any subject race; not even those taken in war, excepting such as have been made prisoners in an actual encounter. 'The slaves among them are only such as are condemned to that state of life for the commission of some crime, or, which is more common, such as their merchants find condemned to die in those parts to which they trade; whom they sometimes redeem at low rates, and in other places have them for nothing[3].' They are thus taken into Utopia from motives of humanity; or, at least, their example is used to show that a humane policy is also the most profit-able. In the first Book, where Hythloday is made to relate the customs of the Polylerites (Utopians under another name), the subject of slaves is treated at considerable length. And when we read how that 'every year divers of them be restored to their freedom, through the commendation of their patience,' we find More combining Augustine's theory of bondage, as the proper punishment of sin, with the most modern theories as to the alleviation of penal servitude. He may be looked on as the first suggester of the 'ticket of leave.'

To the *Republic* of Plato More's indebtedness is obvious and avowed. That 'ancient and sage philosopher' is the one whom Hythloday had copied in his observant voyagings. The judge-ment of Plato on 'weal publics' is more than once quoted. But the *Utopia* is by no means a mere copy of the *Republic*.

Plato

The second, though later, title of Plato's dialogue is 'con-cerning Justice.' In the endeavour to discover what justice

---

[1] Rom. vi. 16.
[2] *De Civit.* Lib xix. cap 15.
[3] Burnet's Translation, ed 1753, p. 112.

Plat.

is, the object under scrutiny is magnified, so to speak. A civil polity so far corresponds to a living human organization, that the constitution and working of the one will illustrate those of the other. They will do more. So close is the analogy, that for the purposes of the inquiry, the commonwealth may be safely regarded as a vaster man. In it, then, as in an enlarged shadow cast upon the canvas, we may see that which, in the smaller organism, our eyes could not discern. To have its perfect form, a state must possess three classes of citizens: rulers, guardians, and producers. The two former are two divisions of one great class, answering to the rational and courageous elements in the human soul. The third is of a lower order, and answers to the concupiscent element. It may possess property, and may live its life in its own way. But the rulers who have to control, and the guards who have to defend, the common state, must be carefully and laboriously trained. No study, no preparation, is too great for them. Their wives must be such among the women as are fitted by mental and bodily qualifications for propagating the lofty race. That being the only object, no private attachments, no permanent unions, must be allowed. The children born to them must be separated from their parents, and brought up as the children of the state. 'In this way, and only in this way, is it possible for the rulers and guardians to lose all sense of private property, and thus become conscious of a perfect unity of interest[1].' To bring about this state of harmony, the supreme power must, by some means, be vested in philosophers. Only when that is achieved will the members work together in proper subordination. And only then will the lineaments of justice be discerned. We shall then recognize her as that which defines the office each member has to fulfil, and which teaches him to fulfil it without encroaching on that of his neighbour.

It is obvious to any reader that Plato adopted many things from the institutions of the Spartans. Their public meals, their

---

[1] See the Analysis of the *Republic*, prefixed to Davies and Vaughan's translation, ed. 1892, p. xxi.

The Spartans

discarding the use of the precious metals for money, the garrison life led by their men, the hardy, gymnastic training of their women, the severe discipline of their children, are familiar topics, which reappear in the *Republic*[1]. Nowhere else was the subjection of the individual to the state so completely realized. Nowhere else did the machinery employed work so efficiently for the production of that which it was intended to produce—the fighting man, or soldier. Plato tempers this, in his ideal state, by an admixture of Athenian freedom, of wisdom and philosophy; but still his ideal citizen has very much of the soldier. Music for him is placed under a strict censorship, poetry under a ban. Commerce is a thing beneath him; art, if not jealously guarded, will lead to effeminacy. In Plato's aristocracy the old idea of *aristos* still survives.

To the mind of More, on the other hand, the thought of war was only repulsive. His typical citizens, therefore, were not to be soldiers, splendidly equipped. His Utopia was not to be a camp. Hence, while he borrowed much from Plato, or from Lycurgus—the community of goods, the public meals, to some degree the equality of the sexes—he did so with another end in view. Instead of the training of the body for war (though this, as a collateral object, was not neglected), he set before him the training of the intellect for peace. To this end, instead of the barracks, he established the lecture-hall; instead of the exercises of the palaestra, he had books, and music, and games of mental skill. In particular, while approving, and that not in Utopia only, but in his own family, of the education of women being similar to that of men, he opens to them an avenue, of which Plato in the *Republic* gives no hint, but for which a precedent was to be found in the religious systems both of Greece and Rome. He admits them to the priesthood. Like their sisters in ancient Sparta, they are trained to martial exercises. Like the Pythian priestess, or the priestesses of Vesta, they administer the rites of the Utopian religion. Very few are so privileged; the number

female priests

[1] See the Introduction to Professor Jowett's translation, 1888, p. clxx.

of priests altogether is very few; but still they are eligible with the men.

It would be idle to connect this with any approval or disapproval by More of the state of the Christian Church in his own time. It is simply a touch of paganism which he introduces, to illustrate better his own views on the education of women. He was giving his own daughters a learned education. The 'Moricae,' like the 'Bilibaldicae,' soon became known as scholars with whom an Erasmus might correspond. In the *Utopia* he shadows forth, of course with some humorous exaggeration, the parts such women might come to play in a state. If he could have foreseen the mighty power for good or evil two daughters of his own sovereign, reared on the same mental food as his own Margaret, would come to wield in the state, he might perhaps have stayed his hand [1].

Imitations of the *Republic* by writers later than More have only a comparatively slight interest for us. But it may be well to notice a few of them, if only to see how far they fall short of his standard.

In 1643 there was published at Utrecht a little volume containing three treatises, in Latin, on ideal commonwealths. These were: the *Mundus alter et idem* of our countryman, Joseph Hall; the *Civitas Solis* of Campanella; and the *Nova Atlantis* of Sir Francis Bacon. Of these we will give a short account, in the order in which they stand.

Joseph Hall, successively bishop of Exeter and Norwich, was born in 1574, and educated at Emmanuel College, Cambridge. In 1597 he published a volume of satires, in English verse, under the title of *Virgidemiarum Libri*. It was a jest of Plautus to turn *Vindemia*, 'vintage,' into *Virgidemia*, 'a harvest of rods'; and so these satires were to be rods for the fool's

---

[1] It would be an interesting subject of speculation, to try to measure the influence on the history of their country exercised by two ladies of a little later date, but trained by their father as More's children were trained by him: I mean, the two daughters of Sir Anthony Coke; one of whom became the second wife of Sir William Cecil, and the other the wife of Sir Nicholas Bacon, and mother of Sir Francis Bacon.

back. Little of them is remembered now except a couple of lines from the prologue :

> I first adventure; follow me who list,
> And be the second English satyrist.

From this we shall not be surprised to find a like tone of satire pervading the *Mundus alter et idem*, the work we are here concerned with, which appeared in 1607. Visions of an austral continent seem to have flitted across his mind, as they did across that of his great contemporary, Bacon. His voyager sails in quest of it, in the good ship Phantasy, and returns after all his discoveries with the wise man's conclusion that there is nothing new under the sun, He has seen another world ; but after all it is but the same as the one he left ;—the same weaknesses, and follies, and vices of men.

This, then, is the great distinction between Hall's imaginative structure and that of Plato ; that whilst in the *Republic* we see embodiments of the higher faculties of the human soul: its reason in the Rulers, its spiritedness in the Guardians : in the *Mundus* we have only localizations of its baser appetites and passions. The *terra incognita* of Hall is mapped out like a cranium as seen by a phrenologist. Here is the region of acquisitiveness ; there the region of gluttony ; there of combativeness ; and the like. The good qualities alone have no territories to represent them. The chief humour is shown in the proper names ; some of which are happily chosen. The first land at which the voyager touches is Crapulia, 'Sick Headache' land, with its two provinces of Pamphagonia (Gluttony) and Yvronia (Drunkenness). Its capital is Ucalegon [1], past which steals softly the lazy river Oysivius ; where birds bring the people their food, and where the only exertion called for is that of cooking and eating it. For coin, they exchange birds, at a fixed rate. One starling is worth two sparrows, one fieldfare two starlings, and so on. As to their religion, 'they hate Jove because his thunder turns the wine sour and he spoils

[1] As Juvenal uses the name of the Trojan chief for his house, so Hall uses it for a city. It is evidently chosen for its etymological meaning, οὐκ ἀλέγων, to express this sort of city of Laish, or N Importe.

ripe fruit by raining on it. Their god is Time, who eats everything [1].'

The next land visited is Viraginia, the country of the Viragoes.
This is really Gynia Nova, in books of geography mistakenly
written New Guinea. Of its many provinces the chief is Lin-
guadocia, with Garrula for its capital. Here the lionesses are
the painters ; and man, the less noble animal, is treated with
much the same consideration as women used to be, in the days
when Judge More had his jest about the eels in the bag, or
Erasmus thought it natural to put *mulierum loquacitas* as an
obvious illustration of the shorter class of proverbs.

The reader will see from this specimen, which it is needless
to extend, that the *Mundus alter et idem* has little in common
with the *Utopia*.

The next piece on the list is of a much more serious character. Its author, Thomas Campanella, was born at Stilo,
a village in Calabria, in 1568, and entered the Dominican order.
In 1590 he went to Naples for the purpose of publishing some
work, the opinions in which were considered heterodox, and
got him into trouble with the Inquisition. In 1599 he was
arrested on a charge of treason, and is said to have been seven
times put to the rack, and sentenced to imprisonment for life.
From this he was delivered by the interposition of Pope
Urban VIII, and ultimately died in a Dominican monastery in
Paris, in 1639. His *Civitas Solis* was first published in 1623.

The *City of the Sun* is thrown into the form of a dialogue
between a Grand Master of the Knights Hospitallers and
a Genoese sea-captain, his guest. This latter is an evident
reminiscence of Hythloday. There is a trace, too, of allusion
to More in the region assigned to the Solar City. In the
Utopia, when Hythloday travelled with his little company from
the Castellum, they got after a while to the 'line equinoctiall,'
where everything was barren and dried up. Only when they

[1] See the late Professor Morley's
Ideal Commonwealths, 1890, p. 269. A
translation is there given of part of
Hall's work, found among the papers
of Dr. William King (b. 1663), a
kindred spirit.

had got some distance past it, did they begin to find cities of human habitation. Campanella fixes on this torrid zone for the site of his ideal City. In Taprobane (Ceylon), which prosaic geographers make to be many miles north of the equatorial line, his navigator, who has landed, is led to 'a large plain immediately under the equator.' There stands the City of the Sun, compassed by seven encircling walls, like the orbits of the planets; each wall having depicted on it scenes from the history of mankind, the contemplation of which would be of use for the education of the young. In the centre is the temple, itself like the rest of a circular pattern, with altar and dome. Over the altar are two globes, the celestial and terrestrial. Inside the dome are painted the stars of the firmament. From the top outside hangs a revolving flag, 'marked with figures up to thirty-six; and the priests know what sort of year the different kinds of winds bring, and what will be the changes of weather on land and sea[1].'

As it has been remarked, the organization of the city is based on the monastic pattern with which the writer was familiar. 'The great ruler among them is a priest whom they call by the name of Hoh, though we should call him Meta-physicus.' He has three assistant princes. The office of Hoh is conferred on the one who has shown the greatest aptitude for acquiring knowledge. He must understand 'all the mechanical arts, the physical sciences, astrology, and mathematics.' 'Not too much attention is given to the cultivation of languages, as they have a goodly number of interpreters who are grammarians in the state . . . but beyond everything else it is necessary that Hoh should understand metaphysics and theology.'

It is in this way that Campanella would fulfil the aspiration of Plato that philosophers should be kings. His theory of higher education is a remarkable protest, considering the age in which he lived, against the notion that 'he was the most

---

[1] See p. 220 of Morley's *Ideal Commonwealths* before quoted. The translation there given was made by Mr. Thomas W. Halliday. A short analysis of the work is also given by Professor Jowett, in his Introduction to the *Republic*, pp. ccxxvi–vii.

learned who knew most of grammar, or logic, or Aristotle, or any other author[1].' Such an one has 'contemplated nothing but the words of books, and has given his mind with useless result to the consideration of the dead signs of things.' For these reasons they consider that their rulers should have been 'philosophers, historians, politicians, and physicists.'

War is an occupation to which they are much more given than the Utopians. But, as with them, their women are trained in martial exercises. Minute directions are given as to their dress. The hours of work are but four a day; for, 'as every one likes to be industrious,' the labour is quickly dispatched. As with Plato, all things are in common; and they reverence the lives of the Apostles, being told that they practised a community of goods. They hold, moreover, the community of wives and children, as Plato did, and for the same reason. 'They say that all private property is acquired and improved for the reason that each of us by himself has his own home and wife and children[2].' When the Grand Master brings the same objection to this doctrine of communism that Aristotle brought against Plato, and More against his spokesman, Hythloday, that 'under such circumstances, no one will be willing to labour, while yet he expects others to labour,' the Captain can only reply that the objection is one he cannot answer; but that, in some way, there is such a strong spirit of brotherly love among the citizens that all works well.

Want of space forbids longer extracts. The close imitation of the *Republic*, in several points, will however have been made sufficiently plain. As More interwove the Platonic theory with that of a peaceful, half learned, half industrial, community, so Campanella wove across the same warp the weft of educational reform, and of a purified life of the cloister. At the public meals, with him, as with More, 'on one side sit the women, on the other the men; and as in the refectories of the monks, there is no noise. While they are eating, a young man reads a book from a platform, intoning distinctly and sonorously.'

---

[1] Halliday's translation, as above, p. 229.

[2] *Ib.* p. 225. Comp. *De Republica*, bk. v. § 464.

With much that is whimsical, there is much that is of value in Campanella's romance. He felt strongly the necessity of training the mind on a knowledge of facts, and not of mere words only, of mitigating the labour of the working classes, of keeping the race from degenerating by undesirable unions. That a Dominican monk should have written as he did in the first quarter of the seventeenth century, is remarkable. Still more remarkable is it that reforms should have been suggested so temperately by one whose best years were spent in unjust imprisonment.

The *New Atlantis* of Bacon is but a fragment. According to his biographer, Dr. Rawley, 'his lordship thought also in this present fable to have composed a frame of laws, or of the best state or mould of a commonwealth; but, foreseeing it would be a long work, his desire of collecting the natural history diverted him, which he preferred many degrees before it.' What we possess is therefore but one wing, so to speak, of an extensive building. It was designed to be 'a model or description of a college, instituted for the interpreting of nature, and the producing of great and marvellous works for the benefit of men, under the name of Solomon's House, or the College of the six days' works[1].' Though this short piece was not published till 1629, three years after its author's death, the subject was one which had long occupied his mind. When, in 1611, Thomas Sutton died, leaving his munificent endowment of the Charterhouse, Bacon tendered his advice to the king on the form which the endowment should take. He grudged that it should be made into a mere hospital for the poor. As for grammar schools, 'there are already too many, and therefore no providence to add where there is excess.' What 'Mr. Sutton meant for teachers of children' he would have the king devote to 'teachers of men.' And he ends by indicating a threefold scheme for the application of the bequest, of which the first part was to provide 'a college for controversies,' and the second

---

[1] See Rawley's Preface in vol. iii. of Bacon's Works, ed. 1730, p 235.

'a receipt' ('for I like not the word "seminary"') for converts
from Spain, Italy, and other foreign countries, to the reformed
faith [1].

The experiment of a College of Polemical Divinity was tried,
about the time when Bacon wrote, by the foundation of King
James's College at Chelsea. This did not long survive its
founder. But we may now discern better what had been in
Bacon's thoughts, and how his romance of Solomon's House
may have been connected with these designs of the 'English
Solomon,' as part of a wider scheme of politics as well as
education.

The *New Atlantis* opens abruptly. A company of voyagers,
fifty-one in number, sail from Peru, for China and Japan, by
the South Sea. We see again the instinctive belief that
a southern continent existed. *Atlantis* had been realized in
America. The *New Atlantis* was to be—as it afterwards
proved—an Austral land. After long buffeting by storms, they
reach a land 'flat to our sight, and full of boscage.' After an
hour and a half's sail they enter a good haven, 'being the port
of a fair city,' and are there hospitably received. The island
is Bensalem, the people are Christians, and the chief glory of
the place is the Society of Solomon's House, 'which house, or
college, is the very eye of this kingdom.' The king who
founded it was Salomona, who reigned 'about one thousand
nine hundred years ago [2].' But as for the name, the writer
inclines to think that 'our king, finding himself to symbolize
in many things with the King of the Hebrews, honoured him
with the title of this foundation.'

Hence its other appellation of the College of the Six Days
Works; for it was to investigate 'the true nature of all things'
created, 'whereby God might have the more glory in the
workmanship of them, and men the more fruit in the use of
them.' In keeping with this, the visitors are informed that

---

[1] *Works, ib.* vol. iv. p. 412.

[2] As More made Utopus to have
lived 1760 years before the scene of
his romance opens, and as Bacon
wrote a century later, it would almost
seem as if in this date there was a
designed allusion to the *Utopia.*

some parts of Solomon's works are still preserved in Bensalem, which had been lost to the rest of the world : 'namely, that natural history which he wrote of all plants, from the cedar of Lebanon to the moss that groweth out of the wall, and of all things that have life and motion.'

Without entering into more details, it seems clear that what Bacon wished most to promote, in his theory of education, was the study of Natural Science. What projects he would have struck out, if he had finished his design, and made a political as well as educational *Utopia*, we can only conjecture. His treatment of this section, it must be admitted, is a little stiff and pedantic. In one place he evidently refers, though not by name, to his great predecessor. This is where his speaker finds fault with More's device for preventing disappointment after marriage, and proposes another in its stead.

It does not seem worth while to pursue this analysis further. As we approach modern times, the field widens so immensely, that it would be impossible even to recount the names of those who have taken a lead in advocating socialist theories. In the 380 years that have passed since More wrote, the difficulties of the problem that occupied him have become, through the growth of population, at once more complex and more pressing. Some of the revolutionary forces, which he discerned to be even then in motion, have since that time gathered, and burst, and spent themselves ; or at least transfused their energy into other movements. He saw the end of feudalism, the disbanding of the retainers of feudal lords, the clearing away of cottagers, that great sheep-farms, reminding us of the old *latifundia*, might bring in increased revenues. He saw the middle class rising into power, and the poor made still poorer by the dissolution of the religious houses.

Later generations have seen the influence of the middle class reach its height, and in turn begin to decline ; while the vast body of wage-earners, now strong by combination as well as numbers, is pressing forward to take their place. Meantime changes have taken place in the implements and modes of labour analogous to those which have arisen in the social and political condition of the labourer. The weaver working at his own loom in his own cottage, or his wife spinning at her own wheel, gave place first to the master employing as many workers as his dwelling would accommodate; and these in turn disappeared to make room for the factory, with its hundred-handed machines. And if in the political world, with its gradual change from absolutism to democracy, what are called the lower classes seem threatening to swamp the higher, they are themselves exposed to a like fate, as workers, from the very machinery they employ. No one can stand long hours each day tending a machine, or more probably some single part of a machine, without becoming dwarfed and stunted in his faculties as a man. Unlike the old weaver at his loom, he can have no interest in the machine he tends. The raw material it works upon has not been procured by any effort of his; he has no hand in the disposal of it when finished. He receives the wages necessary to ensure his working there regularly, just as the machine receives its share of the steam or other motive power. If any alleviations of another kind fall to his lot, they come, not from the strict conditions of business, but from motives exterior to business, in the employer or in fellow-workers.

That discontent should arise among those whose lives are spent under such conditions is but natural. More had the discernment to perceive that, for men to remain happy and contented, they must have periodical change of occupation. And so in Utopia the dwellers in towns spend some time in rotation in agricultural labour. If any way could be found for such alternation in the crowded towns of our own day, who can doubt that it would be a blessing—a blessing not to one side only? The sedentary student would be the better, physically and mentally, for working some time as a farm-labourer [1]; the ditcher and delver, whose hands have grown horny with the

---

[1] See, for an illustration of this, the *Life of the Rev. Samuel Lewis*, by Mrs. Lewis, 1892.

spade and mattock, would have a chance of saving one-half of
his nature from death by atrophy, if he could pass for a little
while to a life of comparative leisure; the loutish boy, if taken
possession of for public gymnastic training, during the hours
when he would otherwise be hanging about the streets, might
grow up into a soldier-like man, possessed of qualities which,
if we had an army of such like, would make it a backbone of
strength to the nation.

That attempts made to bring about results of this kind should
have failed, from time to time, is less to be wondered at than
regretted.   The societies of Robert Owen, the phalansteries
of Fourier, the *ateliers nationaux*, which travestied rather than
carried out the ideas of Louis Blanc, have all had their trial and
failed.   Selfishness, and the timidity begotten of selfishness,
in those who opposed, and want of purity of motive in many of
those who advocated, such schemes, have alike contributed to
their failure.   Above all, the appeal to violence, or the fear of
it, has closed the ranks of those who might otherwise have
been disposed to give new theories a trial.   More, like Budé and
Colet, had much to say in favour of an abstract communism.
But if any one had tried to put into practice the maxim of
Proudhon[1], 'la propriété c'est le vol,' he would have found
scant indulgence if brought before Sir Thomas on the bench.
So far as effecting any great or sudden changes in society at
large was concerned, the *Utopia* was a failure.   During the
author's lifetime it remained, as it began, simply a philosophical
romance.   But its value should not, on that account, be now
described as 'rather historic than prophetic,' or the author
himself as 'the last of the old rather than the first of the
new[2].'   Its influence has sunk deep into the minds of many
generations.

In his own practice, in the patriarchal life led under his rule
by the combined households at Chelsea, we seem to see an

[1] According to Woolsey, the saying should really be ascribed to Brissot de Warville, in 1782. See his *Communism and Socialism*, 1879, p 102.

[2] See the Foreword by Mr. William Morris to his edition of the *Utopia*, 1893, p. iii.

approximation to the solution of the problem. There every one
was busy, every one was happy. The servants varied their
menial labour by cultivating allotments of garden ground, and,
if they had any capacity for it, by the study of music. The
daughters of the family were trained in learned pursuits as well
as the sons; the Moricae became as famous as the Bilibaldicae.
Works of charity were the delight of all. In the diffusion of
such a spirit of Christian brotherhood as this we may hope to
see a remedy for some of the crying evils of our time. A pluto-
cracy, grasping far more than its share of the good things of this
life ; an unbridled competition in business, where the race is
too keen for the weaker followers to get their due ; the deter-
mination to amass a fortune at all costs, *quocunque modo rem*,
till in the effort even our quiet country glades, and the national
monuments of the capital, are made vehicles for advertisements
of wares :—these things, which are our disgrace, may indeed be
abolished by nihilism and anarchy. But those forces, however
they might succeed in producing chaos, have no power to bring
light and order out of it again. 'There is nothing that conquers
evil,' said Colet[1], 'but good'; and Colet's Master had said the
same before him.

§ 5.—Early Editions of the Utopia.

The first edition of the *Utopia*, in Latin, was printed by
Thierry Martin, at Louvain, towards the end of 1516. The
work of printing appears to have been very expeditious. On
Nov. 12, Gerhard of Nimeguen writes to Erasmus that Martin
will undertake the task[2]. A week later, we hear of the work
being in the printer's hands[3]. By February 24, 1516-17, the
book is out ; as Erasmus, in a letter to Cope, begs him to send
for a copy[4]. Its title-page is as follows :—

[1] *Lectures on Romans*, 1873, p. 86.
[2] Brewer : *Letters and Papers*, ii.
no. 2540.
[3] *Ib*. no. 2558.

[4] *Ib*. no. 2962. These references
are collected by Prof. Arber in the
bibliographical Introduction to his reprint of the *Utopia*.

𝕷𝖎𝖇𝖊𝖑𝖑𝖚𝖘 𝖇𝖊𝖗𝖊 𝕬𝖚𝖗𝖊𝖚𝖘 𝖓𝖊𝖈

MINUS SALUTARIS QUAM FESTI-

uus de optimo reip. statu, deq3 noua Insula Vtopia

authore clarissimo viro Thoma Moro inclytæ

ciuitatis Londinensis ciue & vicecomiti cu-

ra M. Petri Aegidii Antuerpiẽsis, & arte

Theodorici Martini Alustensis, Ty

pographi almæ Louaniensium

Academiæ nunc primum

accuratissime edi

tus.   . ˙ .

𝕮𝖚𝖒 𝕲𝖗𝖆𝖙𝖎𝖆 𝔃 𝕻𝖗𝖎𝖚𝖎𝖑𝖊𝖌𝖎𝖔.

The book is in small 4to, 36 lines to a page. There is no pagination. The first four leaves and the last two have no signatures. The rest are numbered a 1, a 2, &c., to m iv. The printed surface measures a little more than $6\frac{3}{4}$ inches by $3\frac{1}{2}$. On the reverse of the title is a rough woodcut sketch of Utopia, headed Vtopiae Insvlae Figura, representing a tract of land, shaped like a horse-shoe, the opening being at the bottom, washed on all sides by the sea. In the middle of the entrance a fort is erected, off which lies a ship. A river follows the inner line of the curve, its source on the left being labelled **fons anydri**, and its mouth on the right **ostium anydri**. Temples, or public buildings, are dotted about at intervals, on the highest of which is the inscription **cibitas amaurotu**.

The second leaf has on the obverse the Utopian alphabet, represented below, with the *Tetrastichon Vernacula Utopiensium*

e

lingua, and on the reverse the *Hexastichon Anemolii.* On the
third leaf begins the letter of Peter Giles to Busleyden, dated
Nov. 1, 1516, 'Superioribus hisce diebus,' etc., ending on the
obverse of leaf 4. On the same page begins the letter of Joannes
Paludanus Cassiletensis[1] to Peter Giles, 'Utopiam Mori tui,'
etc., followed by a set of ten elegiac verses by the same writer,
ending on the fifth leaf (the first with signature, a 1). Then
follow the Latin verses of Gerhard and Cornelius Grapheus,
the letter of Busleyden to More, and More's prefatory letter to
Peter Giles. This preliminary matter ends on the reverse of a iv.
The SERMO RAPHAELIS begins on b 1, and ends on the reverse
of e iii. On the same page begins the second book, ending on
what would be, if signed, m vi; on the back of which leaf is the
printer's device, two leopards with human faces, holding between
them a shield with the monogram of Thierry Martin. The
printing, which is in Roman letter, is close and unattractive to
the eye, and full of contractions. The marginal notes are in
black letter.

What was meant by the author to be a revised and corrected
edition, was entrusted to the care of Froben, to be printed at
Basle, and did in fact appear there, in two issues, dated March
and November, 1518. But before that edition, of which we will
speak more fully presently, was brought out, there appeared one
from the press of Gilles de Gourmont at Paris, about the end
of 1517, which, as being actually the second in point of time, must
take the precedence. Its title is :—

---

[1] Joannes Paludanus (Van der
Broeck) was a professor of rhetoric
in the University of Louvain, an intimate friend of both Erasmus and
Martin Dorp. It has been thought
that the epitaph on the Bishop of
Cambray, included among the printed
works of Erasmus, iii. 287 (Leyden
edition), is his. The omission of Paludanus's letter and verses from the
edition of 1518 was due to the judge-
ment of Erasmus, or perhaps of Beatus
Rhenanus. 'De Utopia rem tuo per-
mitto judicio,' writes Erasmus to his
friend, Dec. 6, 1517; 'Paludanica possunt omitti.'—See p. 99 of the *Briefwechsel des Beatus Rhenanus,* by Horawitz and Hartfelder, 1886. The com-
positions have little intrinsic merit;
the verses especially being rhetorical,
not poetical; such as might be expected
from an 'academiae [Lovaniensis]
rhetor.'

Ad lectorem.   *Paris ed.*

HABES   CANDIDE   LECTOR

opusculum illud vere aureũ Thomæ

Mori nõ min⁹ vtile q̃ elegãs de opti-

mo reipublicę statu, deq₃ noua Insula

Vtopia, iam iterũ, sed multo correcti⁹

q̃ pri⁹, hac Enchiridij forma vt vides

multo℞ tũ senatorũ tũ aliorũ grauissi-

morũ viro℞ suasu æditũ. quod sane ti-

bi ędiscẽdum nõ modo in manib⁰ quo

tidie habendũ cẽseo. Cui quidẽ ab

innumeris mẽdis vndequaq₃ pur

gatio[1] ~pter Erasmi annotatiões

ac Budaei epĩam :virorũ sane

qui hoc sæculo nostro extra

omnẽ ingenij aleam po

siti sunt : addita est

etiã ipsius Mo-

ri epla eru-

ditissima

Vale.

+

❡ Cum gratia & priuilegio.

This little book is in small 8vo, the measurement of the
printed surface being 4 by 2⅛ inches[2]. It is in Roman letter,

[1] It is amusing that there should
be this slip (for *purgato*) in the very
word in which credit is claimed for
the elimination of errors.

[2] A fine copy, in the original stamped
leather binding, is in the Library of St.
John's College, Cambridge. Another,
said to have been Henry VIII's own

copy, is in the British Museum,
formerly marked 714 a 26, but now
C 65 e 1. In the old Catalogue it is
assigned conjecturally to 1520. But
I can detect no difference between it
and the previous ones of 1517. In the
wrong numbering of the last three
leaves, the broken pagination of the

e 2

25 lines to a page.   In spite of its profession of being 'multo correctius editum,' it has a long list of errata at the end, and the execution generally shows signs of haste.   The following is the collation : Leaf A i, title, as above ; on the reverse, the Hexastichon Anemolii.   On A ij begins the long letter of Budé, ending on A vij vers., with the date 'pridie calend. Aug.' [1517]. Then follows the letter of Peter Giles to Busleyden (A viij to B ij) ; the letter and verses of Paludanus (B ij vers. to B iiij), and More's letter to Peter Giles (B iiij vers. to B viij).   On leaf C i (from which point onwards the leaves are paged as well as signed) begins the *Utopia,* ending on Q iij.   On Q iij vers. comes a second letter of More to Peter Giles, now first printed, 'Impendio me, charissime Petre,' etc., ending on Q v vers. On Q vi is the letter of Busleyden to More, dated Mechliniae, M.D.XVI, which ends on R i, followed by the verses of Gerardus Noviomagus and Cornelius Grapheus.   After these, on R i vers. comes 'Sermonis pomeridiani Raphaelis . . . finis.' A page and a half of *errata* extend to the bottom of R ij, and on the back is the fine printer's device of Gilles de Gourmont. No date is added.   We are enabled to refer the book to the end of 1517, or the beginning of 1518, because Erasmus, in a letter to More dated March 5, 1517-8 [1], speaks of having seen a French edition of the *Utopia,* which must be this.

The additional matter in this edition consists of the letter of Budé, and the second letter of More to Peter Giles.   From the wording of the title it might appear that the marginal notes of Erasmus were now first appended.   But nothing of this kind appears here which was not in the previous edition of 1516. The additions just described were included in that of 1518, and are reprinted below.

What More himself thought of Lupset's proceeding, in getting this printed in Paris, we have no evidence to show.   It would seem that Budé, with his usual impetuosity, had urged on the young English scholar, then staying in the French capital, to

last leaf but one, and other particulars,   [1] Brewer: *Letters and Papers,* vol. ii.
they seem to be identical.   no. 3991.

get printed a smaller and more handy edition ('Enchiridii forma'), which might serve to popularize a work he thought so useful to the men of his time. Probably also he and other admirers of the *Utopia* were impatient at Froben's delay in reprinting it as Basle [1]. This delay can be in some measure explained.

There is in the Grenville Library of the British Museum a volume (No. 2398), in binding probably contemporary, which contains (1) the *Utopia*, ending with Froben's device on p. 165 [2]; (2) *Querela Pacis . . . autore Erasmo Roterodamo*, with the *Declamatio de Morte*, and some other short pieces of Erasmus ; and (3) *Epigrammata Thomae Mori Britanni*, which begins, on the reverse of the title, with p. 166, thus being plainly meant to continue on with (1). On the last page of (3) is the date : 'mense martio, 1518.' A note by Froben on p. 643 of the *Querela Pacis* accounts for this dislocation. He meant, he said, to have issued together all the treatises just described. But finding that they would make too bulky a volume, he had resolved to publish the *Utopia* and *Epigrammata* together as soon as possible, 'nitidissime et quamprimum' ; the *Querela Pacis* and the other tracts of Erasmus being already out of the press. The date of this letter is 'postridie Nonas Decembris (Dec. 6), M.D.XVII.' The imprint on the *Querela* is also 'Mense Decembri, 1517.'

It thus appears that, had not Froben lost time by attempting to include too much in one volume, and by thus having to change his plans, the *Utopia* would have been printed at Basle before the end of 1517, and this would have been the second edition. As things were, it was delayed till March of the following year ; and thus, while in the author's intention the second edition, it is in point of actual time the third.

[1] Erasmus, writing to Beatus Rhenanus, Dec. 6, 1517, says : 'De Mori Utopia et Epigrammatis, res mihi magis erat cordi quam mea ipsius negotia : id cum tantopere ab eis efflagitarim, tamen nescio quo pacto video cessatum.' *Op.* iii. 1646. The printers made the long additional letter of Budé an excuse. See Brewer: *Letters*, &c. ii. no. 3991.

[2] The last numbered page is 164 ; then comes one unpaged leaf, on the back of which is the printer's device.

Basel
ed.

Of this edition of 1518 there were two issues, one in March, the other in November. The copy in the Basle Library, formerly belonging to some of the Amerbach family, bears date ' Mense Novembri.' But that from which the ensuing reprint has been made, is ' Mense Martio.' I add a brief collation of this, though its contents will be seen from what follows [1].

On the reverse of the title, given below [2], is the letter of Erasmus to Froben, ' Cum antehac,' etc. ; on leaf a 2 (paged 3) is Budé's letter to Lupset, ending on p. 10 ; on p. 11 is ' Hexastichon Anemolii ; p. 12 the woodcut of Utopia ; p. 13 the Utopian alphabet ; p. 14 the letter of Peter Giles to Busleyden, ending p. 16 ; p. 17 the letter of More to Peter Giles, ' Pudet me,' etc., ending on p. 24 ; p. 25 begins the ' Sermo,' headed by a woodcut drawing of the friends conversing in the garden at Antwerp, and ending on p. 163 ; on the same page begins the letter of Busleyden to More, ' Non sat fuit,' etc., ending on the obverse of the unpaged leaf (165), followed by the verses of Gerhard and Cornelius Grapheus ; and on the reverse of this leaf the imprint before described.

As compared with the first edition (1516), it will be observed that this omits the letter and verses of Paludanus [3] ; while as compared with the French edition (1517 ?) it leaves out the second letter of More to Peter Giles, ' Impendio me,' etc. In typographical execution it is much superior to its predecessors. The Roman letter is used throughout. The size is small 4to, the printed surface being 5¾ by 3⅞ inches. The woodcut of Utopia is better engraved, and has more details introduced. In the foreground three figures are brought in, to represent Hythloday, More himself, and (probably) Peter Giles. The

[1] I quote from a copy kindly lent me by Mr. Seebohm. The division of the words in the imprint of the November issue is slightly different : ' Basileae apvd Ioannem | Frobenivm mense Novembri | M. D. XVIII.'

[2] See the facsimile facing p. lxxvi.

[3] See the note above, p. lxvi. The omission of his complimentary tribute does not seem to have been taken in

ill part by Paludanus. Erasmus, writing to Botzhem in 1524, refers to him as ' hospes meus,' and calls him ' vir, si quis alius, exacto judicio.' Still, it must have seemed a little unkind, especially as it was to Paludanus (whose lectures he had attended at Louvain) that Listrius dedicated his commentary on the *Moriae Encomium* of Erasmus.

drawing of the garden at Antwerp represents four figures; 'Io. Clemens' (John Clement, tutor to More's children) making the fourth with the preceding three.

A very brief notice of some later editions must suffice. In 1519 the *Utopia* was issued from the Juntine press at Venice, in 8vo, as an appendix to *Opuscula Erasmo roterodamo interprete*. An edition appeared at Louvain, in the italic letter, in 8vo, in 1548, and one at Cologne, 8vo, 1555. In 1563 the *Utopia* was included in the *Lucubrationes* published by Episcopius at Basle; and in 1565 and 1566 in the *Opera* at Louvain. In 1591 there appeared a small edition 'ex officina Cratoniana' at Wittenberg.

Venice ed. 1519

It is not necessary to go beyond the end of the century[1]. That no edition should have been published in English during the author's lifetime, and that no English translation of it should have been made till 1551, would be thought strange, if we did not consider the political circumstances of the time.

§ 6.— RALPH ROBYNSON, AND THE ENGLISH TRANSLATIONS.

Our debt to Robynson is so great, for having been the first to translate the *Utopia* into English, that he seems to deserve something more than a passing mention.

Ralph Robynson, a Lincolnshire man, was born in 1521, the son of poor parents who had a large family. He was educated at Grantham and Stamford grammar schools[2], and was thus a schoolfellow of William Cecil, afterwards Lord Burghley. On the acquaintance or friendship thus formed he based a claim to consideration, in more than one urgent petition to the great Secretary later on in life. Being the only one of his family destined for a learned profession, he entered Corpus Christi College, Oxford, in 1536, at the age of 15[3]. He took his B.A.

---

[1] Besides those named, Mr. Sidney Lee, in the article before quoted, cites an edition at Basle, 1520, in 4to, which I have not been able to trace.

[2] 'Cum Robynsonum Granthamien-sem Stamfordiensemque noueris in literis educatum.' — *Letter to Cecil*, Lansdowne MSS., vol. ii. no. 59.

[3] Wood's *Fasti* (Bliss), pt. i. col. 111, *n.* See also Boase's *Register*, i. p. 199.

in 1540, was made Fellow of his College, June 16, 1542, and in March, 1544, supplicated for his M.A., but whether he proceeded is not certain. He afterwards obtained the livery of the Goldsmith's Company[1], and received some appointment as clerk in Cecil's service. This he sought to have assured to him by letters patent, and also to have the stipend attached to it increased.

There are preserved among the Lansdowne MSS.[2] two letters and a copy of elegiac verses, all in Latin, addressed at various times by Robynson to his patron, from which we learn several particulars of his life, and of his struggles for a subsistence. In the first of these letters, endorsed May, 1551, he speaks of both his parents as still living, and needing help from him. He had moreover been lately saddled with the maintenance of two brothers, and had in consequence to run into debt. In the verses, endorsed 'his New Year's gift,' written apparently before 1571 (as he does not yet address his patron as Baron of Burghley), he speaks of the burden of advancing years, and hints at having been serviceable to Cecil in their school-days:—

'Si bene quid de te merui puerilibus annis,
    Quolibet officio si tibi gratus eram;
Id mihi pauperie nunc atque senilibus annis
    Oppresso prosit, vir venerande, precor.'

There is something pathetic, and at the same time humiliating, in these repeated applications. It does not appear that either they, or the dedication of the *Utopia* in 1551, produced much effect; as the last letter, which is addressed to Cecil as Lord High Treasurer, and therefore was not written before July, 1572, is drily endorsed: 'Rodolphus Robynsonus. For some place to relieve his poverty.' In what year Robynson died, I have not been able to discover. He must not be confused with a Ralph Robinson, of Lincoln College, Oxford, who was B.A. in 1609, nor with a Cambridge man of the same name, but

---

[1] Strype: *Eccl. Mem.*, ed. 1822, ii. pt. i. p. 548.

[2] Vol. ii. nos. 57–59. The style is pretentious, as Robynson naturally wishes to show off his Latinity to Cecil, and quotations from Greek and Latin authors are unsparingly introduced.

of a still later date, who was minister of St. Mary Woolnoth, London, and died in 1655[1].

Robynson's style as a translator has undoubted merits. It *Style* is idiomatic and picturesque. In many points it illustrates, and is illustrated by, the English of the Book of Common Prayer, which, in its earlier form, had appeared only two years before the *Utopia*. Its chief fault is redundancy, or rather a constant effort to express the sense of the Latin by an accumulation of partial equivalents. We are reminded, in reading it, of the Prayer for the Queen's Majesty, with its 'health and wealth,' 'vanquish and overcome,' 'joy and felicity.' Thus the single word *instat*, in the Latin, becomes with Robynson 'draweth neare and is at hand'; *seruanda*, 'to be fulfylled, obserued and kept.' *Armis* is rendered 'their armoure or harneis whiche they weare'; while *auguria*, in one place[2], has for its equiva- *See p. 279.* lent a whole sentence. Nor is this characteristic feature subdued in the later edition. On the contrary, the striving to attain greater accuracy now and then leads to a yet more dictionary-like definition, instead of a translation. Thus *sine omni prorsus hostimento*, which in the first edition is 'without annye gage or pledge,' appears in the second as 'without any gage, *pawne* or pledge.'

The first edition of Robynson's translation was published by Abraham Vele[3], at the sign of the Lambe in St. Paul's Churchyard, 1551. It is in black letter, small 8vo size, the

---

[1] Wood's *Fasti* (Bliss), pt. i. col. 334. See also the Preface to *Christ the All and in All*, by Ralph Robinson, 1656. Dr. Lumby, p. 184, identifies our Ralph Robynson with one who trans- lated Leland's *Ancient Order . . . of Prince Arthur*; but that is a mistake. The translator of Leland was a *Richard* Robinson, citizen of London, who in 1583 put forth in 4to ' The Auncient Order, Society and Unitie laudable of Prince Arthure,' &c., translated and collected by himself, under the initials R.R. He had, in 1576, published a treatise of 'A moral Methode of

Ciuile Policie,' abridged from Patricius, Bishop of Gaieta. Hence perhaps the confusion. There is a full account of him in Watt's *Bibliotheca*; and Sir S. E. Brydges in *The British Bibliographer*, vol. i. p. 109, art. iii, distinctly speaks of him as Richard Robinson. He was a voluminous writer.

[2] P. 279.

[3] An account of Abraham Vele, or Veale, with a long list of works pub- lished by him, will be found in Watt's *Bibliotheca*. He was a Draper and Stationer.

height of the page being about 5⅜ inches, the breadth 3½ [1]. It has no marginal summaries, as the second edition has. It contains 142 leaves, unpaged.

The Epistle 'To the right honourable, and his verie singuler good maister, maister William Cecylle esquiere,' occupies leaves ✠ ii–vi. On the reverse of ✠ vi begins the Letter of More to Peter Giles, ending on A iv. The reverse of this last leaf is blank. 'The fyrste Boke' begins on B i, and ends on G iv vers. The second begins on G v and ends on S iv. No translation of verses, or any other matter, is added.

The second edition, of 1556, resembles the first in size and style of printing, being also in black letter, but has six leaves fewer. The leaves, excepting the last five, are paged as well as signed. The most noticeable change in the contents is the omission of the dedicatory letter to Cecil [2].

After the title comes an address of the Translator to the gentle Reader (a ij–a iij vers.); then the letter of More to Giles (a iiij–B i vers.); the first book (B ij–K iii); the second book (K iij vers.–S iij vers.); Giles' Letter to Buslyde (S iiij–S vi); 'A meter of iiij verses' and others (S vj vers.–S vij vers.); the address of the Printer to the Reader, explaining why no reproduction of the Utopian alphabet is given (S viij), with the imprint below. The last page of all is blank.

The third edition of Robynson's translation was printed by Thomas Creede, London, 1597, in small 4to. Signatures to T iv. The body of the work is still in black letter, but the preface in Roman.

The fourth was by Bernard Alsop, at the sign of the Dolphin in Distaff Lane, London, 1624, in small 4to, pp. 138, besides eight at the beginning and six at the end not paged. It is dedicated by Alsop to 'the honourable descended Gentleman, Cresacre More, of More-Place in North-Mimes, in the Countie of Hereford, Esquire; next in Bloud to Sir Thomas More . . .,' and

Cresacre
More

---

[1] The copy from which this description is taken is in the Grenville Library of the British Museum, marked G. 2288.

[2] Are we to infer that by 1556 Robynson had grown weary of courting Cecil's favour? If so, he made another attempt, as we have seen above, in 1572 or soon after.

professes to be 'now after many Impressions, newly Corrected and purged of all Errors hapned in the former Editions.'

The work has been often reprinted since ; notably by Dibdin[1], 'with copious notes and a Biographical and Literary Introduction,' London, 1808, 4to (edited afresh, and printed in a handsome style by Robert Roberts, Boston, 1887, 8vo, with facsimiles and notes) ; by Professor Arber in his 'English Reprints,' 1869, and Professor Lumby, at the Pitt Press, in 1879 ; and, quite recently by Mr. William Morris, at the Kelmscott Press, in 1893.　This last is a sumptuously printed book, in black letter type, with rubricated marginal notes ; pp. i–xiv, 1–283, size 9 inches by 5.　The text is revised by F. S. Ellis, on the basis of the second edition.　It has a 'Foreword' of six pages by Mr. Morris.

W. Morris

Until 1684 Robynson's was the only English translation of the *Utopia*　But in that year, Gilbert Burnet, Bishop of Salisbury, published a new version.　His motives for undertaking the work, as he tells us, were want of diversion and the having on his hands too much leisure.　Accordingly, he thought it 'no unkind nor ill Entertainment to the Nation' to give it the 'fine and well-digested Notions' of 'one of the greatest Men that this Island has produced.'　His opinion of the older translation is curious : 'It was once translated into *English* not long after it was written ; and I was once apt to think it might have been done by Sir Thomas More himself: For as it is in the *English* of his Age, and not unlike his Style ; so the Translator has taken a Liberty that seems too great for any but the Author

---

[1] Dibdin professed to reproduce the text of the *first* edition :—' The text of the present edition is taken from the first English one, which was translated by Raphe Robinson, and printed by Abraham Vele, in 1551 ' (*The Epistle to the Reader*).　But later on (p. clxxx), he finds it ' proper to observe, that the text of the present edition of the Utopia is, in fact, printed from Alsop's edition of 1639; as being the most convenient ancient edition for the compositor to execute.'　As Alsop's was a gradually modernized form, embodying the alterations of the second and subsequent editions, and with the spelling modified, it may easily be judged how far Dibdin's reprint was from representing accurately the first edition. As the reprints of Arber, Lumby, and Morris all follow the second edition, it is believed that the present is, as was said in the Preface, the only exact reproduction of the first edition yet made.

himself, who is Master of his own Book, and so may leave out
or alter his Original as he pleases : Which is more than a
Translator ought to do, I am sure it is more than I have pre-
sumed to do.'

Bishop Burnet's translation was often reprinted [1]. It is undoubtedly closer to the Latin and more correct than Robynson's,
but wants the racy English which gives a charm to the older
book. The reader will, however, be able to form his own
opinion, from specimens given from time to time in the notes.

Another translation was made in 1808 by Arthur Cayly the
younger. His work appeared in two vols. 4to, of which the
first was occupied by Memoirs of Sir Thomas More, while the
second contained the new version of the *Utopia*, the History of
Richard III, and a rendering of some of More's Latin poems.
The translation for the most part closely follows Burnet's, and
has never been reprinted.

[1] A list of these reprints is given
by Professor Arber. The most noticeable of them is that appended by Dr.
F. Warner, in 1758, to his *Memoirs of
Sir Thomas More*.

DE OPTI

MO REIP. STATV DEQVE
noua insula Vtopia libellus uer
re aureus, nec minus salutaris
quàm festiuus, clarissimi disertis
simiq̃ uiri THOMAE MORI in
clytæ ciuitatis Londinensis ciuis
& Vicecomitis.

EPIGRAMMATA clarissimi
disertissimiq̃ uiri THOMAE
MORI, pleraq̃ e Græcis uersa.
EPIGRAMMATA. Des. Eras
mi Roterodami.
Apud inclytam Basileam.

REDUCED FACSIMILE OF THE TITLE-PAGE OF
THE EDITION OF MARCH, 1518

To face p. lxxvi]

ERASMUS OF ROTTERDAM

TO HIS DEAR GOSSIP JOHN FROBEN [1]

GREETING.

I have hitherto been pleased beyond measure with all that my friend More has written, but felt some distrust of my own judgment, by reason of the close friendship between us. But now that I see learned men to be all unanimously of my opinion, even outdoing me in the warmth of their admiration for his transcendant genius,—a proof of their greater discernment, though not of their greater affection; I am quite satisfied that

2   ## ERASMVS ROTERODAMVS IOAN

NI FRODENIO COMPATRI SVO

CHARISSIMO S. D.

CVM antehac omnia Mori mei mihi supra modum semper placuerint, tamen ipse meo iudicio nonnihil diffidebam, ob arctissimam inter nos amicitiam. Caeterum ubi uideo doctos uno ore omneis meo subscribere suffragio, ac uehementius etiam diuinum hominis ingenium suspicere, non quod plus ament, sed quod plus

---

[1] John Froben, the printer, was a native of Hammelburg in Franconia, born in 1460. After studying in the university of Basle, he entered the printing-house of John Amerbach, and in time became himself a printer in that city. Erasmus, many of whose works issued from his press, was an intimate friend, and was godfather to his son John Erasmus, or Erasmius. Hence the term *compater* used in the superscription of this letter. Froben died in 1527. His widow, Gertrud, is mentioned in a letter of Beatus Rhenanus to Boniface Amerbach, dated Aug. 20, 1536. Erasmus's godson was married in that year.—See the *Briefwechsel des Beatus Rhenanus*, ed. by Horawitz and Hartfelder, 1886, pp. 421, 430; and Erasmi *Epist.* 922.

I am in the right, and shall not shrink in future from openly expressing what I think. What would not such marvellous natural gifts have accomplished, if his intellect had been trained in Italy; if it were wholly devoted to literature; if it had had time to ripen for its proper harvest, its own autumn? While quite young, he amused himself with composing epigrams, many of them written when he was a mere boy. He has never gone out of his native Britain, save once or twice, when acting as ambassador for his sovereign in the Netherlands[1]. He is married, and has the cares of a family; he has the duties of a public office to discharge, and is immersed in the business of the law-courts; with so many important affairs of state distracting him besides, that you would wonder at his having leisure even to think of books.

So I have sent you his *Prolusions* and *Utopia*. If you think fit, let them go forth to the world and to posterity with the recommendation of being printed by you. For such is the reputation of your press, that for a book to be known to have been published by Froben, is a passport to the approbation of the learned.

cernant; serio plaudo meae sententiae, nec uerebor posthac quod sentio palam eloqui. Quid tandem non praestitisset admirabilis ista naturae felicitas, si hoc ingenium instituisset Italia? si totum Musarum sacris uacaret, si ad iustam frugem ac uelut autumnum suum maturuisset? Epigrammata lusit adolescens admodum, ac pleraque puer. Britanniam suam nunquam egressus est, nisi semel atque iterum, Principis sui nomine legatione fungens apud Flandros. Praeter rem uxoriam, praeter curas domesticas, praeter publici muneris functionem et causarum undas, tot tantisque regni negociis distrahitur, ut mireris esse ocium uel cogitandi de libris.

Proinde misimus ad te progymnasmata illius, et Vtopiam; ut si uidetur tuis excusa typis orbi posteritatique commendentur: quando ea est tuae officinae autoritas, ut liber uel hoc nomine placeat eruditis, si cognitum sit e Frobenianis aedibus prodiisse.

---

[1] This seems to be a mistake on the part of Erasmus. More, in his letter to Dorp, written in 1515, expressly says that, seven years before, he had been in the universities of Paris and Louvain, though not for long—'non diu quidem.' More's second embassy, to Calais, was in the very month in which Erasmus wrote these words.

Farewell, and greet for me your good father-in-law, your charming wife, and the darling children. Mind you bring up in good learning my little godson Erasmus, in whom I have a claim as well as you ; for learning has rocked his cradle.

godson
claim

    Louvain :

    Aug. 25th, 1517.

Bene uale cum optimo socero, coniuge suauissima ac mellitissimis liberis. Erasmum filiolum mihi tecum communem, inter literas natum, fac optimis literis instituendum cures.

    Louanii. viii. Cal. Septemb. An. M.D.XVII.

GUILLAUME BUDÉ[2]

TO HIS ENGLISH FRIEND THOMAS LUPSET[1]

GREETING.

I owe you many thanks, my learned young friend Lupset, for having sent me Thomas More's *Utopia*, and so drawn my attention to what is very pleasant, and likely to be very profitable, reading. It is not long ago since you prevailed upon me (your en-

GVILLIELMVS   3

BVDAEVS THOMAE LV-

PSETO ANGLO S.

GRATIAM SANE INGENTEM a nobis iniisti, Lupsete adolescentum doctissime, qui me, porrecta mihi VTOPIA THOMAE MORI, ad iucundissimae simul et usui futurae lectionis intentionem auertisti. Nam cum a me dudum precibus id contendisses, id quod,

---

[1] Thomas Lupset (? 1498–1530), a scholar whom Colet had educated under William Lily, was at this time in Paris, where he graduated in arts. He was superintending the publication of works by more than one of his friends.—See more in the Introduction, § 5, and, for the scanty details of his life, Cooper's *Athenae Cantabrigienses*, i. p. 40.

[2] The name of Guillaume Budé is too well known in the world of letters to need much said about him here. He was born in 1467, and was thus a close contemporary of Erasmus and Colet. He died in 1540. Many characteristics of the man are illus-

trated in this letter: his vehemence, his aversion from the law (to the profession of which he was originally destined), his fondness for displaying his command of Greek, and the like. He was invited to the court of the French king as urgently as was More to that of the English, and showed the same disinclination to the service; complying only when he believed that the cause of learning would be benefited by his presence at court. At one period of his life, to counteract the effects of too sedentary habits, he devoted himself to active work in building and planting on his two country estates, at Marly and Saint-

treaties seconding my own strong inclination) to read the six books of Galen *On the preservation of the Health,* to which that master of the Greek and Latin tongues, Dr. Thomas Linacre[1], has lately rendered the service—or rather, paid the compliment[2] —of translating them from the extant originals into Latin. So well has the task been performed, that if all that author's works (which I consider worth all other medical lore put

Linacre's Galen

meapte ipse sponte magnopere exoptaturus eram, ut THOMAE LINACRI, medici utraque lingua praestantissimi, libros sex *De sanitate tuenda* legerem, quos ille ex Galeni monumentis latinitate nuper ita donauit, uel quibus ipse potius latinitatem, ut, si omnia eius autoris opera (quae ego instar omnis medicinae esse puto) latina tandem fiant,

---

Maur. When so occupied, he loved, says his biographer (in *Batesii Vitae,* p. 234), in words that will illustrate an expression in his letter, ' cursu corpus fatigare '

As, besides these country villas, he purchased a house in the Rue Saint-Martin, then accounted the best part of Paris, which he pulled down and rebuilt from top to bottom, and lived in such style there that Vives, the Spanish scholar, when he paid him a visit, ' fut ébloui du train que menait l'illustre helléniste,' it is obvious that his invectives against private property must be taken with some qualification.

How far, or whether at all, Budé was inclined to the principles of the Reformation, has been much disputed. He appears to be very guarded in respect of anything said about doctrine. But in the *Epistolae Posteriores* he animadverts, as bitterly as Erasmus might have done, upon the obstructiveness of the haters of the new learning. His great treatise *De Asse,* 1514, was judged by the Spanish Inquisition to require expurgation (Tribbechovius, *De Doctoribus Scholasticis,* 1719, p. 89) ; and we can hardly wonder at this, after reading the fierce attack (fol. xci vers.) upon the late pope, Julius II.

It is certain that, after his death, his widow and some of his many children migrated to Geneva, and made profession of the reformed faith. And some not unnaturally thought, as Melanchthon tells us, that this pointed to counsel given in that direction by Budé, before his death.—See Bayle, i. p. 751, note L, and the monograph by M. Rebitté, 1846. p. 147.

[1] Thomas Linacre (? 1460-1524), the founder of the Royal College of Physicians, had for some time been engaged in translating treatises of Galen into Latin. His version of the six books *De sanitate tuenda* was first printed at Paris by Guillaume Rubé in 1517.—See Johnson's *Life of Linacre,* 1835, p. 208.

[2] In the Latin a nice distinction is drawn between the two constructions of *donare : donare aliquid alicui,* and *donare aliquem aliqua re.* As Valla points out, the latter has more the notion of supplying a deficiency, or giving a ' consolation prize,' as in the well-known line of Virgil :

Nemo ex hoc numero mihi non donatus abibit.

The former more expresses a voluntary or complimentary gift. See the *De linguae Latinae elegantia,* 1529, leaf 87 vers.

together) be in time translated, the want of a knowledge of Greek is not likely to be seriously felt by our schools of medicine.

I have hastily skimmed over that work, as it stands in Linacre's papers (for the courteous loan of which, for so long a time, I am very greatly indebted to you) with the result that I deem myself much benefited by the perusal. But I promise myself still greater profit when the book itself, on the publication of which at the presses of this city you are now busily engaged, shall have appeared in print.

While I thought myself already under a sufficient obligation to you on this account, here you have presented to me More's *Utopia*, as an appendix or supplement to your former kindness. He is a man of the keenest discernment, of a pleasant disposition, well versed in knowledge of the world. I have had the book by me in the country, where my time was taken up with running about and giving directions to workpeople (for you know something, and have heard more, of my having been occupied for more than a twelvemonth on business connected with my country-house); and was so impressed by reading it, as I learnt and studied the manners and customs of the Utopians, that I well-nigh forgot, nay, even abandoned, the management of my family affairs. For I perceived that all the theory and

non magnopere tum medicorum schola Graecae linguae cognitionem desideratura uideatur.

Eum librum ex schedis LINACRI tumultuaria lectione ita percurri (quarum mihi usum tantisper a te indultum summi loco beneficii duco), ut ea lectione multum me profecisse existimem ; sed ex libri editione quae nunc a te sedulo procuratur in officinis huius urbis, ego maiorem etiam profectum mihi spondeam.

Hoc nomine cum me tibi obstric|tum esse satis crederem, ecce tu 4 mihi, uelut prioris beneficii uel appendicem uel auctarium, VTOPIAM illam MORI donasti, hominis in primis acris, ingenioque amoeno, et in rerum humanarum aestimatione ueteratoris. Eum librum cum ruri in manibus cursitando, satagendo, operis imperitando haberem (partim enim nosti, partim audisti, uillaticis me negociis alterum iam hunc annum multum operae impendisse), usque adeo eius lectione affectus sum, cognitis et perpensis Vtopinorum moribus et institutis, ut paene rei familiaris procurationem intermiserim atque etiam abie-

practice of domestic economy, all care whatever for increasing one's income, was mere waste of time.

And yet, as all see and are aware, the whole race of mankind is goaded on by this very thing, as if some gadfly were bred within them to sting them. The result is that we must needs ↓ confess the object of nearly all legal and civil qualification and training to be this : that with jealous and watchful cunning, as each one has a neighbour with whom he is connected by ties of citizenship, or even at times of relationship, he should be ever conveying or abstracting something from him ; should pare away, repudiate, squeeze, chouse, chisel, cozen, extort, pillage, purloin, thieve, filch, rob[1], and partly with the connivance, partly with the sanction of the laws—he ever plundering and appropriating.

corrupt society

This goes on all the more in countries where the civil and canon law, as they are called, have greater authority in the two courts. For it is evident that their customs and institutions are pervaded by the principle, that those are to be deemed the high-priests of Law and Equity, who are skilled in *caveats*—or *capiats*, rather ; men who hawk at their unwary fellow-citizens ; artists in formulas, that is, in gudgeon-traps ; adepts in con·

vs. laws & lawyers

cerim, cum nugas esse uiderem artem omnem industriamque occonomicam, omnemque omnino curam census ampliatricem : qua tamen ipsa omne genus mortalium uelut oestro quodam intestino et congenito exagitari, nemo est qui non uideat et intelligat ; ut legitimarum (prope dixerim) et ciuilium artium ac disciplinarum eum esse scopum fateri necesse sit, ut tam liuida quam accurata solertia alter ab altero, quicum ciuilitatis ius ei et interdum gentilitatis intercedit, quippiam semper abducat, abstrahat, abradat, abiuret, exprimat, extundat, exculpat, extorqueat, excutiat, excudat, subducat, suffuretur, suppilet, inuolet, legibusque partim conniuentibus partim nutoribus, auferat et interucitat.

Id adeo magis in iis gentibus, apud quas iura quae ciuilia et pontificia uocantur amplius in utroque foro ualent ; quorum moribus et 5 institutis eam inualuis|se opinionem nemo non uidet, ut homines cautionum prudentes, uel captionum potius, et inconsultorum ciuium aucupes, et formularum, id est, excipularum, opifices, ac pactilis iuris

---

[1] If it is impossible to impart elegance to such a string of expletives, I must plead that they are only a close reproduction of the Latin.

cocted law; getters up of cases; jurisconsults of a controverted, perverted, inverted *jus*. These are the only fit persons to give opinions as to what is fair and good; nay, what is far more, to settle with plenary power what each one is to be allowed to have, and what not to have, and the extent and limit of his tenure. How deluded must public opinion be to have determined matters thus [1]!

The truth is that most of us, blind with the thick rheum of ignorance in our eyes, suppose that each one's cause, as a rule, is *just*, in proportion to its accordance with the requirements of the *law*, or to the way in which he has based his claim on the *law*. Whereas, were we agreed to demand our rights in accordance with the rule of truth, and what the simple Gospel prescribes, the dullest would understand, and the most senseless admit, if we put it to them, that, in the decrees of the canonists, the divine law differs as much from the human; and, in our civil laws and royal enactments, true equity differs as much from law; as the principles laid down by Christ, the founder of human society, and the usages of His disciples,

(margin note: Truth & gospel vs. law)

callentissimi, et litium concinnatores, iurisque contrauersi peruersi inuersi consulti, antistites esse iusticiae aequitatisque existimentur; solique digni qui de aequo bonoque responsitent, atque etiam (quod maius est multo) qui cum imperio ac potestate statuant quid unumquemque habere, quid non habere, quatenus quamdiuque liceat; hallucinantis id utique sensus communis iudicio.

Quippe cum plerique hominum, crassis ignorantiae lemis caecutientes, tam aequissimam fere causam unumquemque putemus habere, quam maxime ius postulat, aut iure subnixus est; cum, si ad ueritatis normam et ad simplicitatis Euangelicae praescriptum exigere iura uelimus, nemo sit tam stupidus quin intelligat, nemo tam uaecors quin fateatur si urgeas, tam ius et fas hodie ac tamdiu in sanctionibus pontificiis, et ius atque aequum in legibus ciuilibus et principum placitis dissidere, quam CHRISTI, rerum humanarum conditoris, instituta, eiusque discipulorum ritus, ab eorum decretis et placitis, qui

---

[1] With these denunciations of the law as then administered may be compared the not less severe strictures of DeanColet in his *Exposition of Romans* (edited with the *Letters to Radulphus*, 1876), p. 162; and in his *Lectures on Corinthians*, pp. xviii, 45. Both he and Budé had probably in their minds the language of Cicero, *De Oratore*, i. 55.

differ from the decrees and enactments of those who think the *summum bonum* and perfection of happiness to lie in the money-bags of a Croesus or a Midas. So that, if you chose to define Justice now-a-days, in the way that early writers liked to do, as the power who assigns to each his due[1], you would either find her non-existent in public, or, if I may use such a comparison, you would have to admit that she was a kind of kitchen stewardess: and this, alike whether you regard the character of our present rulers, or the disposition of fellow-citizens and fellow-countrymen one towards another.

Perhaps indeed it may be argued, that the law I speak of has been derived from that inherent, world-old Justice called *natural* law[2]; which teaches that the stronger a man is, the more he should possess; and, the more he possesses, the more eminent among his countrymen he ought to be : with the result that now we see it an accepted principle in the Law of Nations, that persons who are unable to help their fellows by any art or practice worth mentioning, if only they are adepts in those complicated knots and stringent bonds, by which men's pro-

Croesi et Midae aceruos bonorum finem esse putant et felicitatis cumulum. Adeo si iusticiam finire nunc uelis, quomodo priscis autoribus placuit, quae ius suum unicuique tribuat, uel nullibi eam in publico inuenias, uel (si dicere id mihi permittam) culinariam quan-
6 dam dispensatricem esse ut fateamur ne|cesse sit; siue nunc imperitantium mores spectes, siue ciuium inter se et popularium affectus.

Nisi uero a germana mundique aequali iusticia (quod ius naturale uocatur) manasse ius id contenderint, ut quo quisque plus polleat, eo etiam plus habeat; quo autem plus habeat, eo plus eminere inter ciues debeat. Quo fit ut iam iure gentium receptum esse uideamus, ut qui nec arte nec industria memorabili iuuare ciues suos et populares possunt, si modo pactiles illos nexus et contractiles nodos teneant, queis hominum patrimonia obstringuntur, quosque uulgus ignarum hominesque literis humanioribus dediti, ac procul foro,

---

[1] 'Quae animi affectio, suum cuique tribuens, . . . iusticia dicitur.' Cic. *de Fin.* v. 23.
[2] 'The good old rule' of Wordsworth :

'the simple plan,
That they should take, who have the power,
And they should keep, who can.'

perties are tied up (things accounted a mixture of Gordian knots and charlatanry, with nothing very wonderful about them, by the ignorant multitude, and by scholars living, for the sake of recreation or of investigating the truth, at a distance from the Courts),—that these persons, I say, should have an income equal to that of a thousand of their countrymen, nay, even of a whole state, and sometimes more than that; and that they should then be greeted with the honourable titles of wealthy men, thrifty men, makers of splendid fortunes. Such in truth is the age in which we live; such our manners and customs; such our national character. These have pronounced it lawful for a man's credit and influence to be high, in proportion to the way in which he has been the architect of his own fortunes and of those of his heirs: an influence, in fact, which goes on increasing, according as their descendants in turn, to the remotest generation, vie in heaping up with fine additions the property gained by their ancestors; which amounts to saying, according as they have ousted more and more extensively their connections, kindred, and even their blood relations.

Christian Communism

But the founder and regulator of all property, Jesus Christ, left among His followers a Pythagorean communion and love; and ratified it by a plain example, when Ananias was condemned to death for breaking this law of communion. By laying down

animi causa aut ueritatis indagandae ergo agentes, partim Gordii uincula esse ducunt, partim circulatoria nec magnopere miranda, ii millenorum ciuium censum, et saepe singularum ciuitatum aut etiam ampliorem habeant; iidemque tum locupletes, tum frugi homines, tum magnifici conquisitores honorifice uocitentur: quippe iis seculis, iis institutis, iis moribus, in iis gentibus, quae id ius esse statuerunt, ut tam summa fide atque autoritate quisque sit, quam maximis opibus penates suos architectatus est ipse haeredesque eius; idque eo magis atque magis, quo eorum adnepotes, horumque rursus abnepotes, patrimonia a maioribus parta luculentis certatim accessionibus cumulauerint; id est, quo longius latiusque confines, affines, cognatos, consanguineos summouerint.

At uero CHRISTVS, possessio num conditor et moderator, Pytha goricam communionem et charitatem inter asseclas suos relictam luculento sanxit exemplo, damnato capitis Anania ob temeratam communionis legem. Quo certe instituto CHRISTVS omne iuris istius

this principle, Christ seems to me to have abolished, at any rate among his followers, all the voluminous quibbles of the civil law, and still more of the later canon law; which latter we see at the present day holding the highest position in jurisprudence, and controlling our destiny.

As for the island of Utopia, which I hear is also called *Udepotia*[1], it is said (if we are to believe the story), by what must be owned a singular good fortune, to have adopted Christian usages both in public and in private; to have imbibed the wisdom thereto belonging; and to have kept it undefiled to this very day. The reason is, that it holds with firm grip to three divine institutions:—namely, the absolute equality, or, if you prefer to call it so, the civil communication[2], of all things good and bad among fellow-citizens; a settled and unwavering love of peace and quietness; and a contempt for gold and silver. Three things these, which overturn, one may say, all fraud, all imposture, cheating, roguery, and unprincipled deception. Would that Providence, on its own behalf[3], would cause these

ciuilis pontificiique adeo recentioris argumentosa uolumina inter suos quidem abrogasse mihi uidetur; quod ipsum ius hodie arcem tenere prudentiae uidemus, ac fata nostra regere.

VTOPIA uero insula, quam etiam VDEPOTIAM appellari audio, mirifica utique sorte (si credimus) Christianos vero[a] ritus ac germanam ipsam sapientiam publice priuatimque hausisse perhibetur, intemeratamque ad hunc usque diem seruasse : utpote quae tria diuina instituta, hoc est, bonorum malorumque inter ciues aequalitatem, seu malis ciuilitatem, numeris omnibus absolutam; et pacis ac tranquillitatis amorem constantem ac pertinacem; et auri argentique contemptum, consertis (ut aiunt) manibus retinet : tria (ut ita loquar) euerticula omnium fraudum, imposturarum, circunscriptionum, uersutiarum et planicarum improbitatum. Superi suo nomine facerent ut

[a] *om. ed.* 1548, *recte.*

---

[1] As much as to say *Nunquamia*, as well as *Nusquamia*; *Kennaquhan*, as well as *Kennaquhair*.—On the meanings which the name *Utopia* can be made to bear, see the Introduction, p. xl.

[2] I do not feel sure what Budé exactly meant by *ciuilitas*, but have taken it to signify the title to share, as citizens, in the common property.

[3] Lat. *suo nomine*: unless the reading should be *suo numine*.

three principles of Utopian law to be fixed in the minds of all men by the rivets of a strong and settled conviction. We should soon see pride, covetousness, insane competition, and almost all other deadly weapons of our adversary the Devil, fall power-less ; we should see the interminable array of law-books, [the work of]¹ so many excellent and solid understandings, that occupy men till the very day of their death, consigned to book-worms, as mere hollow and empty things, or else given up to make wrapping-paper for shops.

The question:

Good heavens! what holiness of the Utopians has had the power of earning such a blessing from above, that greed and covetousness have for so many ages failed to enter, either by force or stealth, into that island alone ? that they have failed to drive out from it, by wanton effrontery, justice and honour ?

Would that great Heaven in its goodness had dealt so kindly with the countries which keep, and would not part with, the appellation they bear, derived from His most holy name! Of a truth, greed, which perverts and sinks down so many minds, otherwise noble and elevated, would be gone from hence once for

haec tria Vtopianae legis capita trabalibus clauis firmae ac statae persuasionis in sensibus omnium mortalium figerentur. Protinus superbiam, cupiditatem, contentionem uaesanam, atque alia pene omnia uulnifica Stygii aduersarii tela concidere languereque uideres ; iurisque illam uoluminum uim immensam, tot eximia solidaque | ingenia ad libitinam usque detinentia, ut cassa et uacantia, teredinibus 8 permitti aut inuolucris officinarum dicari.

Proh diui immortales : quae nam Vtopianorum sanctitas eam diuinitus beatitudinem emereri potuit, ut auaritia et cupiditas in eam unam insulam irrumpere aut irrepere tot seculis non potuerit ? nec inde iusticiam cum pudore proteruitate sua impudentiaque explodere et exigere ?

Deus nunc optimus maximus tam benigne cum iis prouinciis egisset, quae ab eius sacratissimo nomine cognomentum retinent et amplec-tuntur : certe auaritia, tot mentes alioquin egregias arduasque depra-uans et pessumdans, semel hinc facesseret, et aureum seculum

---

¹ If *detinentia* in the Latin be cor-rect, this is the only way in which I can understand the passage. But it seems more likely that *detinentium* was originally written :—'law-books, that keep so many excellent and solid understandings occupied on them, till the very day of death.'

all, and the golden age of Saturn would return. In Utopia one   *Golden Age*
might verily suppose that there is a risk of Aratus and the early
poets having been mistaken in their opinion, when they made
Justice depart from earth, and placed her in the Zodiac [1]. For,
if we are to believe Hythloday, she must needs have stayed
behind in that island, and not yet made her way to heaven.

But in truth I have ascertained by full inquiry, that
Utopia lies outside the bounds of the known world. It is in
fact one of the Fortunate Isles, perhaps very close to the
Elysian Fields ; for More himself testifies that Hythloday has
not yet stated its position definitely. It is itself divided into
a number of cities, but all uniting or confederating into one
state, named Hagnopolis [2] ; a state contented with its own
customs, its own goods, blest with innocence, leading a kind
of heavenly life, on a lower level indeed than heaven, but
above the defilements of this world we know [3], which amid the
endless pursuits of mankind, as empty and vain as they are

Saturniumque rediret. Hic enimuero periculum esse quispiam
autumarit, ne forte Aratus et poetae prisci opinione falsi fuerint ; qui
iusticiam e terris decedentem in signifero circulo collocauerunt ;
restitisse enim eam In Vtopia insula necesse est, si Hythlodaeo
credimus, necdum in coelum peruenisse.

Verum ego Vtopiam extra mundi cogniti fines sitam esse percunc-
tando comperi, insulam nimirum fortunatam, Elysiis fortasse campis
proximam (nam Hythlodaeus nondum situm eius finibus certis tra-
didit, ut Morus ipse testatur), multas quidem ipsam in urbes distractam,
sed unam in ciuitatem coeuntes aut conspirantes, nomine Hagnopolin,
suis utique ritibus bonisque acquiescentem, innocentia beatam, coeles-
9 tem quodammodo uitam agentem, ut infra | coelum, sic supra mundi
huius cogniti colluuionem ; quae in tot mortalium studiis, ut acribus

---

[1] ' Sic iusta in populos mox Vir-
    ginis inculpatae
    Exarsere odia, et caelum per-
    nicibus intrat
    Diua alis.'
    Festi Avieni *Aratea Phaenomena*.
    The allusions to Astraea are com-
mon in the poets.

[2] As Budé had suggested that the

island was also called *Udepotia*, he
here takes the further liberty of calling
the imaginary state *Hagnopolis*, ' Holy
City,' or ' City of the Saints.' Compare
the last words of the passage quoted
above, p. xxxvi, n. 3, and what was
said before about More's lectures on
the *Civitas Dei*, p. xlix.

[3] See Colet's *Lectures on 1 Cor.*, p. 30.

keen and eager, is being hurried in a swollen and eddying tide
to the cataract.

It is to Thomas More, then, that we owe our knowledge of
this island. It is he who, in our generation, has made public
this model of a happy life and rule for leading it, the discovery,
as he tells us, of Hythloday : for he ascribes all to him. For
while Hythloday has built the Utopians their state, and established for them their rites and customs ; while, in so doing,
he has borrowed from them and brought home for us the repre-
sentation of a happy life ; it is beyond question More, who
has set off by his literary style the subject of that island and
its customs. He it is who has perfected, as by rule and square,
the City of the Hagnopolitans itself, adding all those touches
by which grace and beauty and weight accrue to the noble
work ; even though in executing that work he has claimed for
himself only a common mason's share. We see that it has
been a matter of conscientious scruple with him, not to assume
too important a part in the work, lest Hythloday should have
just cause for complaint, on the ground of More having plucked
the first flowers of that fame, which would have been left for
him, if he had himself ever decided to give an account of his
adventures to the world. He was afraid, of course, that Hythloday, who was residing of his own choice in the island of

et incitatis, sic inanibus et irritis, turbide et aestuose in praecipitium
rapitur.

Eius igitur insulae cognitionem Thomae MORO debemus, qui beatae
uitae exemplar ac uiuendi praescriptum aetate nostra promulgauit,
ab Hythlodaeo, ut ipse tradit, inuentum, cui omnia fert accepta. Qui
ut Vtopianis ciuitatem architectatus sit, ritusque illis et instituta con-
diderit, id est, beatae uitae argumentum nobis inde mutuatus sit et
importarit ; MORUS certe insulam et sancta instituta stilo orationeque
illustrauit, ac ciuitatem ipsam Hagnopolitanorum ad normam regulam-
que expoliuit, omniaque ea addidit, unde operi magnifico decor
uenustasque accedit et autoritas ; etiam si in ea opera nauanda sibi
tantum partes structoris uendicauit. Videlicet religio fuit maiores
sibi partes in eo opere sumere, ne Hythlodaeus iure queri posset,
gloriam sibi a MORO praecerptam praefloratamque relinqui, si quando
suos ipse labores literis mandare constituisset : ἐυλαβουμένου δῆθεν
αὐτοῦ, μὴ ὑθλόδαιος αὐτός, ὁ τῇ οὐδεποτίαγε νήσῳ ἐμφιλοχωρῶν, ἐπιφανεῖς ποτε

Udepotia, might some day come in person upon the scene, and be vexed and aggrieved at this unkindness on his part, in leaving him the glory of this discovery with the best flowers plucked off. To be of this persuasion is the part of good men and wise.

Now while More is one who of himself carries weight, and has great authority to rest upon, I am led to place unreserved confidence in him by the testimony of Peter Giles of Antwerp. Though I have never made his acquaintance in person—apart from recommendations of his learning and character that have reached me—I love him on account of his being the intimate friend of the illustrious Erasmus, who has deserved so well of letters of every kind, whether sacred or profane; with whom personally I have long corresponded and formed ties of friendship.

Farewell, my dear Lupset. Greet for me, at the first opportunity, either by word of mouth or by letter, Linacre, that pillar of the British name in all that concerns good learning; one who is now, as I hope, not more yours than ours. He is one

δυσχεράνειε καὶ βαρύνοιτο ταύτην ἀγνωμοσύνην αὐτοῦ τοῦγε ἐγκαταλιπόντος αὐτῷ προαπηνθισμένον τὸ κλέος τοῦ εὑρέματος τούτου. οὕτω γὰρ πεπεῖσθαι, πρὸς ἀνδρῶν ἐστὶν ἀγαθῶντε καὶ σοφῶν [1].

MORO autem homini per se graui et autoritate magna subnixo, fidem plane ut habeam, efficit Petri Aegidii Hantuerpiensis testimonium; 10 quem uirum | nunquam coram a me cognitum (mitto nunc doctrinae morumque commendationem), eo nomine amo, quod ERASMI clarissimi uiri, ac de literis sacris, profanis omneque genus meritissimi, amicus est iuratissimus; quicum etiam ipso iamdiu societatem amicorum contraxi, literis ultro citroque obsignatis.

Vale, Lupsete mi dilectissime, et LINACRUM Britannici nominis columen (quod quidem ad literas bonas attinet) non magis iam uestrum (ut spero) quam nostrum, uerbis meis saluta, uel coram uel epistola internuncia, idque primo quoque tempore. Is enim unus est

---

[1] The Greek is here printed as it stands, with the breathings over the first vowels of diphthongs. It is quite in keeping with Budé's general style, to branch off in this way into Greek. Perhaps he was tempted by the occurrence to his mind of δῆθεν, as a word specially suited to the irony of his tone in this passage.

of the few whose good opinion I should be very glad, if possible, to gain. When he was himself known to be staying here, he gained in the highest degree the good opinion of me and of Jehan Ruelle, my friend and the sharer in my studies [1]. And his singular learning and careful industry I should be the first to look up to and strive to copy.

Greet More also once and again for me, either by message, as I said before, or by word of mouth. As I think and often repeat, Minerva has long entered his name on her selectest album ; and I love and revere him in the highest degree for what he has written about this isle of the New World, Utopia.

In his history our age and those which succeed it will have a nursery, so to speak, of polite and useful institutions ; from which men may borrow customs, and introduce and adapt them each to his own state.   Farewell.

From Paris, the 31st of July [2].

paucorum, quibus me perlubens approbarim, si possim ; cum et ipse coram hic agens mihi se summe Ioannique Ruellio amico meo studiorumque conscio probauerit ; et eius excellentem doctrinam exactamque diligentiam in primis suspiciam aemularique contendam. Velim etiam ut MORO salutem unam et alteram mandato meo uel mittas, ut dixi, uel dicas ; quem uirum in Mineruae sacratius album iamdiu opinione mea sermoneque meo relatum, de Vtopia noui orbis insula summe et amo et ueneror. Eius enim historiam aetas nostra posteraeque aetates habebunt uelut elegantium utiliumque institutorum seminarium, unde translaticios mores in suam quisque ciuitatem important et accommodent.   Vale, Parisiis pridie Cal. August.

---

[1] Joannes Ruellius is mentioned in a letter of Erasmus, dated Antwerp, 1517, as a physician who, like Linacre, had had the good fortune to learn Greek in early life. *Epist.* ed. 1642, col. 629.   He published in 1536 a treatise *De natura stirpium,* printed at Paris by Colinaeus, in folio ; 'a magnificent book,' as it is called by Greswell : *View of the Parisian Greek Press,* i. 91 n.

[2] No year is given ; but it must have been 1517.

❡ A shorte meter of Utopia, written by Ane= molius[1] poete laureate, and nephewe to Hythlodaye by his sister[2].

vs. Skelton?

M E Vtopie cleped Antiquitie,
Voyde of haunte and herboroughe.
Nowe am I like to Platoes citie,
Whose fame flieth the worlde throughe.
Yea like, or rather more likely

Plato's republic surpassed:

Platoes platte[3] to excell and passe.
For what Platoes penne hathe platted briefely
In naked wordes, as in a glasse,
The same haue I perfourmed fully,
With lawes, with men, and treasure fyttely.
Wherfore not Vtopie, but rather rightely
My name is Eutopie[4]: A place of felicitie.

HEXASTICHON ANEMOLII POETAE LAV
RFATI, HYTHLODAEI EX SORO-
RE NEPOTIS IN VTOPI-
AM INSVLAM.

Vtopia priscis dicta ob infrequentiam,
Nunc ciuitatis aemula Platonicae,
Fortasse uictrix, (nam quod illa literis
Deliniauit, hoc ego una praestiti,
Viris et opibus, optimisque legibus)
Eutopia merito sum uocanda nomine.

Eutopia

---

[1] The name is familiar from the use of the word in Homer, ἀνεμώλιος, in its figurative sense of 'braggart,' lit. 'windy.' *Ventosus* is used in a similar way in Latin, as in Cicero's 'homo ventosissimus' (*Epp. ad Fam.* xi. 9). So the name of Anemolians (*inf.* p. 177) is given to a vain, boastful people. It is probable that, in calling Anemolius 'poet laureate' here, a hit is intended at John Skelton, who bore that title in More's time.—See the references in Dyce's ed. of Skelton's works (1843),

vol. i. p. xii. Skelton was the great opponent of More's friend Lily.

[2] Hythlodaye would thus be his *avunculus*, not *patruus*; a distinction that may have been here intended. For Hythlodaye see note below, p. 26.

[3] The sense of this word is defined by 'platted' in the next line, and that by the Latin 'deliniauit,' 'marked out,' 'plotted out,' as is said of an estate in the hands of surveyors.

[4] See the Introduction, p. xl.

❡ A Meter of .iiii. verses in the Utopian

tongue, briefely touchinge afwell the straunge ꞓbeginning, as also the happie and wealthie continuance of the same common wealthe.

M Y kinge and conquerour Vtopus by name
  A prince of much renowne and immortall fame
Hath made me an yle that earst no ylande was,
Ful fraight[1] with worldly welth, with pleasure and solas.
I one of all other without philosophie
Haue shaped for man a philosophicall citie.
As myne I am nothinge daungerous[2] to imparte,
So better to receaue I am readie with al my harte.

HORVM VERSVVM AD VERBVM HAEC

EST SENTENTIA.

Vtopus me dux ex non insula fecit insulam.
Vna ego terrarum omnium absque philosophia
Ciuitatem philosophicam expressi mortalibus.
Libenter impartio mea, non grauatim accipio meliora.

NOTE TO THE UTOPIAN ALPHABET.— In the first edition this is printed on the obverse of leaf 2, the 'Hexastichon Anemolii' being on the reverse. In the first edition also the shape of the Utopian letters is a little simpler, the curves not being turned in at the extremities. Some of the words, as 'gymnosophon,' are evidently reminiscences of Greek; but I have not discovered any key to them, if indeed they were ever intended to have any meaning. The alphabet is not printed in the editions of 1517 or 1548. Robynson prefaces his rendering of the lines, given on the facsimile opposite, by the words : 'Whiche verses the translator, accordinge to his simple knowledge, and meane vnderstanding in the Vtopian tongue, hath thus rudely englished.'

[1] That is, fraught, or laden.

[2] That is, I make no obstacle. 'Difficultas,' 'mora,' are among the interpretations of 'dangerium' given by Maigne d'Arnis.

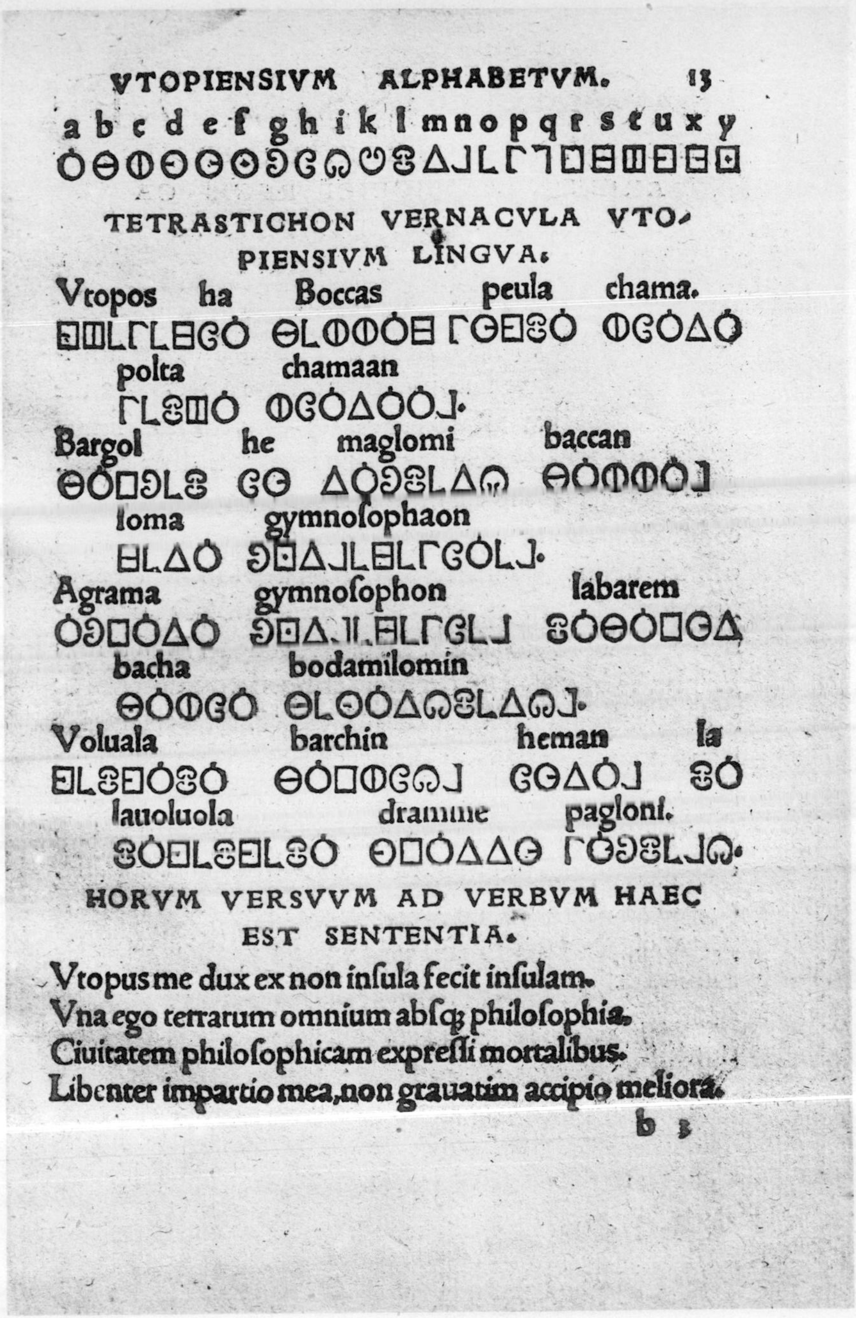
VTOPIENSIVM ALPHABETVM. 13

a b c d e f g h i k l m n o p q r s t u x y

TETRASTICHON VERNACVLA VTOPIENSIVM LINGVA.

Vtopos ha Boccas peula chama.
polta chamaan
Bargol he maglomi baccan
soma gymnosophaon
Agrama gymnosophon labarem
bacha bodamilomin
Voluala barchin heman la
lauoluola dramme pagloni.

HORVM VERSVVM AD VERBVM HAEC EST SENTENTIA.

Vtopus me dux ex non insula fecit insulam.
Vna ego terrarum omnium absq; philosophia.
Ciuitatem philosophicam expressi mortalibus.
Libenter impartio mea, non grauatim accipio meliora.

b 3

REDUCED FACSIMILE OF THE WOODCUT OF THE UTOPIAN ALPHABET

To face p. xciv]

❡ To the right honourable Hie= rome Buslyde, prouost of Arien, and counselloure to the catholike kinge Charles, Peter Gyles [1] Citizein of Antwerpe, wisheth health and felicitie [2].

THomas More the singular ornamente of this our age, as you your self (right honourable Buslide) can witnesse, to whome he is perfectly wel knowen, sent vnto me this other day the ylande of Vtopia, to very few as yet knowen, but most worthy which, as farre excelling Platoes commen wealthe, all

beyond Plato

14

❧ CLARISSIMO D◄

HIERONYMO BVSLIDIO PRAEPOSITO

ARIENSI. CATHOLICI REGIS CA

ROLI A CONSILIIS, PETRVS

AEGIDIVS ANTVERPI-

ENSIS S. D.

SVPERIORIBVS hisce diebus, amantissime Buslidi, misit ad me Thomas ille Morus, te quoque teste, cui notissimus est, eximium huius aetatis nostrae decus, Vtopiam insulam, paucis adhuc mortalibus cognitam, sed dignam imprimis quam ut plusquam plato-

---

[1] For Peter Giles, see below. p. 1.

[2] The translation of this letter is taken from Robynson's second edition, where it occupies leaves S iiii. and v., ending on the obv. of S. vi. It did not appear in his first edition.

Hierome Busleyden, or, as Robynson variously calls him, Buslyde, Buslide, and Buslid, was, at the time when this letter was written, Provost (Propst) of the church of Aire, a town now reckoned in the Pas de Calais, at the confluence of the Lys and the Laquette. He was of a good Luxembourg family. One of his brothers, Francis, had been tutor to the Archduke Philip. Another, Giles, held a position in the Spanish Exchequer,

people shoulde be willinge to know: specially of a man most
eloquent so finely set furth, so conningly painted out, and so
euidently subiect to the eye, that as oft as I reade it, me
thinketh that I see somwhat more, then when I heard Raphael
Hythloday[1] himselfe (for I was present at that talke aswell
as master More) vtteryng and pronouncing his owne woordes:
yea, though the same man, accordinge to his pure eloquence,
did so open and declare the matter, that he might plainely
enough appeare to reporte not thinges, which he had learned
of others onelye by hearesay, but which he had with his own
eyes presently sene, and throughly vewed, and wherin he had
no smal time bene conuersant and abiding: a man trulie, in
mine opinion, as touching the knowledge of regions, peoples,
and worldly experience, muche passinge, yea euen the very
famous and renowmed trauailer Vlysses: and in dede suche
a one, as for the space of these viij. c. yeres past I think nature

nicam omnes uelint cognoscere, praesertim ab homine facundissimo
sic expressam, sic depictam, sic oculis subiectam, ut, quoties lego,
aliquanto plus mihi uidere uidear, quam cum ipsum Raphaelem
Hythlodaeum (nam ei sermoni aeque interfui ac Morus ipse) sua
uerba sonantem audirem; etiam si uir ille haud uulgari praeditus
eloquentia sic rem exponeret, ut facile appareret eum non ea referre
quae narrantibus aliis didicisset, sed quae cominus hausisset oculis,
et in quibus non exiguum tempus esset uersatus; homo mea quidem
sententia regionum, hominum, et rerum experientia uel ipso ulysse

---

Hierome himself was a canon of Brussels, and also of Mechlin (where he had a splendid house, more than once alluded to by More), and Cambray. He was Master of Requests and a Councillor of Charles, the young King of the Netherlands. But he is best known by his foundation of the Collegium Trilingue in the University of Louvain, for teaching the three learned tongues— Hebrew, Greek, and Latin. His will, containing the bequest for this purpose, was dated June 22, 1517. He died on the 26th of August in the same year. His foundation at Louvain met for a time with the same kind of opposition from the obstructive party (who, as Erasmus says, would rather be *bilingues* than *trilingues*), as did Colet's foundation in London.

For more about Busleyden, see Mullinger's *University of Cambridge*, pt. i. p. 565; and especially Nève's *Mémoire historique et littéraire sur le Collége des trois Langues*, 1856, pp. 36–40.

[1] See below, p. 29.

into the worlde brought not furth his like : in comparison of *beyond*
whome Vespuce maye be thought to haue sene nothing. *Vespuce*

Moreouer, wheras we be wont more effectually and pitthely
to declare and expresse thinges that we haue sene, then whiche
we haue but onelye hearde, there was besides that in this man
a certen peculiar grace, and singular dexteritie to discriue and
set furth a matter withall. Yet the selfe same thinges as ofte
as I beholde and consider them drawen and painted oute with
master Mores pensille, I am therwith so moued, so delited,
so inflamed, and so rapt, that sometime me think I am presently
conuersaunt, euen in the ylande of Vtopia. And I promise you,
I can skante beleue that Raphael himselfe by al that fiue yeres
space that he was in Vtopia abiding, saw there somuch, as here
in master Mores description is to be sene and perceaued.
Whiche description with so manye wonders and miraculous
thinges is replenished, that I stande in great doubt wherat first
and chieflie to muse or marueile : whether at the excellencie
of his perfect and suer memorie, which could welniegh worde
by woorde rehearse so manye thinges once onely heard : or
elles at his singular prudence, who so well and wittyly marked *wittily*
and bare away al the originall causes and fountaynes (to the
vulgare people commenly most vnknowen) wherof both yssueth
and springeth the mortall confusion and vtter decaye of a
commen wealth, and also the auauncement and wealthy state
of the same may riese and growe : or elles at the efficacie and

superior, et qualem octingentis hisce annis nusquam arbitror natum ;
ad quem collatus Vespucius nihil uidisse putetur.

15 Iam praeterea quod uisa quam audita narramus efficatius, aderat
homini peculiaris quaedam ad explicandas res dexteritas. | Attamen
eadem haec quoties Mori penicillo depicta contemplor, sic afficior, ut
mihi uidear nonnunquam in ipsa uersari Vtopia. Et hercle crediderim Raphaelem ipsum minus in ea insula uidisse per omne quin-
quennium quod illic egit, quam in Mori descriptione uidere liceat.
Tantum hic occurrit undique miraculorum, ut ambigam quid primum
aut potissimum admirer : felicissimae memoriae fidem, quae tot res
auditas duntaxat pene ad uerbum reddere potuerit ; an prudentiam,
qui uulgo ignotissimos fontes, unde omnia reipublicae uel oriuntur
mala, uel oriri possent mala, sic animaduertit ; an orationis uim ac

pitthe of his woordes, which in so fine a latin stile, with suche
force of eloquence hath couched together and comprised so
many and diuers matters, speciallie beinge a man continuallie
encombred with so manye busye and troublesome cares, both
publique and priuate, as he is. Howbeit all these thinges cause
you litle to maruell (righte honourable Buslid) for that you are
familiarly and throughly acquainted with the notable, yea almost

divine wit

diuine witte of the man.

But nowe to procede to other matters, I suerly know nothing
nedeful or requisite to be adioyned vnto his writinges. Onely

Giles added verses & alphabet

a meter of .iiij. verses written in the Vtopian tongue, whiche
after master Mores departure Hythloday by chaunce shewed
me, that haue I caused to be added thereto, with the Alphabete
of the same nation, and haue also garnished the margent of the
boke with certen notes. For, as touchinge the situation of the
ylande, that is to saye, in what parte of the worlde Vtopia
standeth, the ignoraunce and lacke whereof not a litle troubleth
and greueth master More, in dede Raphael left not that vn-
spoken of. Howbeit with verie fewe wordes he lightly touched it,
incidentlye by the way passing it ouer, as meanyng of likelihod
to kepe and reserue that to an other place. And the same,
I wot not how, by a certen euell and vnluckie chaunce escaped
vs bothe. For when Raphael was speaking therof, one of
master Mores seruauntes came to him, and whispered in his

facultatem, qua tanta sermonis latini puritate, tantis dicendi neruis,
tot res complexus est, praesertim unus in tot publica simul et domes-
tica negocia distractus. Verum haec omnia tu minus admiraris,
doctissime Buslidi, qui familiari etiam consuetudine penitus habes
cognitum homine maius ac prope diuinum hominis ingenium.

In caeteris igitur nihil est, quod illius scriptis queam adiicere.
Tantum tetrastichum uernacula Vtopiensium lingua scriptum, quod
a Mori discessu forte mihi ostendit Hythlodaeus, apponendum
curaui, praefixo eiusdem gentis alphabeto, tum adiectis ad margines
aliquot annotatiunculis. Nam quod de insulae situ laborat Morus, ne
id quidem omnino tacuit Raphael, quanquam paucis admodum ac
uelut obiter attigit, uelut hoc alii seruans loco. Atque id sane nescio
quomodo casus quidam malus utrique nostrum inuidit. Siquidem,
cum ea loqueretur Raphael, adierat Morum e famulis quispiam, | qui 16

eare. Wherefore I beyng then of purpose more earnestly addict to heare, one of the company, by reason of cold taken, I thinke, a shippeborde, coughed out so loude, that he toke from my hearinge certen of his wordes[1]. But I wil neuer stynte, nor rest, vntil I haue gotte the full and exacte knowledge hereof: insomuche that I will be hable perfectly to instructe you, not onely in the longitude or true meridian of the ylande, but also in the iust latitude therof, that is to say, in the subleuation or height of the pole in that region, if our frende Hythloday be in safetie, and aliue. For we heare very vncerten newes of him. Some reporte, that he died in his iorney homewarde. Some agayne affirme, that he retorned into his countrey; but partly, for that he coulde not away with the fashions of his countrey folk, and partly for that his minde and affection was altogether set and fixed vpon Vtopia, they say that he hathe taken his voyage thetherwarde agayne.

Now as touching this, that the name of this yland is nowhere founde amonge the olde and auncient cosmographers, this doubte Hythloday himselfe verie well dissolued. For why, it is possible enoughe (quod he) that the name, whiche it had in olde time, was afterwarde chaunged, or elles that they neuer had knowledge of this iland: forasmuch as now in our time

illi nescio quid diceret in aurem ; ac mihi quidem tanto attentius auscultanti comitum quispiam clarius, ob frigus opinor nauigatione collectum, tussiens, dicentis uoces aliquot intercepit. Verum non conquiescam donec hanc quoque partem ad plenum cognouero ; adeo ut non solum situm insulae, sed ipsam etiam poli sublationem sim tibi ad unguem redditurus, si modo incolumis est noster Hythlodaeus ; nam uarius de homine rumor adfertur : alii affirmant periisse in itinere ; rursum alii reuersum in patriam ; sed partim suorum mores non ferentem, partim Vtopiae desyderio sollicitatum, eo remigrasse.

Nam quod huius insulae nomen nusquam apud Cosmographos reperiatur, pulchre dissoluit Hythlodaeus ipse. Si quidem fieri potuit, inquit, ut nomen quo ueteres sint usi postea sit commutatum, aut etiam illos hacc fugerit insula ; quando et hodie complures

---

[1] For this artistic touch, reminding us of More's own hand, see the Introduction, p. xliii.

Peter Giles to Buslyde.

diuers landes be found, which to the olde Geographers were vnknowen. Howbeit, what nedeth it in this behalfe to fortifie the matter with argumentes, seynge master More is author hereof sufficient? But whereas he doubteth of the edition or imprinting of the booke, in deede herein I both commende, and also knowledge the mannes modestie. Howbeit vnto me it semeth a worke most vnworthie to be long suppressed, and most worthy to go abrod into the handes of men, yea, and vnder the title of youre name to be publyshed to the worlde: either because the singular endowmentes and qualities of master More be to no man better knowen then to you, or els bicause no man is more fitte and meete then you, with good counselles to further and auaunce the commen wealth, wherin you haue many yeares already continued and trauailed with great glory and commendation, bothe of wisedome and knowledge, and also of integritie and vprightnes. Thus o liberall supporter of good learninge, and floure of this oure time,

I byd you moste hartely well to fare. At

Antwerpe .1516. the first daye of

Nouember.

oriuntur terrae, priscis illis Geographis intactae. Quanquam quorsum attinet hic argumentis astruere fidem, cum Morus ille sit author? Caeterum quod is ambigit de acditione, equidem laudo et agnosco uiri modestiam. At uisum mihi est opus modis omnibus indignum quod diu premeretur, et cum primis dignum quod exeat in manus hominum; idque tuo potissimum nomine commendatum orbi: uel quod Mori dotes tibi praecipue sint perspectae, uel quod nemo magis idoneus qui rectis consiliis iuuet rem publicam, in qua iam annis compluribus summa cum laude uersaris tum prudentiae tum integritatis. Bene uale, studiorum Maecenas, et huius saeculi decus. Antuerpiae, An. M.D.XVI. Cal. Nouembr.

¶ Thomas

More to Peter Giles[1] sendeth gretynge.

I Am almoste ashamed, right welbeloued Peter Giles, to sende vnto you this boke of the vtopian commen wealth, welnigh after a yeares space, which I am suer you loked for within a moneth and a half. And no marueil. For you knewe welenough, that I was already disbourdened of all the labour and study belonging to the inuention in this work, and that I had no nede at all to trouble my braynes about the disposition or con- ueyaunce of the matter; and therfore had herin nothing els to do, but only to rehearse those thinges, which you

invention & disposition

THOMAS

MORUS PETRO

AEGIDIO

S.D.

PVdet me prope modum, charissime Petre Aegidi, libellum hunc, de Vtopiana re publica, post annum ferme ad te mittere, quem te non dubito intra sesquimensem expectasse. quippe
10 quum scires mihi demptum in hoc opere inueni|endi laborem, neque de dispositione quicquam fuisse cogitandum, cui tantum erant ea

---

[1] Petrus Gillius, or Aegidius, was born at Antwerp about 1486. His father Nicholas was 'quaestor urbis.' His studies were directed by Erasmus, with whom, as well as with More and Conrad Goclenius, he lived on terms of cordial friendship. The Epithalamium in Erasmus's Colloquies was composed for his marriage. In 1510 he was made Town Clerk (Stadtschreiber) of Antwerp. He died November 11, 1533. Some Latin poems of his are preserved

Raphael's
style

{eloquence

Greek
less eloquent?{

Truth

and I togethers hard maister Raphaell tel and declare.
Wherefore there was no cause whie I shold study to set
forth the matter with eloquence; for asmuch as his talke
cold not be fine and eloquent, being firste not studied for,
but sodein and vnpremeditate, and then, as you know, of
a man better sene in the greke language then in the latine
tong. And my writing, the nigher it shold approche to
his homely, playne, and simple speche, somuch the nigher
shold it go to the trueth ; whiche is the only marke, wherunto I do and ought to direct all my trauail and study
herin.   Fateor

I (graunt and confesse,) frende Peter, mcself discharged
of somuch labour, hauing all thies thinges redy done to
my hand, that almoost there was nothing lefte for me to
do. Elles other the inuention, or the disposition of this
matter, might haue requyred of a witte, nother base nother
at all vnlearned, bothe some time and leasure, and also

recitanda, quae tecum una pariter audiui narrantem Raphaelem.
quare nec erat quod in eloquendo laboraretur [a], quando nec illius
sermo potuit exquisitus esse, quum esset primum subitarius atque
extemporalis, deinde hominis, ut scis, non perinde Latine docti
quam Graece, et mea oratio quanto accederet propius ad illius
neglectam simplicitatem, tanto futura sit propior ueritati, cui hac
in re soli curam et debeo et habeo.

Fateor, mi Petre, mihi adeo multum laboris hiis rebus paratis
detractum, ut pene nihil fuerit relictum. alioquin huius rei uel
excogitatio, uel oeconomia, potuisset ab ingenio neque infimo neque
prorsus indocto postulare tum temporis nonnihil tum studii, quod

[a] laboretur, A[1].

at the beginning of vol. i. of the *Delitiae
Poetarum Belgicorum*, 1614. Like
More's *Epigrammata*, they are imitations of the classical style, and sometimes coarse. In 1519 he published
a *Threnodia* on the death of the Emperor Maximilian, with other pieces.
There is a charming letter of Erasmus
to him on the death of his father, and
on the bringing up of his child Nicholas, called after his grandfather. *Epist.*

1642, p. 761.—See Foppens, *Bibliotheca
Belgica*, 1739, ii. p. 948 b.
[1] The various readings at the foot of
the Latin text, denoted by A, are from
the first edition of 1516; those denoted
by B, from the Paris edition of 1517.
Those at the foot of the English text
are from Robynson's second edition of
1556. The figures on the inner margin
refer to the pages of the edition of
1518.

some studye. But yf yt were requysyte and necessary,
that the matter shoulde also haue bene wryten elo-
quentelye, and not alone truelye : of a suerty that thynge
coulde I haue perfourmed by no tyme nor studye. But
nowe, seynge all thyes cares, stayes, and lettes were taken
awaye, wherin elles somuche laboure and studye shoulde
haue bene employed ; and that there remayned no other
thynge for me to doo, but onelye to wryte playnlye the
matter as I hard it spoken ; that in dede was a thynge
lyghte and easye to be done. Howe beit, to the dyspatch-
ynge of thys so lytell busynes my other cares and troubles
did leaue almooste lesse then no leasure. Whyles [1] I doo
daylye bestowe my tyme abowte lawe matters ; some to
pleade, some to heare, some as an arbytratour wyth myne
awarde to determyne, some as an vmpier or a judge with
my sentence finallye to discusse ; whiles I go one way to
see and visite my frend, an other way about mine owne
privat affaires ; whiles I spend almost al the day abrode
emonges other, and the residue at home among mine own ;
I leaue to meselfe, I meane to my boke, no time.

For when I am come home, I muste commen with my

si exigeretur, ut diserte etiam res, non tantum uere, scriberetur, id
uero a me praestari nullo tempore, nullo studio potuisset. Nunc uero
quum ablatis curis hiis, in quibus tantum fuit sudoris exhauriendum,
restiterit tantum hoc, uti sic simpliciter scriberentur audita, nihil erat
negocii. Sed huic tamen nihilo negocii peragendo, caetera negocia
19 mea minus fere quam nihil tempo|ris reliquerunt. Dum causas foren-
seis assidue alias ago, alias audio, alias arbiter finio, alias iudex
dirimo ; dum hic officii causa uisitur, ille negocii , dum foris totum
ferme diem aliis impartior, reliquum meis ; relinquo mihi, hoc est
literis, nihil.

Nempe reuerso domum, cum uxore fabulandum est, garriendum

---

[1] The sentence which follows is an
example of Robynson's diffuse style.
Burnet renders more compactly, but
less pleasantly : ' For while in plead-
ing, and hearing, in judging or composing of Causes, in waiting on some
Men upon Business, and on others
out of Respect, the greatest part of
the Day is spent on other Men's
Affairs,' &c.

wife, chatte with my chyldren, and talke wyth my seruauntes. All the whyche thynges I reken and accompte
emonge busynes, forasmuche as they muste of necessytye
be done: and done muste they nedes be, oneles a man
wyll be a straunger in hys owne howse [1]. And in any
wyse a man muste so fassyon and order hys condytyons,
and so appoynte and dyspose hym selfe, that he be merye,
iocunde, and pleasaunte amonge them, whome eyther
nature hath prouyded, or chaunce hathe made, or he hymselfe hathe chosen, to be the fellowes and companyons of
hys lyfe: so that wyth to muche gentle behauyoure and
famylyaryte he doo not marre them, and, by tomuche
sufferaunce, of hys seruauntes make them hys maysters.
Emonge thyes thinges nowe rehearsed stealethe awaye
the daye, the moneth, the yeare. When doo I wryte,
then? And all thys whyle haue I spoken no woorde of
slepe, nother yet of meate, whyche emonge a greate number doth waste no lesse tyme then dothe slepe, wherin
almooste halfe the lyfe tyme of man crepethe awaye.
I therefore doo wynne and gette onelye that tyme, whyche
I steale from slepe and meate [2]. Whyche tyme bycause

cum liberis, colloquendum cum ministris. quae ego omnia inter
negocia numero, quando fieri necesse est (necesse est autem, nisi
uelis esse domi tuae peregrinus) et danda omnino opera est, ut quos
uitae tuae comites aut natura prouidit, aut fecit casus, aut ipse dele-
gisti, hiis ut te quam iucundissimum compares, modo ut ne comitate
corrumpas, aut indulgentia ex ministris dominos reddas. Inter haec
quae dixi elabitur dies, mensis, annus. Quando ergo scribimus? nec
interim de somno quicquam sum loquutus, ut nec de cibo quidem, qui
multis non minus absumit temporis quam somnus ipse, qui uitae

---

[1] For this picture of More's domestic
life, see above, p. xxi.

[2] According to Stapleton, More's
habit was to give but four or five hours
each night to sleep. He rose at two.
' Hora secunda matutina surgere solitus, usque ad septimam studiis ac
precibus se dabat.' *Tres Thomae*, ed.

1689, p. 14. The contemporary French
adage was more lenient :—
  ' Lever à cinq, diner à neuf,
  Souper à cinq, coucher à neuf,
  Fait vivre d'une nonante et neuf.'
See Southey's *Common-Place Book*,
iii. p. 11.

yt ys verye littell, and yet somwhat it is, therfore haue
I ones at the last, thoughe it be longe first, finished
Vtopia, and haue sent it to you, frende Peter, to reade and
peruse ; to the intent that if anye thynge haue escaped
me, you might putte me in remembraunce of it. For
though in this behalf I do not greatly mistruste meself
(whiche woulde God I were somewhat in witte and learnyng, as[1] I am not all of the worste and dullest memory),
yet haue I not so great trust and confidence in it, that
I thinke nothing could fall out of my mynde.

For John Clement[2] my boye, who as yow knowe was
there present with vs, whome I suffer to be awaye from
no talke, wherin may be anye profit or goodnes (for out
of this yong bladed and newe shotte vp corne,) whiche
hath alredy begonne to sprynge vp bothe in Latine and
Greke learnynge, I looke for plentiful increase at length

absumit ferme dimidium. At mihi hoc solum temporis adquiro, quod
somno ciboque suffuror, quod quoniam parcum est, lente, quia tamen
aliquid, aliquando perfeci, atque ad te, mi Petre, transmisi Vtopiam, ut
20 legeres, et si quid ef|fugisset nos, uti tu admoneres. Quanquam enim
non hac parte penitus diffido mihi (qui utinam sic ingenio atque doctrina aliquid essem, ut memoria non usquequaque destituor) non
usqueadeo tamen confido, ut credam nihil mihi potuisse excidere.
Nam et Ioannes Clemens, puer meus, qui adfuit, ut scis[a], una, ut
quem a nullo patior sermone abesse in quo aliquid esse fructus potest,
quoniam ab hac herba, qua[b] et latinis literis et Graecis coepit evires-

[a] sis, A. [b] *Leg.* quae.

---

[1] That is, in proportion as.

[2] John Clement was educated under
Lily, and then taken into the household of Sir Thomas More, whose
adopted daughter, Margaret Gigs, he
afterwards married. The high expec-
tations More entertained of his proficiency in Greek and Latin were
fulfilled. He assisted Colet in his
study of Greek. In 1519 he was Reader
of Wolsey's Greek lecture at Oxford,
in which office he was succeeded by
Lupset. Turning his attention to medicine, he was made a member of the
newly-founded College of Physicians.
More, in an undated letter to Erasmus
(Jortin, iii. 342) speaks of him as 'nemini
aliquando cessurus' in that capacity.
Under the reigns of Edward VI and
Elizabeth he went abroad, to escape
persecution, and died at Mechlin in
1572. His wife had died two years
before. For an account of his family,
see Bridgett's *Life of More*, p. 126 *n.*

of goodly rype grayne), he, I saye, hath brought me into
a greate doubte. For wheras Hythlodaye (oneles my
memory fayle me) sayde that the bridge of Amaurote[1],
which goeth ouer the riuer of Anyder[2], is fyue hundreth
paseis, that is to saye, half a myle, in lengthe; my Jhon
sayeth that ii. hundred of those paseis must be plucked
awaye; for that the ryuer conteyneth there not aboue thre
hundreth paseis in bredthe. I praye yow hartely call the
matter to youre remembraunce. For if you agree with
hym, I also wyll saye as you saye, and confesse me selfe
deceaued. But if you cannot remember the thynge, then
suerly I wyl write as I haue done, and as mync owne
remembraunce serueth me. For as I will take good hede
that there be in my booke nothyng false, so, if there be
anythynge in doubte, I wyll rather tell a lye then make
a lye; bicause I had be good then wise rather[a].

Howbeit this matter maye easely be remedied, if yow
wyll take the paynes to aske the question of Raphaell

[a] rather be good then wilie.

cere[3], egregiam aliquando frugem spero, in magnam me coniecit
dubitationem[a]. si quidem quum, quantum ego recordor, Hythlodaeus
narrauerit Amauroticum illum pontem, quo fluuius Anydrus insterni-
tur, quingentos habere passus in longum, Ioannes meus ait detra-
hendos esse ducentos : latitudinem fluminis haud supra trecentos ibi
continere. Ego te rogo rem ut reuoces in memoriam. Nam si tu
cum illo sentis, ego quoque adsentiar et me lapsum credam. sin
ipse non recolis[b], scribam ut feci quod ipse re-
cordari uideor mihi. nam ut maxime curabo ne
quid sit in libro falsi, ita si quid sit in ambiguo,
potius mendacium dicam quam mentiar, quod malim
bonus esse quam prudens.

Nota Theologicam differentiam inter mentiri et menda-cium dicere.

Quanquam | facile fuerit huic mederi morbo, si ex Raphaele ipso aut 21
praesens scisciteris, aut per literas, quod necesse est facias uel ob

[a] magnum . . . dubium, A.   [b] recolas, A.

[1] Described more fully below, p. 128, where see the note.
[2] See note below, p. 127.
[3] *Eviresco,* in the sense of 'fade,' is given in the *Cornucopiae* on the authority of Varro, but appears to have no classical authority.

himselfe, by worde of mouthe, if he be nowe with yow, or els by youre letters. Which you must nedes do for an other doubte also, whiche hath chaunced, throughe whoes faulte I cannot tell, whether throughe myne or youres or Raphaels. For neither we remembred to enquire of hym, nor he to tell vs, in what parte of that newe worlde Vtopia is situate. The whiche thinge I had rather haue spent no small somme of money then that it should thus haue escaped vs; aswell for that I am ashamed to be ignoraunt in what sea that Ilande standeth, wherof I write so longe a treatyse, as also because there be with vs cer-tayne men, and especially one deuoute [a] and godly man, and a professour of diuinitie [1], who is excedynge desier-ous to go vnto Vtopia; not for a vayne and curious desiere to see newes, but to the intent he maye further and increase oure religion, whiche is there already luckely begoune. And that he may the better accomplyshe and

[a] vertuous.

alium scrupulum, qui nobis incidit, nescio mea ne culpa magis, an tua, an Raphaelis ipsius. Nam neque nobis in mentem uenit quaerere, neque illi dicere, qua in parte noui illius orbis Vtopia sita sit. Quod non fuisse praetermissum sic uellem profecto mediocri pecunia mea redemptum, uel quod subpudet me nescire, quo in mari sit insula de qua tam multa recenseam, uel quod sunt apud nos unus et alter, sed unus maxime, uir pius et professione Theologus, qui miro flagrat desyderio adeundae Vtopiae, non inani et curiosa libidine collustrandi noua, sed uti religionem nostram, feliciter ibi coeptam, foueat atque adaugeat. Quod quo faciat rite, decreuit ante curare ut mittatur

---

[1] In the edition of Robynson's trans-lation published in 1624 is the mar-ginal note opposite this: 'It is thought of some that here is vnfainedly meant the late famous Vicar of Croyden in Surrey.' This was Rowland Phillips, Canon of St. Paul's and Warden of Merton College, Oxford, who was collated to the vicarage of Croydon in 1497. He was 'esteemed a notable preacher' (Holinshed), and is said to have foretold, in a sermon preached at St. Paul's, that 'the introduction of printing would be the bane of the Roman Catholic religion.' He resigned the vicarage of Croydon in 1538, re-tiring on a pension of £12 for life. See Lysons' *Environs of London* (1792), i. p. 189. In what follows Robynson seems to have hesitated about translat-ing Pontifex by Pope — see his later rendering in the note.

perfourme this his good intent, he is mynded to procure
that he maye be sent thether of the byshoppe[a], yea and
that he hymselfe may be made bishop of Vtopia; beynge
nothynge scrupulous herein, that he must obteyne this
byshopricke with suete. For he counteth that a godly
suete, whiche procedeth not of the desiere of honour or
lucre, but only of a godly zeale.

Wherfore I moste earnestly desyere you, frende Peter,
to talke with Hythlodaye, if you can, face to face, or els to
wryte youre letters to hym; and so to worke in this
matter, that in this my booke there maye neyther any
thynge be founde whiche is vntruc, neither any thinge be
lacking whiche is true. And I thinke verely it shalbe well
done that you shewe vnto hym the booke it selfe. For if
I haue myssed or fayled in any poynte, or if any faulte
haue escaped me, no man can so well correcte and amende
it, as he can: and yet that can he not do, oneles he peruse
and reade ouer my booke written. Moreouer by this
meanes shal you perceaue, whether he be well wyllynge
and contente that I should vndertake to put thys worke in
wryting. For if he be mynded to publyshe and put forth
his owne labours and trauayles hymselfe, perchaunce he
would be lothe, and so would I also, that in publyshynge

[a] by the hieghe Byshoppe.

a Pontifice, atque adeo ut creetur Vtopiensibus Episcopus, nihil eo
scrupulo retardatus, quod hoc antistitium sit illi precibus impetrandum. Quippe sanctum ducit ambitum,
quem non honoris aut quaestus ratio, sed pietatis respectus pepererit.

Sanctus ambitus.

Quamobrem te oro, mi Petre, uti aut praesens, si potes commode,
aut absens per epistolam, compelles Hythlo|daeum atque efficias, ne 22
quicquam huic operi meo aut insit falsi aut ueri desyderetur. Atque
haud scio an praestet ipsum ei librum ostendi. Nam neque alius
aeque sufficit, si quid est erratum corrigere, neque is ipse aliter hoc
praestare potest, quam si quae sunt a me scripta perlegerit. Ad
haec : fiet ut hoc pacto intelligas; accipiat ne libenter, an grauatim
ferat, hoc operis a me conscribi. Nempe si suos labores decreuit ipse

the Vtopiane weale publyque, I should preuente[a] and take
from hym the flowcr and grace of the noueltie of this his
historie.

Why publish?

Howbeit, to saye the verie truthe, I am not yet fully
determined with meselfe, whether I wyll put forth my booke
or no. For the natures of men be so diuers, the phan-
tasies of some so wayewarde, theire myndes so vnkynde,
theire iudgementes so corrupte, that they which leade a
merie and a iocunde lyfe, followinge theire owne sensuall
pleasures and carnal lustes [1], maye seme to be in a muche
better state or case, then they that vexe and vnquiete them
selfes with cares and studie for the puttynge forth and
publyshynge of some thynge, that maye be either profett
or pleasure to other; whiche[b] neuertheles wyl disdayn-
fully, scornefully, and vnkyndly accepte the same. The
moste parte of al be vnlearned: and a great numbre
hath learnynge in contempte. The rude and barbarous
alloweth nothynge but that which is verie barbarous in
dede. If it be one that hath a lytell smacke of learnynge,
he reiecteth as homely[c] and commen warc whatsoeuer is

Variable
Readers:

Sensualists

[a] preuente him.   [b] whiche others.   [c] homely geare.

mandare literis, nolit fortasse me : neque ego certe uelim, Vtopiensium per me uulgata republica, florem illi gratiamque nouitatis
historiae suae praeripere.

Quanquam ut uere dicam, nec ipse mecum satis adhuc constitui, an
sim omnino aediturus. Etenim tam uaria sunt palata
mortalium, tam morosa quorundam ingenia, tam ingrati *Ingrata*
animi, tam absurda iudicia, ut cum hiis haud paulo felicius *hominum*
agi uideatur, qui iucundi atque hilares genio indulgent *iudicia,*
suo, quam qui semet macerant curis, ut aedant aliquid quod aliis, aut
fastidientibus aut ingratis, uel utilitati possit esse uel uoloptati. Plu-
rimi literas nesciunt : multi contemnunt. Barbarus ut durum reiicit,
quicquid non est plane barbarum. Scioli aspernantur ut triuiale,

---

[1] This is going wide of *indulgent genio*, which is simply 'follow their bent,' or gratify their natural inclina- tion. Erasmus notes the proverb in his *Adagia*.

Bad Readers

not stuffed full of olde moughteaten wordes[a], and that be worne out of vse. Some there be that haue pleasure onely in olde rustie antiquities; and some onely in theire owne doinges. One is so sowre, so crabbed, and so vnpleasaunt [1], that he can awaye with no myrthe nor sporte. An other is so narrow in [b] the sholders [2], that he can beare no iestes nor tawntes. Some selie poore soules be so aferd that at euery snappishe worde theire nose shalbe bitten of, that they stande in no lesse drede of euerye quicke and sharpe worde, then he that is bytten of a madde dogge feareth water. Some be so mutable and wauer-yng, that euery houre they be in a newe mynde, sainge one thynge syttynge, and an other thynge standynge. An other sorte sytteth upon theire allebencheis, and there amonge theire cuppes they geue iudgement of the wittes of wryters, and with greate aucthoritie they condemne euen as pleaseth them euery wryter accordyng to his writinge; in moste spiteful maner mockynge, lowtynge, and flowtynge them: beynge themselfes in the meane season sauffe, and, as sayth the proverbe [3], out of all daunger of gonneshotte.

[a] termes.   [b] betwene.

quicquid obsoletis uerbis non scatet. quibusdam solum placent 23 uetera, plerisque tantum sua. Hic tam tetricus est, ut non admittat iocos, hic tam insulsus, ut non ferat sales. tam simi *Simos uocat homines nullo naso.* quidam sunt, ut nasum omnem, uelut aquam ab rabido morsus cane, reformident. adeo mobiles alii sunt, ut aliud sedentes probent, aliud stantes. Hi sedent in tabernis, et inter pocula de scriptorum iudicant ingeniis, magnaque cum autoritate condemnant utcumque lubitum est, suis quenque *Prouerbium.* scriptis, ueluti capillicio uellicantes, ipsi interim tuti et, { quod dici solet, ἔξω βέλους. quippe tam leves et abrasi

in Greek

---

[1] The three attempts at *tetricus* may be noted.

[2] As we should now say, 'so strait-laced.' Robynson amplifies considerably the single word *insulsus*, 'tasteless.' Erasmus, under the heading 'Collo valido' in his *Adagia*, quotes a somewhat similar proverbial expression as used by Marius in tbe Senate: 'non ita latum sibi esse collum.' But the application is not the same.

[3] The proverb and its cognates are given under *Extra telorum jactum* in the *Adagia* of Erasmus, ed. 1629, p. 351 a.

For whye, they be so smugge and smoethe, that they haue not so much as one heare[1] of an honest man, whereby one may take holde of them. There be moreouer some so vnkynde and vngentell, that thoughe they take great pleasure and delectation in the worke, yet for al that they can not fynde in theire hartes to loue the author therof, nor to aforde hym a good worde; beynge muche lyke vncourteis, vnthankefull, and chourlishe guestes, whiche, when they haue with good and deyntie meates well filled theire bellyes, departe home, geuynge no thankes to the feaste maker. Go youre wayes, nowe, and make a costly feaste at youre owne chargeis for guestes so deyntie mouthed, so dyuers in taste, and bisydes that of so vnkynde and vnthankefull natures[2].

To the Reader

But neuertheles, frende Peter, do I praye you with Hythlodaye as I willed you before. And as for this

undique, ut ne pilum quidem habeant boni uiri, quo possint apprehendi. Sunt praeterea quidam tam ingrati, ut quum impense delectentur opere, nihilo tamen magis ament autorem; non absimiles inhumanis hospitibus, qui quum opiparo conuiuio prolixe sint excepti, saturi demum discedunt domum, nullis habitis gratiis ei, a quo sunt inuitati. I nunc[3], et hominibus tam delicati palati, tam varii gustus, animi praeterea tam memoris et grati, tuis impensis epulum instrue.

Mira collatio.

Sed tamen, mi Petre, tu illud age quod dixi cum Hythlodaeo.

---

[1] That is, are so close cropped and shaven (abrasi), like wrestlers prepared for a conflict, that they present nothing to lay hold of, not even so much as a single hair.

[2] Referring to what he had said (p. 8) about consulting Hythloday. Warner's note here is to the point:— 'Sir Thomas More not only intended that this should pass for a true history, but also wished to conceal from the public that he had any hand in it as an author: and as there would be no great probability that the fiction could be long undiscovered, we may suppose

he was the more solicitous to succeed in the last intention; having said so many free things about religion and government in his narrative, repugnant to the principles of the times he wrote in.'

[3] Erasmus, in commenting on the proverb *Inanis Opera*, breaks out into a similar denunciation of the ingratitude experienced by authors. 'I nunc,' he exclaims, in a strain reminding us of the present passage, 'et hoc tam magnificum praemium tot tamque diuturnis uigiliis .. redime' *Adagia*, ed. 1629, p. 330 b.

matter, I shalbe at my lybertie afterwardes to take newe
aduisement. Howebeit, seynge I haue taken great paynes
and laboure in wrytynge the matter, if it may stande with
hys mynde and pleasure, I wyll, as touchinge the edition or
publishing of the booke, followe the counsell and aduise of
my frendes, and specially yours. Thus fare you well, ryght

hartely beloued frende Peter, with
youre gentell wyfe ; and loue
me as you haue euer done ;
for I loue you better
then euer I dyd.
(. · .)

postea tamen integrum erit hac de re consultare denuo.   Quan|-

quam si id ipsius uoluntate fiat, quandoquidem   25
scribendi labore defunctus nunc sero sapio,
quod reliquum est de aedendo se-
-quar amicorum consilium, at-
-que in primis tuum. Va-
-le, dulcissime Petre
Aegidi, cum
optima
con-
-iuge ; ac
me ut soles a-
-ma ; quando ego te
amo etiam plus quam soleo [a].

[a] serio, A.

A fruteful/

and pleasaunt worke of the

beste state of a publyque weale, and
of the newe yle called Utopia : written
in Latine by Syr Thomas More
knyght, and translated into Englyshe
by Raphe Robynson Citizein and
Goldsmythe of London, at the
procurement, and earnest re=
quest of George Tadlowe
Citezein & Haberdassher
of the same Citie.

(∴)

❡ Imprinted at London

by Abraham Vele, dwelling in Pauls
churcheyarde at the sygne of
the Lambe.   Anno,

1 5 5 1.

To the right

honourable, and his berie sin
guler good maister, maister William
Cecylle esquiere[1], one of the twoo prin=
cipal secretaries to the kyng his moste
excellent maiestie, Raphe Robynson
wissheth continuaunce of health,
with dayly increase of ver=
tue, and honoure.

VPon a tyme[2], when tidynges came too the citie of
Corinthe that kyng Philippe, father to Alexander
surnamed the Great, was comming thetherwarde with an
armie royall to lay siege to the citie ; the Corinthians,
being forth with stryken with greate feare, beganne busilie
and earnestly to looke aboute them, and to falle to worke of

---

[1] William Cecil, afterwards Lord
Burghley, was born in 1520, being the
only son of Richard Cecil of Burleigh
in Northamptonshire. He was educated at Stamford and Grantham
Schools, and afterwards at St. John's
College, Cambridge, then at the height
of its reputation. Owing to a romantic
attachment to a sister of John Cheke,
he was taken from the University
before obtaining a degree, and was
entered at Gray's Inn, where his
portrait still hangs in the Hall. He
was knighted in October, 1551 ; made
Secretary of State, Nov. 20, 1558,

three days after Elizabeth's accession ;
Baron of Burghley, Feb. 25, 1571, and
Lord High Treasurer in July, 1572.
He died in 1598. See Dr. Jessopp's
article in the Dict. of National Biography, and, for his connection with
Robynson, the Introduction, above,
p. lxxi.
[2] The story which follows is taken
from Lucian's Quomodo historia con-
scribenda sit, § 3. The readers of Sir
Walter Scott will remember the description in Waverley of David Gellatly,
'idle as Diogenes at Sinope, while his
countrymen were preparing for a siege.'

all handes ; some to skowre and trymme vp harneis ; some
to carry stones ; some to amende and buylde hygher the
walles ; some to rampiere and fortyfie the bulwarkes and
fortresses ; some one thynge and some an other, for the
defendinge and strengthenynge of the citie. The whiche
busie labour and toyle of theires when Diogenes the
phylosopher sawe, hauing no profitable busines wherupon
to sette himself on worke (neither any man required his
labour and helpe as expedient for the commen wealth in
that necessitie), immediatly girded about him his phylo-
sophicall cloke, and began to rolle and tumble vp and
downe hether and thether vpon the hille syde, that lieth
adioyninge to the citie, his great barrel or tunne, wherein
he dwelled : for other dwellynge place wold he haue none.

This seing one of his frendes, and not alitell musynge
therat, came to hym : And I praye the, Diogenes (quod
he), whie doest thou thus, or what meanest thou hereby ?
Forsothe I am tumblyng my tubbe to, (quod he) bycause
it were no reason that I only should be ydell, where so
many be working.

In semblable maner, right honorable sir, though I be,
as I am in dede, of muche lesse habilitie then Diogenes
was, to do any thinge, that shall or may be for the auauncement and commoditie of the publique wealth of my natiue
countrey ; yet I, seing euery sort and kynde of people in
theire vocation and degree busilie occupied about the common wealthes affaires, and especially learned men dayly
putting forth in writing newe inuentions and deuises to
the furtheraunce of the same ; thought it my bounden
duetie to God and to my countrey, so to tumble my tubbe,
I meane so to occupie and exercise meself in bestowing
such spare houres, as I, beinge at the becke and commaundement of others, cold conueniently winne to me
self ; that, though no commoditie of that my labour and
trauaile to the publique weale should arise, yet it myght

v.

cf. Lyly :
Campaspe

Diogenes
in tub

cf. Tale
of a Tub

by this appeare, that myne endeuoire, and good wille hereunto was not lacking.

To the accomplishement therfore and fulfyllyng of this
my mynde and purpose, I toke vpon me to tourne and
translate out of Latine into oure Englishe tonge the frutefull and profitable boke, which sir Thomas more, knight,
compiled and made of the new yle Vtopia, conteining and
setting forth the best state and fourme of a publique weale:
a worke (as it appeareth) written almost fourtie [1] yeres ago
by the said Sir Thomas More, the authour therof. The
whiche man, forasmuche as he was a man of late tyme,
yea almost of thies our dayes ; and for the excellent quali
ties, wherewith the great goodnes of God had plentyfully
endowed him, and for the high place and rowme, wherunto his prince had most graciously called him, notably
wel knowen, not only among vs his countremen, but also
in forrein countreis and nations ; therfore I haue not much
to speake of him. This only I saye : that it is much to be
lamented of al, and not only of vs English men, that a man
of so incomparable witte, of so profounde knowlege, of so
absolute learning, and of so fine eloquence, was yet neuerthelesse so much blinded, rather with obstinacie then with
ignoraunce, that he could not, or rather would not, see the
shining light of godes holy truthe in certein principal
pointes of Christian religion ; but did rather cheuse to
perseuer and continue in his wilfull and stubbourne obstinacie euen to the very death : this I say is a thing much
to be lamented.

But letting this matter passe, I retourne again to vtopia ;
which (as I said befor) is a work not only for the matter
that it conteineth fruteful and profitable, but also for the
writers eloquent latine stiele [2] pleasaunt and delectable.

---

[1] Thirty-six, reckoning from 1515 to
1551. Sir Thomas More had been dead
sixteen years when Robynson wrote.

[2] Erasmus was probably thinking of
More's latinity, when, in his letter to
Froben (above, p. lxxviii), he indulged

Which he that readeth in latine, as the authour himself
wrote it, perfectly vnderstanding the same, doubtles he
shal take great pleasure and delite both in the swete eloquence of the writer, and also in the wittie inuencion, and
fine conueiaunce, or disposition of the matter; but most
of all in the good and holsome lessons, which be there in
great plenty and aboundaunce.

But nowe I feare greatly that in this my simple translation, through my rudenes and ignoraunce in our english
tonge, all the grace and pleasure of the eloquence, wher-
with the matter in latine is finely set forth, may seme to be
vtterly excluded and lost; and therfore the frutefulnes of
the matter it selfe muche peraduenture diminished and
appayred. For who knoweth not, whiche knoweth any
thyng, that an eloqent styele setteth forth and highly
commendeth a meane matter; where as, on the other side,
rude and vnlearned speche defaceth and disgraceth a very
good matter? According as I harde ones a wise man
say: A good tale euel tolde were better vntold, and an
euell tale well tolde nedeth none other sollicitour.

This thing I well pondering and wayinge with me self,
and also knowing and knowledging the barbarous rudenes
of my translation, was fully determined neuer to haue put
it forth in printe; had it not bene for certein frendes of
myne, and especially one, whom aboue al other I regarded;
a man of sage and discret witte, and in wordly matters by
long vse well experienced, whoes name is GeorgeTadlowe [1];
an honest citizein of London, and in the same citie well

---

in speculation as to the perfection
More's genius might have reached, if
trained in Italy. Some of the pecu-
liarities of his Latin style will be
pointed out in the course of the notes.
There are traces in it of the study of
Plautus. As a rule, it is fluent and
vigorous, with a great command of
vocabulary. But it has not the elegance of Erasmus; and it shows
occasionally the same tendency as
appears in the author's English writings, to run off into inordinately long
sentences.

[1] I have not been able to discover
anything about this person.

accepted and of good reputation; at whoes request and
instaunce I first toke vpon my weake and feble sholders
the heauie and weightie bourdein of this great enterprice.

This man with diuers other, but this man chiefely (for he
was able to do more with me then many other), after that
I had ones rudely brought the worke to an ende ceassed
not by al meanes possible continualy to assault me, vntil
he had at the laste, what by the force of his pitthie argumentes and strong reasons, and what by hys authority,
so persuaded me, that he caused me to agree and consente
to the impryntynge herof. He therefore, as the chiefe
persuadour, must take vpon him the daunger, whyche
vpon this bolde and rashe enterpryse shall ensue. I, as
I suppose, am herin clerely acquytte and discharged of
all blame.

Yet, honorable Syr, for the better auoyding of enuyous
and malycyous tonges, I (knowynge you to be a man, not
onlye profoundely learned, and well affected towardes all
suche as eyther canne, or wyll, take paynes in the well
bestowing of that poore talente, whyche GOD hath endued
them wyth; but also for youre godlye dysposytyon and
vertuous qualytyes not vnworthelye nowe placed in aucthorytye, and called to honoure), am the bolder humblye
to offer and dedycate vnto youre good maystershyppe thys
my symple woorke : partly that vnder the sauffe conducte
of your protection it may the better be defended from the
obloquie of them, which can say well by nothing that
pleaseth not their fond and corrupt iudgementes, though
it be els both frutefull and godly ; and partlye that, by the
meanes of this homely present, I may the better renewe
and reuiue (which of late, as you know, I haue already
begonne to do) the old acquayntaunce, that was betwene
you and me in the time of our childhode, being then
scolefellowes togethers [1] : not doubting that you, for your

Robinson schoolmate of Cecil

---

[1] See the Introduction, § 6.

C 2

natiue goodnes and gentelnes, will accept in good parte this poore gift, as an argument or token that mine old good wil and hartye affection towardes you is not, by reason of long tract of time and separrtion of our bodies, any thinge at all quayled and diminished, but rather (I assuer you) much augmented and increased.

This verely is the chieffe cause, that hath incouraged me to be so bolde with youre maistershippe. Els truelye this my poore present is of such simple and meane sort, that it is neyther able to recompense the least portion of your great gentelnes to me, of my part vndeserued, both in the time of our olde acquayntance, and also now lately again bountifully shewed; neither yet fitte and mete, for the very basenes of it, to be offered to one so worthy as you be. But almighty god (who therfore euer be thanked) hath auaunced you to such fortune and dignity, that you be of hability to accept thankefully aswell a mans good will as his gift. The same god graunte you and all yours long and joyfully to

contynue in all godlynes

and prosperytye.

(∴)

¶ The fyrste

boke of the communyca

cion of Raphaell hythlodaye concernynge the best state of a commen
wealthe.

THe moste vyctoryous and tryumphante Kynge of
Englande, Henry the ight of that name, in all royal
vertues Prince moste peerlesse, hadde of late in contra-
uersie with ᵃ the right hyghe and myghtie king of Castell ¹
weightye matters, and of greate importaunce; for the
[debatement and final determination] wherof the kinges
Maieste sent me Ambassadour into flaunders, ioined in   *More*
                                                          &

ᵃ with Charles.

25   S E R M O N I S   Q V E M

RAPHAEL HYTHLODAEVS VIR EXIMIVS

DE OPTIMO REIPVBLICAE STATV HA-

BVIT, LIBER PRIMVS, PER ILLVSTREM

VIRVM THOMAM MORVM INCLYTAE

BRITANNIARVM VRBIS LONDINI

ET CIVEM ET VICECOMITEM.   *Basel, 1518.*

QVVM NON EXIGVI MOMENti negocia quaedam inuictissi-
mus Angliae Rex HENRICVS, eius nominis octauus, omni-
26   bus egregii principis artibus ornatissimus, cum serenissi|mo
Castellae principe CAROLO controuersa nuper habuisset, ad ea
[tractanda componendaque]oratorem me legauit in Flandriam, comitem

---

¹ See the Introduction, § 2.

Tunstall

commission with cuthebert Tunstall[1], a man doubteles owte of comparison, and whom the kinges maiestie of late, to the greate reioysyng of all men, did preferre to the office of maister of the Rolles. But of thys mans prayses I will saye nothynge; not bycause I do feare that small credence shalbe geuen to the testymony that commyth owt of a frindes mouthe, but bicause hys vertue and lernyng be greater and of more excellencye, than that I am able to prayse them; and also in all places so famous, and so perfectlye well knowne, that they nede not nor ought not of me to be praysed, onles I wolde

et collegam uiri incomparabilis Cuthberti Tunstalli, quem sacris [a] scriniis nuper ingenti omnium gratulatione praefecit. de cuius sane laudibus nihil a me dicetur, non quod uerear ne parum syncera fidei testis habenda sit amicitia, sed quod uirtus eius ac doctrina maior est, quam ut a me praedicari possit, tum notior ubique atque illustrior,

[a] *om.* A.

---

[1] Cuthbert Tunstall, brother of the Sir Brian Tunstall who fell at Flodden, and uncle of the famous Bernard Gilpin, was born at Hackforth in Yorkshire, 1474. After studying at both the English Universities and in Padua, and holding various ecclesiastical preferments, he was made Master of the Rolls, May 16, 1516 (Brewer: *Letters and Papers*, vol. i. no. 1882). Hence the words of More in the text, *quem . . . nuper*, &c., should be rendered not 'did preferre,' but 'hath lately preferred.' Tunstall was not yet Master of the Rolls at the time of the embassy. For the amount of public business that passed through his hands as ambassador on various occasions, see the reference given above. p. xxvii, *n.* In 1516 he was again in Flanders, and on that occasion stood godfather to Peter Giles' infant daughter (Erasm. *Epist.*, ed. 1642, p. 400). He was an attached friend of Erasmus as well as of More, and shared their liberal sentiments. In 1522 he was made Bishop of London, and in 1530 Bishop of Durham. He accepted the oath of supremacy to Henry VIII, but drew back, like many other good men, from the sweeping reforms under Edward VI. After being deprived of his see in that reign, and restored under Queen Mary, he finally refused to take the oath, on Elizabeth's accession, and was again deprived in 1559. The short remainder of his life he spent at Lambeth, under the kindly charge of Archbishop Parker. High praise is given to one of his works, the *De arte supputandi*, 1522, by a critic not very lavish of praise—the late Professor De Morgan (*Arithmetical Books*, 1847, p. 13). To his honour it is stated that no one suffered death for heresy in his diocese, during his administration.

seme to shew and set furth the brightenes of the sonne
wyth a candell, as the Prouerbe sayth [1].

sun/candle

There met vs at Bruges (for thus yt was before agreed)
they whome theire prince hadde for that matter appoynted
commyssyoners, excellente men all. The chiefe and the
head of them was the Marcgraue (as they cal him) of
Bruges, a right honorable man: but the wisest and the
best spoken of them was George Temsice, prouoste of
Casselles [2]; a man not onlye by lernyng but also by
nature of singuler eloquence, and in the lawes profounde-
lye lerned; but in reasonynge, and debatynge of matters,
what by his naturall witte, and what by daylye exercise,
suerlye he hadde fewe fellowes. After that we hadde
ones or twise mette, and vpon certeyne poyntes or artycles
could not fully and throughlye agre; they for a certeyne
space toke their leaue of vs, and departed to Bruxelle,
there to knowe theire princes pleasure. I in the meane

at Bruges

of Latin

quam ut debeat, nisi uideri uelim solem lucerna, quod aiunt,
ostendere.   Paroemia

Occurrerunt nobis Brugis (sic enim conuenerat) hi, quibus a principe
negotium demandabatur, egregii uiri omnes, in his praefectus Bru-
gensis, uir magnificus, princeps et caput erat ; caeterum os et pectus
Georgius Temsicius, Cassiletanus Praepositus, non arte solum uerumetiam natura facundus, ad haec iure consultissimus, tractandi uero
negocii cum ingenio tum assiduo rerum usu eximius artifex. ubi
semel atque iterum congressi quibusdam de rebus non satis consen-
tiremus, illi in aliquot dies uale nobis dicto Bruxellas profecti sunt,

---

[1] The proverb is given by Erasmus
in the form *lucernam adhibere in meridie*
(*Adag.* 1629, p. 12 b). A kindred one
(*ib.*, p. 18 b) is *solem adiuuare facibus.*
The comment on this latter by Erasmus : 'superuacuis laborat impendiis,
qui solem,' &c., is curiously imitated,
whether consciously or not, by Shakspeare in *King John*, iv. 2 ; where 'with
taper-light | To seek the beauteous eye
of heaven to garnish' is pronounced to

be 'wasteful and ridiculous excess,'

[2] Cassel, now a town in the Dép.
du Nord of France, is a little north of
Hazebrouck, on the line between it
and Dunkirk. Its provost, Georgius
a Tempseca (de Theimsecke), was a
native of Bruges, and wrote a history
of Artois. See König's *Bibliotheca
vetus et nova*, 1678, p. 749 b, with a
reference to Sweert, p. 276 ; and
Gairdner's *Henry VII*, p. 201.

More to Antwerp

tyme (for so my busynes laye) wente streyghte thens to Antwerpe[1].

Peter Giles

Whyles I was there abydinge, often tymes amonge other, but whyche to me was more welcome then annye other, dyd vysite me one Peter Gyles, a Citisien of Antwerpe[2]; a man there in hys contrey of honest reputatyon, and also preferred to hyghe promotyons, worthye truelye of the highest. For it is harde to saye whether the yong man[3] be in lernynge or in honestye more excellent. For he is bothe of wonderfull vertuous condytyons, and also singulerlye well lerned, and towardes all sortes of people excedynge gentyl; but towardes his fryndes so kynde harted, so louynge, so faythfull, so trustye, and of so earneste affectyon, that yt were verye harde in any place to fynd a man, that wyth hym in all poyntes of frendshyppe maye be compared. No man can be more lowlye or courteys. No man vsithe lesse symulatyon or dyssymulatyon; in no man ys more prudente symplycytye. Besydes this, he is in his talke and communycatyon so merye and plcasaunte, yea, and that wythout harme, that, throughe hys gentyll intertaynement and hys swete and delectable communycatyon, in me was greatlye abated and dymynyshed the feruent desyre that I hadde

principis oraculum sciscitaturi. Ego me interim (sic enim res ferebat) Antuerpiam confero.

Ibi dum uersor, saepe me inter alios, sed quo non alius gratior, inuisit Petrus Aegidius, Antuerpiae natus, magna fide, et loco apud suos honesto, dignus honestissimo, quippe iuuenis haud scio doctior ne an moratior. est enim et optimus et literatissimus, ad haec animo in | omnes candido, in amicos uero tam propenso pectore, amore, fide, **27** adfectu tam syncero, ut uix unum aut alterum usquam inuenias, quem illi sentias omnibus amicitiae numeris esse conferendum. Rara illi modestia; nemini longius abest fucus; nulli simplicitas inest prudentior; porro sermone tam lepidus, et tam innoxie facetus, ut patriae

---

[1] See the Introduction, § 2.
[2] See note above, p. 1.
[3] At the time of More's visit he would be twenty-nine.

to see my natyue contreye, my wyffe and my chyldren; whome then I dyd muche longe and couett to see, bicause that at that tyme I hadde byn more then .iiii. monythes from them [1].

Upon a certeyne daye as I was herynge [a] the deuyne seruyce in our ladies churche [2], whyche is the fayrest, the moste gorgious and curyous churche of buyldynge in all the cytye, and also moste frequented of people, and when the deuyne [3] was done [b], was readye to goo home to my lodgyng, I chaunced to espie thys forsayde Peter talkynge wyth a certeyne straunger, a man well stryken in age, wyth a blake sonne burned face, a longe bearde, and a cloke caste homely aboute hys shoulders [4]; whom by

[a] when I hadde herde.   [b] the seruice beynge done.

desyderium, ac laris domestici, uxoris, et liberorum, quorum studio reuisendorum nimis quam anxie tenebar (iam tum enim plus quatuor mensibus abfueram domo) magna ex parte mihi dulcissima consuetudine sua et mellitissima confabulatione leuauerit.

Hunc quum die quadam in templo diuae Mariae, quod et opere pulcherrimum, et populo celeberrimum est, rei diuinae interfuissem, atque peracto sacro pararem inde in hospitium redire, forte colloquentem uideo cum hospite quodam, uergentis ad senium aetatis, uultu adusto, promissa barba, penula neglectim ab humero depen-

---

[1] This would make the time referred to in the text the middle of September, or later, as the embassy left England on May 12, 1515. See the Introduction, § 2.

[2] The Cathedral of Notre Dame at Antwerp, which More would see in all the freshness of its beauty, as it was not completed till the sixteenth century, though begun early in the fifteenth, has always been counted one of the most superb specimens of Gothic architecture on the Continent. It possesses two master-pieces of Rubens.

[3] The word *service* is omitted, as seen by the reading of the second edition. Burnet renders, more naturally, 'One

day, as I was returning home from mass.'

[4] This little trait comes in so naturally, that it may be doing it wrong to give prominence to it. But the Latin word, *neglectim*, seems to suggest that More is here playfully bringing in a habit of his own — that of wearing his gown in a careless fashion. In this, as has happened since, he had his imitators. Ascham mentions one such, 'who, being most unlike him in wit and learning, nevertheles in wearing his gowne awrye upon the one shoulder, as Syr *Tho. More* was wont to do, would nedes be counted lyke unto him.'—*The Scholemaster*, ed. by Mayor, p. 180.

hys fauour and apparrel forthwythe I iudged to be a
maryner. But when thys Peter sawe me, he cummythe
to me and saluteth me[a]. And as I was abowte to answere
hym: 'see you thys man?' sayeth he (and therwyth he
poynted to the man that I sawe hym talkynge wyth
before). 'I was mynded,' quod he, 'to brynge hym
streyghte home to you.' 'He should haue bene verye
welcome to me,' sayd I, 'for your sake.' 'Naye' (quod
he) 'for hys owne sake, if you knewe hym; for there ys
no man this daye lyuynge that can tell you of so manye
strange and vnknowne peoples and contreis as this man
can. And I know well that you be verye desyrous to
heare of suche newes.' 'Than I coniectured not farre
a mysse' (quod I) 'for euen at the fyrste syghte I iudged
hym to be a maryner.' 'Naye' (quod he) 'there ye were
greatlye deceaued. He hayth sayled indede, not as the
maryner Palynure[1], but as the experte and prudent prince
Ulisses; yea, rather as the auncyent and sage Philosopher
Plato.

'For thys same Raphaell Hythlodaye[2] (for thys ys hys

[a] But the sayde Peter seyng me, came vnto me and saluted me.

Marginal notes:
More curious of strange places:
not Palinurus —
Ulysses &
Plato

dente, qui mihi ex uultu atque habitu nauclerus esse uidebatur. At
Petrus ubi me conspexit, adit ac salutat. respondere conantem
seducit paululum, et, uides, inquit, hunc? (simul designabat eum cum
quo loquentem uideram) eum, inquit, iam hinc ad te recta parabam
ducere. Venisset, inquam, pergratus mihi tua causa. Imo, inquit
ille, si nosses hominem, sua. Nam nemo uiuit hodie mortalium
omnium, qui tantam tibi hominum, terrarumque incognitarum narrare
possit historiam. quarum rerum audiendarum scio | auidissimum 28
esse te. Ergo, inquam, non pessime coniectaui. Nam primo aspectu
sensi hominem esse nauclerum. Atqui, inquit, aberrasti longissime:
nauigauit quidem non ut Palinurus, sed ut Vlysses: imo, uelut Plato.
Nempe Raphael iste, sic enim uocatur, gentilicio nomine Hythlo-

---

[1] The pilot of Aeneas. Virg. *Aen.* iii.
202.
[2] The name is plainly formed from
ὔθλος 'idle talk,' and δαίειν 'to dis-

tribute' (the second element being
found in prefixes, as δαϊτρός), as if to
express, like ὑθλορρήμων, 'a teller of
idle tales.' No commentator seems

name) is verye well lerned in the Latyne tonge; but profounde and excellent in the greke tonge[a], wherein he euer bestowed more studye than in the lattyne, because he had geuen hym selfe holye to the studye of Phylosophy. Wherof he knewe that there ys nothynge extante in the lattyne tonge[b], that is to anny purpose, sauynge a few of Senecaes and Ciceroes doinges[1]. His patrymonye that he was borne vnto he lefte to his bretherne (for he is a Portugalle borne); and for the desyre that he hadde to see and knowe the farre contreys of the worlde, he joyned him selfe in companye wyth Amerike vespuce[2], and in the .III. laste voyages of thoes .iiii., that be nowe in prynte and abrode in euerye mans handes, he contynued styll in

(margin notes in hand: Raphael more proficient in Greek than Latin. Hythloday Portugese. A Vespucci 4 books of voyages.)

[a] language.   [b] in Latine.

---

daoua, et latinae linguae non indoctus, et Graecae doctissimus (cuius ideo studiosior quam Romanae fuit, quoniam totum se addixerat philosophiae; qua in re nihil quod alicuius momenti sit, praeter Senecae quaedam ac Ciceronis extare latine cognouit) relicto fratribus patrimonio, quod ei domi fuerat (est enim Lusitanus) orbis terrarum contemplandi studio Americo Vespucio se adiunxit, atque in tribus posterioribus illarum quatuor nauigationum, quae passim iam leguntur,

---

to have thought it worth while to suggest any reason for the traveller's other name being Raphael. It may have been borrowed from Raphael Volaterranus, whose voluminous *Commentarii Urbani* were printed at the Ascensian Press in 1511. See Freytag's *Adparatus Litterarius*, 1755, iii. p. 518. Vives often refers to Volaterranus as a geographical writer. Cf. *De discip.* (ed. 1636), p. 633. Paulus Jovius, after finding fault with his style, says that 'multum hercle debemus ingenuo gratuitoque labori.'—*Elogia*, 1571, p. 260. Jean Saugrain, the author of an early French translation of the *Utopia*, takes a different view. After defining 'Hythloday' as 'facteur de non veritables et plaisans

propos,' he adds: 'lequel en propre nom il appelle Raphael, nom d'un Ange spirituel, signifiant que de son propre et bon esprit ha esté inuentée ladite Republique de nul lieu.'— *La Republique d'Vtopie*, Lyons, 1559, p. 5.

[1] That is, works. The want of originality in Latin philosophical writings, referred to in the text, is a matter of common remark. Ascham went farther, and, after excepting Cicero, declared that 'if there be any good' in Latin and certain other languages, 'it is either lerned, or borowed, or stolne, from some of those worthie wittes of Athens.'—*Scholemaster*, ed. Mayor, p. 52.

[2] See the Introduction, § 3.

hys companye; sauynge that in te [the] laste voyage he came not home again wyth hym. For he made suche meanes and shyfte, what by intreataunce and what by importune sute, that he gotte lycence of mayster Amerycke (thoughe it were sore agaynst his will) to be one of the .xxiiii. whyche in the ende of the laste voyage were leftc in the contrye of Gulike [1].) He was therfore lefte behynde for hys mindes sake, as one that toke more thoughte and care for trauaylyng then dyinge; hauynge customablye in hys mouthe theis sayinges: He that hathe no graue ys couered wyth the skie; and, The way to heauen owte of all places is of like lenghth and distance. Which fantasye of his (if God had not bene his better frende) he hadde suerlye bought full deere.

'But after the departynge of Mayster vespuce, when he

perpetuus eius comes fuit, nisi quod in ultima cum eo non rediit. Curauit enim atque adeo extorsit ab Americo, ut ipse in his xxiii esset, qui ad fines postremae nauigationis in Castello relinquebantur. Itaque relictus est, uti obtemperaretur animo eius, peregrinationis magis quam sepulchri curioso; quippe cui haec assidue sunt in ore, Apophthegma [a].   Caelo tegitur qui non habet urnam [2], et Vndique ad superos tantundem esse uiae. Quae mens eius, nisi deus ei propitius adfuisset, nimio fuerat illi constatura.

Caeterum postquam digresso Vespucio [b] multas regiones cum quin-

[a] *Deest in* B.   [b] Vespusio, A.

---

[1] From its being printed with a capital letter, Robynson seems to have taken the 'Castellum' of the Latin to be a proper name, instead of rendering the words 'in the fort.' See above, p. xxxix. With this idea, he rendered it 'Gulike,' because in the old dictionaries Castellum is given as the ancient name of Jülich (the French Juliers, 23 miles west of Cologne), and this is sometimes spelt *Gulike*, as in Cooper's *Thesaurus*, ed. 1584: 'Castellum, the name of a country called Juliers or Gulike.' That More's Castellum was in South America, not in Gallia Belgica, does not seem to have troubled the translator.

[2] The line is from Lucan, vii. 819. What follows is an adaptation of the oft-quoted saying of Anaxagoras of Clazomenae, when dying at Lampsacus: 'Quaerentibus amicis, velletne Clazomenas in patriam, si quid accidisset, auferri: *Nihil necesse est*, inquit; *undique enim ad inferos tantundem viae est.*'—Cic. *Quaestiones Tusc.* I. § 104.

[margin left: 24 left]
[margin left: Proverbs]

hadde trauayled thoroughe and abowte manye contreis, with v. of his companyons Gulykyans, at the laste by maruelous chaunce he arryued in Taprobane[1], from whens he wente to Calyquit[2], where he chaunced to fynde certeyne of hys contrey shyppes, wherin he retorned again into hys countreye, nothynge lesse then lokyd for.'

All thys when Peter hadde tolde me, I thankyd hym for his gentyll kyndnes, that he hadde vouchesaufed to brynge me to the speche of that man, whose communication he thought sholde be to me pleasaunte and acceptable. And there wyth I turned me to Raphaell; and when we hadde haylsede[3] thone thother, and hadde spoken thies comen wordes, that be customably spoken at the fyrste metynge and acquentaunce of straungers, we wente thens to my house, and there in my gardeyne, vpon a benche coueryd wyth grene torues[4], we satte downe talking togethers.

que Castellanorum comitibus emensus est, mirabili tandem fortuna Taprobanem delatus, inde peruenit in Caliquit, ubi repertis commode Lusitanorum | nauibus, in patriam denique praeter spem reuehitur.

Haec ubi narrauit Petrus, actis ei gratiis quod tam officiosus in me fuisset, ut cuius uiri colloquium mihi gratum speraret, eius uti sermone fruerer, tantam rationem habuisset, ad Raphaelem me conuerto. tum ubi nos mutuo salutassemus, atque illa communia dixissemus, quae dici in primo hospitum congressu solent, inde domum meam digredimur, ibique in horto, considentes in scamno cespitibus herbeis constrato, confabulamur.

[1] That is, Ceylon. Robynson retains the Latin name.

[2] It was at Calicut, 'Caliquit,' on the Malabar coast, that Vasco de Gama landed in May, 1498. 'Here a *factory* was formed, and after De Gama's return a large fleet followed him up and planted factories all along the coast.'—Caldecott's *English Colonization*, 1891, p. 17.

[3] That is, hailed, or greeted. The spelling of the word recalls its connexion with the Scandinavian forms *heilsa*, *helsa*, and *hilse*; on which see Professor Skeat.

[4] In the edition of 1518 there is a woodcut (p. 25) representing this garden scene. The artist seems to have taken the 'bench covered with green torves' to be a kind of crate stuffed with turf. I cannot realize to myself what More's description meant.

Hythloday's story

There (he) tolde vs howe that, after the departynge of vespuce, he and hys fellowes, that tarryed behynde in Gulyke, beganne by lytle and lytle, thoroughe fayre and gentle speche, to winne the loue and fauour of the people of that contreye ; in so muche that within shorte space, theye dydde dwell amonges them not onlyc harmelese, but also occupyed [a] wyth them verye famylyerly. He tolde vs also that they were in hyghe reputatyon and fauoure

?

wyth a certeyne greate man (whose name and contreye ys nowe quyte owte of my remembraunce), which of hys mere lyberalytye dyd beare the costes and charges of hym

5 companions

and his fyue companions, and besydes that gaue them a trustye guyde, to conducte them in theyre iorney (whyche by water was in botys and by lande in wagains), and to bring them to other princes withe verye frindlye commendatyons. Thus after manye dayes iourneis, he

a number of weal publics

sayd they found townys and cytyes, and weale publyques full of people, gouerned by good and holsom lawes.

equator

For vnder the lyne equynoctyall and of bothe [b] sydes of the same, as farrc as the sonne doth extend hys course, lyeth (quod he) greate and wyde desertes and wylder-

[a] occupiyng.   [b] and bothe.

Narrauit ergo nobis, quo pacto posteaquam Vespucius abierat, ipse sociique eius, qui in Castello remanserant, conueniendo atque blandiendo coeperint se paulatim eius terrae gentibus insinuare, iamque non innoxie modo apud eas, sed etiam familiariter uersari, tum principi cuidam (cuius et patria mihi et nomen excidit) grati charique esse. eius liberalitate narrabat commeatum atque uiaticum ipsi et quinque eius comitibus affatim fuisse suppeditatum, cum itineris (quod per aquam ratibus, per terram curru peragebant) fidelissimo duce, qui eos ad alios principes, quos diligenter commendati petebant, adduceret. Nam post multorum itinera dierum, oppida atque urbes aiebat reperisse se, ac non pessime institutas magna populorum frequentia respublicas.

Nempe sub aequatoris linea tum hinc atque inde ab utroque latere quantum fere spatii solis orbita complectitur, uastas obiacere [a] soli-

[a] subiacere, A.

Too much
Sun:

nesses, parched, burned and dryed vppe with continuall
and intollerable heate. All thynges be hydeous, terryble,
lothesome, and vnpleasaunte to be holde; all thynges
owte of fasshyon and comylynes, inhabyted wyth wylde
beastes and serpentes, or at the leaste wyse wyth people
that be no lesse sauage, wylde, and noysome then the
verye beastes themselfes be. But a lytle farther beyonde
that all thynges begyn by lytle and lytle to waxe pleasaunte ; the ayre softe, temperate, and gentle ; the ground
couered wyth grene grasse; less wildnes in the beastes.
At the laste shall ye come again to people, cities, and
townes, wherin is contynuall entercourse and occupyinge
of marchandyse and chaffare, not onelye amonge them
selfes and wyth theyre borderers, but also wyth marchauntes of farre contreys bothe by lande and water.
Ther I had occasion' (sayde he), 'to go to manye
contreys of ª euery syde. For there was no shyppe reddye
to anye voyage or iorney, but I and my fellowes were
into it verye gladlye receauyde. The shyppes that they
founde fyrste were made playne, flatte, and broade in the
botome, troughewyse. The sayles were made of greate
russhes, or of wyckers, and in some places of lether.
Afterwarde they founde shyppes wyth rydged kyeles, and

ª of omitted.

Temperate
Zone
of
civilization

Commerce,
(communism?)

First
person
narration ?
begins ?

cf. Latin:
no direct
discourse

tudines perpetuo feruore torridas. Squalor undique et tristis rerum
30 facies; | horrida atque inculta omnia, feris habitata serpentibusque,
aut denique hominibus, neque minus efferis quam sint beluae, neque
minus noxiis. Caeterum ubi longius euectus sis, paulatim omnia
mansuescere : caelum minus asperum, solum uirore blandum, miliora
animantium ingenia. tandem aperiri populos, urbes, oppida. in his
assidua, non inter se modo ac finitimos, sed procul etiam dissitas
gentes, terra marique commercia.
  Inde sibi natam facultatem multas ultro citroque terras inuisendi,
quod nulla nauis ad iter quodlibet instruebatur, in quam non ille
comitesque eius libentissime admittebantur. Naues quas primis
regionibus conspexerunt, carina plana fuisse narrabat; uela consutis
papyris aut uiminibus intendebantur, alibi coriacea. post uero acu-

sayles of canuas; yea, and shortelye after hauynge all thynges lyke owers; the shyppemen also verye experte and connynge both in the sea and in the wether [1].'

But (he) sayde that he founde greate fauour and fryndeshyppe amonge them for teachynge them the feate and vse of the lode stone [2], whych to them before that tyme was vnknowne; and therefore they were wonte to be verye tymerous and fearefull vpon the sea, nor to venter vpon it but onlye in the somer time. But nowe they haue such a confidence in that stone, that they feare not stormy wynter; in so doynge, ferther frome care then ieopardye [a]. In so muche that it is greatlye to be doubtyd, leste that thynge, thoroughe theyre owne folyshe hardynes, shall tourne them to euyll and harme, whyche at the fyrste was supposyde shoulde be to them good and commodyous.

But what he tolde vs that he sawe, in euerye contrey wheare he came, it were verye longe to declare. Nother is it my purpose at this time to make rehersall therof.

[a] daunger.

minatas carinas, canabea [a] uela reppererunt, omnia denique nostris similia. nautae maris ac caeli non imperiti.

Sed miram se narrabat inisse gratiam, tradito magnetis usu, cuius antea penitus erant ignari: ideoque timide pelago consueuisse sese, neque alias temere quam aestate credere. Nunc uero eius fiducia lapidis contemnunt hyemem, securi magis quam tuti; ut periculum sit, ne quae res magno eis bono futura putabatur, eadem per imprudentiam magnorum causa malorum fiat.

Quid quoque in loco se uidisse narrauit, et longum fuerit explicare, neque huius est operis institutum, et alio fortasse loco dicetur a nobis,

[a] canobea, A.

---

[1] Burnet, in more sounding phrase : ' the Seamen understood both Astronomy and Navigation.'

[2] The polarity of the magnetic needle had been known long before More wrote; but its application to the purposes of navigation does not seem to have been thought of before the fifteenth century. It was in the latter part of the same century that the capability of the ancient astrolabe, for observations at sea, was discovered.' See Prescott's *Ferdinand and Isabella*, 1886, p. 305.

But peraduenture in an other place [1], I wyll speake of yt; chyefelye suche thynges as shalbe profytable to be knowne; as in specyall be thoese decrees and ordinaunces that he marked to be well and wyselye prouyded and enacted amonge suche peoples as do lyue to gethere in a cyuyle pollycye and good ordre. For of suche thynges dyd we busilie enquyre and demaunde of hym, and he lyke wise verye wyllynglye tolde vs of the same. But as for monsters, because they be no newes, of them we were nothynge inquysitiue. For nothynge is more easye to be founde, then be barking Scyllaes [2], rauenyng Celenes, and Lestrygones deuourers of people, and suche lyke great and vncredyble monsters; but to fynde cytyzyns ruled by good and holsome lawes, that ys an excedynge rare and harde thynge.

other profitable governmentis

monsters

Virgil & Maundeville?

praesertim quicquid ex usu fuerit non ignorari, qualia sunt in primis
31 ea, quae apud po|pulos usquam ciuiliter conuiuentes animaduertit, recte prudenterque prouisa [a]. His enim de rebus et nos auidissime rogabamus, et ille libentissime disserebat, omissa interim inquisitione monstrorum, quibus nihil est minus nouum. Nam Scyllas et Celenos [b] rapaces, et Lestrigonas populiuoros [3], atque eiuscemodi immania portenta, nusquam fere non inuenias; at sane ac sapienter institutos ciues haud reperias ubilibet.

[a] prouisum, A.   [b] celonos. A.

---

[1] The writer's art is noticeable in thus leading up to the Second Book, which had in fact been written first.

[2] Virgil, *Aen.* iii. 426 *sqq.* For Celaeno, chief of the Harpies, *ib.* 211. The man-eating Laestrygonians are described in Hom. *Od.* x. 82 *sqq.*; but as More has taken his previous examples from Virgil, he may have had in his mind the *Culex*, where Scylla and the Laestrygones are mentioned together (vv. 329–330). More may have intended, by the slighting expressions

in the text, to ridicule such travellers' tales as those in *The Voiage and Travaile* of Sir John Maundeville. In the *Description of the West Indies* by Antonio de Herrera (a translation of which is in vol. iii of Purchas's *Pilgrim*), p. 997, we have an account of a sea-monster higher than a caravel, and immediately after of strange birds 'with talons like Hawkes;' which may recall the Scyllas and Celaenos of the text.

[3] This appears to be a word of More's own invention.

D

But as he markyd manye fonde and folyshe lawes in
thoose newe founde lands, so he rehersyde manye [a] actes
and constytutyons wherby thies our cytyes, nations, contreys, and Kyngdomes maye take ensample [b], to amende
theyre faultes, enormytyes and errors ; wherof in another
place, as I sayde, I wyll intreate. Now at thys tyme
I am determyned to reherse onlye that he tolde vs of the
maners, customes, lawes, and ordinaunces of the vtopians.
But fyrste I wyll repete our former communycatyon ; by
thoccasyon, and, as I myghte saye, the dryfte wherof he
was browghte into the mentyon of that weale publyque.

For when Raphaell hadde verye prudently touched
dyuers thynges that be amysse, sume here and sume
there ; yea, verye manye of [c] bothe partes ; and agayne
hadde spoken of suche wyse and prudent lawes and
decrees [d] as be establyshed and vsyde bothe here amonge
vs and also there emonge them ; as a man so connynge [e]
and experte in the lawes and customes of euery seuerall
countreye, as though into what place soeuer he came
geaste wyse, there he had lede al his life: then Peter,
much meruellyng at the man : 'Surely mayster Raphaell'

Utopiensium

See
Hexter
p. 26,
introduction
to dialogue
of
counsel:

Dialogue

[a] diuers.   [b] example.   [c] on.
[d] wise lawes and prudente decrees.   [e] perfecte.

Caeterum ut multa apud nouos illos populos adnotauit perperam
consulta, sic haud pauca recensuit, unde possint exempla sumi corri-
gendis harum urbium, nationum, gentium ac regnorum erroribus
idonea, alio, ut dixi, loco a me commemoranda. Nunc ea tantum
referre animus est, quae de moribus atque institutis narrabat Vtopiensium, praemisso tamen eo sermone, quo uelut tractu quodam ad eius
mentionem reipublicae deuentum est.

Nam quum Raphael prudentissime recensuisset alia hic alia illic
errata, utrobique certe plurima, tum quae apud nos quaeue item sunt
apud illos cauta sapientius, quum uniuscuiusque populi mores atque
instituta sic teneret, tanquam in quencumque locum diuertisset, totam
ibi uitam uixisse uideretur, admiratus [a] hominem Petrus, Miror profecto, mi Raphael, inquit, cur te regi cuipiam non adiungas, quorum

[a] admiratur, A. *Omittit* hominem B.

(quod he), 'I wondere greatlye whie you gette you not
into some Kinges courte; for I am sewre there is no
prynce lyuynge that wolde not be very gladde of yowe;
as a man not onlye able hyghelye to delyte hym wyth
youre profounde lernynge, and thys youre knowledge of
contreis and peoples, but also are[a] meat to instructe him
with examples, and helpe hym wyth counsell. And thus
doynge yowe shal bring yowre selfe in a verye good case,
and also be in[b] habylytye to helpe all youre frindes and
kynsfolke[1].'

'As concernyng my fryndes and kynsfolke' (quod he),
'I passe not greatly for them: for I think I haue suffycyentlye done my parte towardes them all readye. For
thies thinges that other men doo not depart from vntyll
they be olde and sicke, yea, which they be then verye
lothe to leaue when they can no lenger kepe, those verye
same thynges dyd I, beynge not onlye lustye and in good
helth, but also in the flowere of my youthe, deuyde among
my fryndes and kynsfolkes; which I think wyth thys my
liberalytye owghte to holde them contentyd, and not to

        [a] are *omitted*.   [b] of.

neminem esse satis scio, cui tu non sis futurus uehementer gratus,
utpote quem hac doctrina atque hac locorum hominumque peritia
non oblectare solum, sed exemplis quoque instruere, atque adiuuare
32 consilio | sis idoneus; simul hoc pacto et tuis rebus egregie con-
sulueris, et tuorum omnium commodis magno esse adiumento
possis.

  Quod ad meos attinet, inquit ille, non ualde commoueor, nempe in
quos mediocriter opinor me officii mei partes impleuisse nam
quibus rebus alii non illsl senes et aegri cedunt, immo tum quoque
aegre cedunt, quum amplius retinere non possunt, eas res ego non
sanus modo ac uegetus, sed iuuenis quoque cognatis amicisque dis-
partiui, quos debere puto hac mea esse benignitate contentos, neque

---

[1] With these same arguments Wolsey
may have plied More, to draw him
into the service of Henry VIII. See
the Introduction, § 2, p. xxxi, and
Erasmus's Letter to Hutten (*Epist.*
ccccxlvii).

requyre nor to looke that besydes thys I shoulde for
theyre sakes gyue my selfe in bondage to^a kynges.'

cf. Erasmus
fear of
bondage

'Naye god forbedde^b' (quod peter), 'it is not my
mynd that you shoulde be in bondage to kynges, but as
a retaynoure to them at youre pleasure; whyche sewrelye
I thynke ys the nygheste waye that you can deuyse[1],
howe to bestowe youre tyme frutefullye, not onlye for the
pryuate commoditye of your fryndes, and for the general
proffytte of all sortes of people, but also for the auaunce-
mente of your selfe to a muche welthier state and condytyon then you be nowe in.'

Raphael
prefers
liberty

'To a welthyer condition' (quod Raphael), 'by that
meanes that my mynde standethe cleane agaynst? Nowe
I lyue at lybertye, after myn owne mynde and pleasure;
whiche I thynke verye fewe of thes greate states and
peeres of realmes can saye. Yea, and there be ynowe of

^a vnto.   ^b forbyd that.

id exigere atque expectare praeterea, ut memet eorum causa regibus
in seruitium dedam.

Bona uerba, inquit Petrus ; mihi uisum est non ut seruias regibus,
sed ut inseruias. Hoc est, inquit ille, una syllaba plus quam seruias.
At ego sic censeo, inquit Petrus, quoquo tu nomine rem appelles, eam
tamen ipsam esse uiam, qua non aliis modo et priuatim et publice
possis conducere, sed tuam quoque ipsius conditionem reddere feliciorem.

Feliciorem ne, inquit Raphael, ea uia facerem, a qua abhorret
animus? Atqui nunc sic uiuo ut uolo, quod ego certe suspicor pauci-
simis purpuratorum contingere. Quin satis est eorum, qui potentum

---

[1] Robynson's translation is here defective, as he leaves out altogether
the reply of Hythloday, *Hoc est, inquit
ille*, &c. There is a play on the words
servias and *inservias*. 'This latter,'
says Hythloday, 'is only a syllable
more than the former:' that is, *service*
at a court, is only short for *servitude*.
It is difficult to reproduce the play on
the words in English. Burnet renders
the whole passage thus : 'Soft and
fair,' said Peter, 'I do not mean that
you should be a *Slave* to any King, but
only that you should assist them, and
be useful to them.' 'The Change of
the Word,' said he, 'does not alter the
Matter.' 'But term it as you will,'
replied Peter, 'I do not see any other
Way in which you can be so useful,'
&c.

them that sike[a] for greate mens frindeshippes; and therfore thynke it no great hurte, if they haue not me, nor .ii.
or .iii.[b] suche other as I am.'

(margin: MORE) 'Well, I perceyue plainlye, frind Raphaell' (quod_I), *(margin handwritten: More joins the discussion: cf. end of Bk. II on magnificence)*
'that yowe be desierous nother of riches nor of powre.
And truly I haue in no lesse reuerence and estimacyon
a man that is[c] of your mind, then anny of them al that be
so high in pour and aucthoritie. But you shall doo as it
becommith yow, yea, and accordinge to this wisedome
and[d] thys highe and free couraghe of youres, yf yowe can
fynde in youre harte so to appoynte and dyspose your
selfe, that you maie apply your wytte and delygence to the
proffyt of the weale publyque, though it be sume what to
youre owne payne and hyndraunce. And thys shall yow
neuer so well doo, nor wyth so greate proffitte perfourme,
as yf yowe be of sum great prynces councell, and put in[e]
his heade (as I doubte not but you wyll) honeste opynyons,
and vertuous persuasyons. For from the prynce, as from *(margin handwritten: The Prince: a Well)*
a perpetuall well sprynge, cummythe amonge the people
the floode of all that is good or euell. But in yowe is so
perfitte lernynge, that wythowte anye experience; and

[a] sue.   [b] iii. or iiii.   [c] that is *omitted.*   [d] to.   [e] into.

amicitias ambiunt, ne magnam putes iacturam fieri si me atque uno
aut altero mei similibus sint carituri.
  [Tum ego, perspicuum est, inquam, te, mi Raphael, neque opum *(margin: More)*
esse neque potentiae cupidum ; atque ego profecto huius tuae mentis
hominem non minus ueneror ac suspicio, quam eorum quemuis qui
33 maxime rerum | sunt potentes. Caeterum uideberis[a] plane rem te
atque isthoc animo tuo tam generoso, tam uere philosopho dignam
facturus, si te ita compares, ut uel cum aliquo priuatim incommodo
ingenium tuum atque industriam publicis rebus accommodes, quod
nunquam tanto cum fructu queas, quanto si a consiliis fueris magno
alicui principi, eique (quod te facturum certe scio) recta atque honesta
persuaseris. nempe a principe bonorum malorumque omnium torrens
in totum populum, uelut a perenni quodam fonte promanat. In te
uero tam absoluta doctrina est, ut uel citra magnum rerum usum,

[a] uidebaris, A.

agayne so greate experyence, that wythoute anye lernynge ; yowe maye well be anny kinges councellour.'

Raphael :   'Yow be twyse deceaued, maister More' (quod he), 'fyrste in me, and agayne in the thing it selfe. For nother is in me that[a] habilitye that yowe force vpon me ; and yf it were neuer so muche, yet in dysquieting

Criticism : myne owne quietnes I should nothing further the weale

I   publique. For, fyrst of all, the moste parte of all princes haue more delyte in warlike matters and feates of cheualrie

vs.   *chivalry :* (the knowlege wherof I nother haue nor desire), than in the good feates of peace ; and employe muche more study howe by right or by wrong to enlarge their dominions, than howe well and peaceablie to rule and gouerne that they haue all redie. Moreouer, they that be counsellours

II   to kinges, euery one of them eyther is of him selfe so wyse in dede, that he nede[b] not, or elles he thinketh him

Competition of counsellors self so wise, that he will not allowe an other mans councell ; sauing that they do shamefully[1] and flatteringly geue

             [a] the.   [b] nedeth.

---

porro tanta rerum peritia, ut sine ulla doctrina egregium consiliarium cuiuis regum sis praestaturus [a].

    Bis erras, inquit ille, mi More, primum in me, deinde in re ipsa. nam neque mihi ea est facultas, quam tu tribuis, et si maxime esset, tamen quum ocio meo negocium facesserem, publicam rem nihil promoueam. Primum enim principes ipsi plerique omnes militaribus studiis (quorum ego neque peritiam habeo neque desydero) libentius occupantur quam bonis pacis artibus, maiusque multo studium est, quibus modis per fas ac nefas noua sibi regna pariant, quam uti parta bene administrent. Praeterea quicunque regibus a consilio sunt, eorum nemo est qui aut non uere tantum sapit, ut non egeat, aut tantum sibi sapere uidetur, ut non libeat alterius probare consilium ;

                      [a] praestiturus, A.

---

[1] This word does not seem well chosen. Burnet gives the spirit of it better :—' If they court any, it is only those for whom the Prince has much personal Favour ; whom by their Faunings and Flatteries they endeavour to fix to their own Interests.' But both translators miss the humour of ' always applauding the great man's jests, however absurd.' Erasmus, com-

assent to the fond and folishe sayinges of certeyn greate
men, whose fauours, bicause they be in high aucthoritie
with their prince, by assentacion and flattering [a] they labor
to opteyne. And verily it is naturally geuen to all men
to esteame their owne inuentyons best. So both the
rauen and the ape thincke their owne yong ones fayrest [1].

raven
ape

'Than if a man in such a company, where some disdayne
and haue despite at other mens inuentions; and some
cownte their owne best; if among suche men, (I) saye,
a man shoulde bringe furth any thinge that he hayth
redde done in tymes paste, or that he hathe sene done in
other places, there the hearers fare as thoughe the hole
existimacion of theyr wisdome were in ieopardy to be
ouerthrowen, and that euer after they should be counted
for very diserdes [2], onles they colde in other mens inuentions pycke out matter to reprehende and find fawt at.
If all other pore helpes faile, then this is their extreame

*human
enry
&
perversity*

(clowns)

[a] flatterie.

---

nisi quod absurdissimis quibusque dictis assentiuntur et supparasi-
tantur [3] eorum, quos ut maxime [a] apud prin|cipem gratiae student
assentatione demereri sibi. Et certe sic est natura comparatum, ut
sua cuique inuenta blandiantur. Sic et coruo suus arridet pullus, et
suus simiae catulus placet.

Quod siquis in illo coetu uel alienis inuidentium, uel praeferentium
sua, aliquid afferat, quod aut aliis temporibus factum legit, aut aliis
fieri locis uidit, ibi qui audiunt perinde agunt ac si tota sapientiae suae
periclitaretur opinio, et post illa pro stultis plane sint habendi, nisi
aliquid sufficiant inuenire, quod in aliorum inuentis uertant uitio. Si
caetera destituant, tum huc confugiunt : haec nostris, inquiunt, placuere

[a] *i. q.* maximae.

---

menting on the proverb 'Simia in
purpura,' ends with some remarks
in a like spirit: 'Quam multos id
genus simios videre est in Principum
aulis; quibus si purpuram, si tor-
quem, si gemmas detrahas, meros cer-
dones deprehendes.'—*Adagia*, 1629,
p. 255 a.

[1] 'Canis cani videtur pulcherrima,
et bovi bos, et asina asino, et sus
sui.'—*Ib.*, p. 642.

[2] That is, clowns. See the Glossary.

[3] Like many other words employed
by More, this is borrowed from Plautus.
Comp. *Mil. Glor.* ii. 3. 77.

refuge: "Thies thinges" (say they) "pleased oure forefathers and auncetours: wolde god wee coulde be so wise as
they were." And as though they had wittely concluded the
matter, and with this answere stoppid euery mans mouthe,
they sitt downe agayn. As who should saye it were
a very daungerous matter, if a man in any pointe should
be founde wiser then his forefathers were [1]. And yet be
we content to suffer the best and wittiest of their decrees
to lye vnexecuted; but if in any thinge a better ordre
mighte haue bene taken, than by them was, theare we
take faste holde, and finde [a] many fawtes. Many times
haue I chaunced vpon suche prowde, lewde, ouerthwarte,
and waywarde iudgementes ; yea, and ones in Englande.'
'I praye yow, Syre' (quod I), 'haue yow bene in owr
contrey ?' 'Yea forsothe' (quod he), 'and their I tarried
for the space of iiii. or v. monythes together, not longe
after the insurreccion, that the westerne Englishe men
made agaynst their kynge [2]; whych by their owne myser-

[a] holde, findyng therin.

maioribus, quorum prudentiam utinam nos aequaremus. itaque hoc
dicto ueluti egregia perorata re confidunt. Tanquam magnum sit
periculum, siquis ulla in re deprehendatur maioribus suis sapientior.
a quibus tamen, ut quicque optime consultum est, ita aequissimo
animo ualere sinimus. at siqua de re potuit consuli prudentius, eam
protinus ansam cupide arreptam mordicus retinemus. Itaque in haec
superba, absurda ac morosa iudicia, cum saepe alibi, tum semel in
Anglia quoque, incidi.
'Obsecro, inquam, fuisti apud nos? Fui, inquit, atque aliquot menses
ibi sum uersatus, non multo post eam cladem, qua Anglorum occi-
dentalium ciuile aduersus regem bellum miseranda ipsorum strage

---

[1] It is against this 'nouitatis calumnia' that Erasmus protests forcibly in
his comment on St. John i. 1. He had
often been made the object of it himself. 'Sed offendit, inquiunt, nouitas
. . . Actum, inquiunt, de re Christiana,
posteaquam nouum habemus Euan-

gelium,' &c.—See the *Annotationes*,
ed. 1535, p. 219.
[2] The reference is to the rising of
the Cornishmen in 1497, who marched
upon London, and were defeated,
June 22, at Blackheath. Besides the execution of their leaders, Lord Audely,

able and pitefull slaughter was suppressed and endyd. In
the meane season I was much bounde and beholden [a] to
the righte reuerende father Jhon Morton [1], Archebishop,
and cardenall of Canterburye, and at that tyme also Lord
chauncellour of England; a man, maister Peter (for
maister More knoweth all reddy that I wyll saye), not more
honorable for his aucthority, then for his prudence and
vertue. He was of a meane stature, and though streken
in age yet bare he his body vpryght. In his face did
shine such an amiable reuerence, as was pleasaunte to

[b] beholdynge

compressum est. Interea multum debui reuerendissimo patri Ioanni
Mortono Cantuariensi Archiepiscopo et Cardinali, ac tum quoque
35 Angliae Cancella|rio, uiro, mi Petre (nam Moro cognita sum narra-
turus) non autoritate magis quam prudentia ac uirtute uenerabili.
Etenim statura ei mediocris erat, nec aetati, quanquam serae, cedens.
uultus quem reuereare, non horreas. in congressu non difficilis,

---

Flammock an attorney, and others,
there was, as More says, a 'pitiful
slaughter' on the field of battle.

[1] John Morton, afterwards Cardinal,
was born in Dorsetshire, at Bere Regis,
as is commonly said, about 1420.
After studying at Balliol College, he
practised for some years as an ecclesiastical lawyer. In that capacity he
came under the favourable notice of
Archbishop Bourchier, then Chancellor, and rose to various preferments
in the Church. His attachment to the
House of Lancaster brought him to
Towton in 1461, whence he narrowly
escaped with his life. He followed
the fortunes of the exiled queen, but
on his submission after Tewkesbury
was kindly treated by Edward IV, who
made him Master of the Rolls in 1473,
and Bishop of Ely in 1479. Shakspeare has made us familiar with the
scene in which he took part under
Richard III. To the timely warning

he sent, Henry of Richmond probably
owed his escape from the machina-
tions of that king. In 1486, as a reward
for his faithful services to Henry VII,
he was raised to the see of Canterbury.
In 1487 he was made Lord Chancellor,
and afterwards, by much solicitation
on the king's part, a Cardinal. He
died in 1500. The circumstance of
More, as a youth, having been brought
up in his household, has been mentioned before (Introd. § 1). He is
naturally introduced here, in connexion
with the Cornish rising; as one of the
demands of the insurgents was the
punishment of the king's ministers,
Morton and Sir Reginald Gray. The
character of him given by Sir Francis
Bacon is not so favourable as More's.
—See Gairdner's *Henry the Seventh*,
1892, p. 41; Campbell's *Lives of the
Lord Chancellors*, 1845, i. p. 425; and
the article by Mr. Archbold in the
Dict. of National Biography.

beholde[1]. Gentell in communycatyon, yet earneste and sage. He had greate delyte manye tymes wyth roughe speche to hys sewters to proue, but wythowte harme, what prompte wytte and what bolde sprite were in euery man. In the which, as in a vertue much agreinge with his nature, so that therewyth were not ioyned impudency, he toke greate delectatyon; and the same person, as apte and mete to haue an administratyon in the weale publique, he dyd louingly enbrace. In hys speche he was fyne, eloquent, and pythye. In the lawe he had profounde knowledge; in witte he was incomparable; and in memory wonderfull excellent. Thies qualytyes, whych in hym were by nature synguler, he by learnynge and vse had made perfytte.

'The Kynge putt muche truste in hys councell: the weale publyque also in a maner leaned vnto hym, when I was there. For euen in the chiefe of hys youth[2] he was taken from schole into the Courte, and there passyd all hys tyme in muche trouble and busynes, and was[a] contynually troubled and tossed with[b] dyuers mysfortunes and aduersytyes. And so by many and great daungers

<hr>

[a] being.   [b] tumbled and tossed in the waues of.

serius tamen et grauis. libido erat asperius interdum compellando supplicantes experiri, sed sine noxa, quid ingenii, quam animi praesentiam quisque prae se ferret; qua uelut cognata sibi uirtute, modo abesset impudentia, delectabatur, et ut idoneam ad res gerendas amplectebatur. Sermo politus et efficax. Iuris magna peritia, ingenium incomparabile, memoria ad prodigium usque excellens. Haec enim natura egregia discendo atque exercendo prouexit.

Huius consiliis rex plurimum fidere, multum Respublica niti (cum ego aderam) uidebatur. quippe qui ab prima fere iuuenta protinus a schola coniectus in aulam, maximis in negociis per omnem uersatus aetatem, ac uariis fortunae aestibus assidue iactatus prudentiam rerum

<hr>

[1] Burnet, much better: 'his Looks begot Reverence rather than Fear.'   [2] Lat. *ab prima fere*, &c , ' wellnigh from boyhood.'

he lerned thee^a xperience of the worlde, whyche so
beynge learned can not easely be forgotten.
'It chaunced on a certayne daye, when(I)sate at hys
table, there was also a certayne laye man, cunnynge in
the lawes of yowre Realme. Whyche^b, I can not tel
wherof takyng occasyon, began dyligently and busily^c
to prayse that strayte and rygorous iustice, which at that
tyme was there executed upon fellones, who, as he sayde,
were for the moste part[1] .xx. hanged together vpon one
gallowes. And, seyng so fewe escapyd punyshement, he
sayd he coulde not chewse but greatly wonder and maruell,
howe and by what euill lucke it should so cum to passe,
that theues neuertheles were in euery place so ryffe and^d
ranke[2]. "Naye, Syr," quod I (for I durst boldely speake
my mind before the cardynall), "maruell nothing herat;

^a the experience.   ^b Who.   ^c earnestly.   ^d and so.

(quae sic recepta non facile elabitur) multis magnisque cum periculis
didicerat.
    Forte fortuna quum die quodam in eius mensa essem, laicus quidam
legum uestratium peritus aderat. Is nescio unde nactus
occasionem, coepit accurate laudare rigidam illam Iusti-   De legibus
tiam, quae tum illic exercebatur in fures, quos passim   parum aequis.
narrabat nonnunquam suspendi uiginti in una cruce ; atque eo uehementius dicebat se mirari, cum tam pauci elaberentur supplicio, quo
malo fato fieret, uti tam multi tamen ubique grassarentur. Tum ego
36 (ausus enim sum libere apud Cardin|alem loqui) nihil mireris, inquam.

---

[1] Render : ' were being hanged in
all directions, sometimes twenty on
one gallows.'
[2] See the Introduction, § 2. To
what is there said may be added the
expressions put by Starkey into the
mouth of Pole. If certain abuses were
removed, Pole is made to say, then
' as for beggarys lusty and strong, ye,
and thefys also, schold be but few or
non at al of that sorte as they be
now.' He thinks the root of the mis-
chief to be ' thys multytude of seruyng

men.' And it is noticeable, when
taken in connexion with More's stay
in the Netherlands, that he commends
a method of providing for the poor
observed by him at Ypres. The rem-
nant of helpless folk, Pole says, ' easely
schold be nuryschyd, after a maner
lately deuysyd by the wysedome of the
cytyzyns of Ipar, a cyte in Flaundres,
the wych I wold wysch to be put in
vse wyth vs, or els some other of
the same sort.'—Dialogue, as above,
pp. 175, 176.

*on
Justice*

for thys punyshement of theues passeth of the lymytes [a]
Justyce, and is also very hurtefull to the weale publyque.
For it is to extreame and crewell a punishement for thefte,
and yet not sufficient to refrayne [b] men from thefte. For
simple thefte is not so greate an offence, that it owght to
be punished with death. Nother there is any punishmente
so horrible, that it can kepe them from stealynge whych
haue no other crafte wherby to get their liuing. Therefore
in this poynte, not yow only, but also the moste part of
the worlde, be lyke euyll scholemasters, whych be readyare
to beate then to teache their scholers [1]. For great and
horryble punyshementes be appoynted for theues ; whereas
muche rather prouysyon should haue bene made, that there
were some meanes wherby they might gett theyr lyuynge,
so that no man should be dreuen to thys extreame necessitie, fyrst to steale, and then to dye." "Yes" (quod he),

*Lawyer
replies*

"this matter is well ynoughe prouyded for all ready.

[a] passeth the limites of. [b] refrayne and withhold.

Nam hacc punitio furum et supra iustum est et non ex usu publico.
Est enim ad uindicanda furta nimis atrox, nec tamen ad refrenanda
sufficiens. Quippe neque furtum simplex tam ingens facinus est, ut
capite debeat plecti, neque ulla poena est tanta, ut ab latrociniis
cohibeat eos, qui nullam aliam artem quaerendi uictus habent. Itaque
hac in re non uos modo, sed bona pars huius orbis imitari uidentur
malos praeceptores, qui discipulos uerberant libentius
quam docent. Decernuntur enim furanti grauia atque
horrenda supplicia, cum potius multo fuerit prouidendum
uti aliquis esset prouentus uitae, ne cuiquam tam dira sit
furandi primum, dehinc pereundi necessitas. Est, inquit

*Qua ratione
fieri possit,
ne tam multi
sint fures.*

---

[1] Such were the ' imperiti paeda-
gogi' of whom Pace writes : ' quales
olim scio apud nos fuisse multos, et
nescio an adhuc supersint. Nam is, si
videt puerum ad discendum tardiorem,
non nisi verberibus agendum censet,
et indoctus homo verbera plus posse
quam naturam credit.' — *De Fructu*,
1517, p. 97. This treatise of Pace is
dedicated to Colet ; and Lily, the first
High Master of St. Paul's School, was
during his lifetime one of More's
closest friends. And yet, strange to
say, there are people ready to believe,
or at least to propagate, the application
to Lily and Colet of a story of Erasmus
about barbarous flogging in school.
See App. B of an edition by the present writer of Erasmus's *Letter to Justus
Jonas*, 1883.

There be handy craftes, there is husbandry, to gett their liuinge by, if they wolde not wyllingely be nowght." "Nay" (quod I), "you shall not skape so; for, fyrste of all, I wyll speake nothynge of them that come home owte of warre [a] maymede and lame, as not longe ago owte of blacke heath [1] filde, and a lityll before that owt of the warres in Fraunce [2] : suche (I say) as put their lyues in ieopardy for the weale publiques or the kinges sake, and by the reason of weakenes and lamenes be not able to occupy their olde craftes, and be to aged to lerne newe: of them I wyll speake nothinge, because warre lyke the tyde ebbeth and floweth [b]. But let vs consydere those thinges that chaunce dayly before our eyes.

' " Fyrste, there is a great number of gentilmen, which can not be content to lyue ydle them selfes, like dorres [3], of that whiche other haue laboryd for: their tenauntes

[a] the warres.   [b] forasmuch as warres haue their ordinarie recourses [4].

---

ille, satis hoc prouisum: sunt artes mechanicae; est agricolatio; ex his tueri uitam liceat, ni sponte mali esse mallent. At non sic euades, inquam. Nam primum omittamus eos, qui saepe uel ab externis bellis uel ciuilibus mutili redeunt domum, ut nuper apud uos e Cornubiensi praelio, et non ita pridem e Gallico, qui uel Reipublicae impendunt membra, uel regi; quos neque pristinas artes exercere debilitas patitur, neque aetas nouam discere. hos, inquam, omittamus, quando bella per intermissas uices commeant. Ea contemplemur quae nullo die non accidunt.

Tantus est ergo nobilium numerus, qui non ipsi modo degant ociosi, tanquam fuci laboribus aliorum, quos puta suorum praediorum colonos

---

[1] See the note above, p. 40.

[2] The intervention of Henry VII in the affairs of France was partly due to his personal obligations to the Duke of Brittany. When Francis of Brittany died, at the end of 1488, and his territory was being overrun by the French, Henry promised the aid of an English force to the orphan princess, Anne. When she had been coerced into a marriage with the French king,

Charles VIII, Henry, by way of re prisals, in October, 1492, landed at Calais, and invested Boulogne. But he was secretly in treaty with Charles, and the expedition ended in a money payment.

[3] That is, drones. See the Glossary.

[4] It is difficult to believe that any one could have deliberately altered the first version, given in the text, to this.

(marginalia: IV Idle servants on the road.)

I meane, whom they polle and shaue to the quycke by
reysing their rentes [1] (for this only poynte of frugalitye
do they vse, men els thoroughe their lauasse and prodigall
spendynge able to bringe them selfes to very beggery):
thies gentilmen (I say) do not only liue in ydilnes them
selfes, but also carry about with them at their tayles
a greate flocke or trayne of ydell and loytrynge seruynge
men, whyche neuer learned any crafte wherby to get their
liuinges. Thies men, as sone as theyr mayster is dead,
or be sicke them selfes, be incontinent thruste owte of
doores. For gentlemen had rather kepe ydil persones
then sycke men; and many times the dead mans heyr
is not able to mainteyne so great a howse, and kepe so
many seruinge men, as his father dydde. Then in the
meane season they that be thus destytute of seruice other
starue for honger, or manfully playe the theaues. For
what wolde yow haue them to do? When they haue
wandred abrode so longe, untyll they haue worne threde
bare their apparell, and also appayred their health, then
gentlemen, because of their pale and sicke [a] faces and

[a] sickely.

augendis reditibus ad uiuum usque radunt : nam eam | solam frugali- 37
tatem nouere, homines alioquin ad mendicitatem usque prodigi :
uerum immensam quoque ociosorum stipatorum turbam circumferunt,
qui nullam unquam quaerendi uictus artem didicere. Hi simul atque
herus obierit [a], aut ipsi aegrotauerint, eiiciuntur ilico. nam et ociosos
libentius quam aegrotos alunt, et saepe morientis heres non protinus
alendae sufficit paternae familiae. interim illi esuriunt strennue, nisi
strennue latrocinentur. Nam quid faciant? Si quidem ubi errando
paululum uestes ac ualetudinem attriuere, morbo iam squalidos atque

[a] obiit, A.

---

[1] On this subject, see the Introduction, § 2. Archdeacon Crowley, half a century after, has an epigram ' Of Rente Raysers':—

' For thys thynge, he sayde,
    full certayne he wyste,

That wyth his owne he myghte
    alwayes do as he lyste.'
Select Works (E. E. T. S.), 1872, p. 46. Henry Brinklow's Complaynt of Roderyck Mors is full of the same thing.

patched cotes, wyll not take them into seruyce. And husbandmen dare not sett them a worke, knowyng well ynough that he is nothynge mete to doo trewe and faythfull seruice to a poore man wyth a spade and a mattoke, for small wages and harde fare, whyche, beynge deyntely and tenderly pampered vp in ydilnes and pleasure, was wont with a sworde and a buckeler by hys syde to iette [1] through the strete with a bragging looke, and to thynke hym selfe to good to be any mans mate."

' " Naye by saynt Marie [2], ser " (quod the lawier) " not so, for this kinde of men muste we make most of. For in them, as men of stowter stomackes, bolder spyrytes, and manlyer currages, then handy craftes men and plowe men be, doth consyste the hole powre, strengthe, and puisaunce of oure hoste, when we muste fight in battaill."

' " Forsothe, ser, aswel yowe myghte saye " (quod I) " that for warres sake you must cheryshe theues. For sewerly yow shal neuer lacke theues [3] whyles yowe haue them.

(marginal notes in hand:) Lawyer argues military use / military power. / Rapael.

obsitos pannis, neque generosi dignantur acciperc, neque audent rustici: non ignari eum qui mollitei educatus in ocio ac deliciis solitus sit, accinctus acinace ac cetra, totam uiciniam uultu nebulonico despicere et contemnere omnes prae se, haudquaquam idoneum fore, qui cum ligone ac marra, maligna mercede ac uictu parco, fideliter inseruiat pauperi.

Ad haec ille, atqui nobis, inquit, hoc hominum genus in primis fouendum est. In his enim, utpote hominibus animi magis excelsi ac generosioris quam sunt opifices aut agricolae, consistunt uires ac robur exercitus, si quando sit confligendum bello.

Profecto, inquam ego, eadem opera dicas licet, belli gratia fouendos esse fures, quibus haud dubie nunquam carebitis, dum habebitis hos.

---

[1] To strut, or swagger. See the Glossary.

[2] A little insertion of the translator's.

[3] In the Latin two terms are used, *fures* and *latrones*, both of which are rendered ' thieves ' in the text, to the injury of the sense. Burnet renders more correctly:—'You may as well say,' replied I, 'that you must cherish Thieves on the Account of Wars; for you will never want the one, as long as you have the other: and as Robbers prove sometimes gallant Soldiers, so Soldiers often prove brave Robbers: so near an Alliance there is between these two Sorts of Life.'

Thieves are bad soldiers

France.

mercenaries
(cf.
Machiavelli)

Morosophis

cf. p. 172.
252.

No, nor theues be not the most false and faynt harted soldiers, nor souldiours be not the cowardliste theues : so well thees .ii. craftes agree together. But this fawte, though it be muche vsed among yow, yet is it not peculiar to yow only, but commen also almost to all natyons. Yet Fraunce, besydes thys, is troubled and infected wyth a muche sorer plage. The hole realme is fylled and besieged wyth hierede souldiours in peace tyme[1], yf that be peace ; whyche be brought in under the same coloure and pretence, that haith persuaded yow to kype thies ydell seruynge men. For thies wysefooles and very archedoltes thought the wealth of the hole contrey herin to consist, yf there were euer in a readynes a stronge and a sewer garrison, specyallye of olde practysed soldyours ; for they put no truste at all in men vnexercysed.

Quin neque latrones sunt instrennui milites, neque milites ignauissimi latronum, adeo inter has artes belle conuenit. At hoc uitium tamen frequens est uobis[a], non proprium. est enim | omnium fere 38 gentium commune. Nam Gallias infestat alia praeterea pestis pestilentior : tota patria stipendiariis in pace quoque (si illa pax est) oppleta atque obsessa militibus, eadem persuasione inductis, qua uos ociosos hic ministros alendos esse censuistis ; nempe quod Morosophis[2] uisum est, in eo sitam esse publicam salutem, si in promptu semper adsit ualidum firmumque praesidium, maxime ueteranorum : neque enim confidunt inexercitatis quicquam : ut uel ideo quaerendum eis

[a] nobis, A.

---

[1] More exactly, 'in peace time also,' that is, as well as in war. The state of things described by More as prevailing in France had come in with the discontinuance of levies according to the old feudal tenure. These had given place, says Hallam, 'in an evil hour for the people, and eventually for sovereigns, to contracts with mutinous hirelings, frequently strangers, whose valour in the day of battle inadequately redeemed their bad faith and vexatious rapacity. France, in her calamitous period under Charles VI and Charles VII, experienced the full effects of military licentiousness.'— *Middle Ages*, ed. 1869, p. 145. Charles VII in 1444 had tried to remedy this by the establishment of regular French troops ; but More writes as if the evil were still unabated in his time.

[2] A Greek word, taken by More from Lucian. It occurs in the *Alexander*, § 40.

And therfore they must be fayne[a] to seke for warre, to thende they maye euer haue practysed souldyours and cunnynge mansleers; leaste that (as it is pretilie sayde of Saluste[1]) their handes and their myndes thoroughe ydylnes or lacke of exercyse shoulde waxe dull.

Sallust, Catiline

' " But howe pernycyous and pestylente a thynge it is to maynteyne suche beastes, the Frenche men by there owne harmes haue learned; and the examples of the Romaynes, Carthaginiens, Siriens and of many other contreys, do manyfestly declare[2]. For not only the empire, but also the fieldys and cityes of all thies, by diuers occasyons haue bene ouerrunned and destroyed of their owne armies before hand had in a reddines[3]. Now how vnnecessary a thynge thys is, hereby it maye appere: that the Frenche souldiours, whyche from their youthe haue byne practysed and vrede[b] in feates of armes, doo not cracke nor auaunce them selfes to haue verye often gotte the vpperhande and mastcrye of your newe made and vnpractysed

evils of mercenaries

<hr>

[a] forced.　　　　　　　　　[b] inured.

<hr>

bellum sit, ne imperitos habeant milites, et homines iugulandi gratis, ne (ut habet facete Salustius) manus aut animus incipiat per ocium torpescere.

At quam sit perniciosum huiusmodi beluas alere, et Gallia suo malo didicit, et Romanorum, Carthaginiensium, ac Syrorum, tum multarum gentium exempla declarant, quorum omnium non imperium modo sed agros quoque atque adeo urbes ipsas parati ipsorum exercitus aliis atque aliis occasionibus euerterunt. Quam uero non magnopere necessarium, uel hino olucescit, quod ne Galli quidem milites armis ab unguiculis exercitatissimi cum euocatis comparati uestris, admodum saepe gloriantur superiores sese discessisse, ut ne

Quam perniciem adferant perpetua militum praesidia.

<hr>

[1] Sall. *Cat.* xvi, 'Ne per otium torpescerent manus aut animus.'

[2] Lat. *parati exercitus,* 'standing armies.' More had probably in his mind the Janizaries and Mamelukes: of the latter of whom Gibbon writes

that 'the rage of these ferocious animals, who had been let loose on the strangers, was provoked to devour their benefactor.'—*Decline and Fall,* ch. lix, *sub fin.*

[3] That is, previously prepared.

soldiours¹. But in thys poynte I wyll not vse manye wordes, leaste perchaunce I maye seme to flatter yow. No nor those same handy craft men of yours in cities, nor yet the rude and vplandishe ploughemen of the contrcy, are not supposed to be greatly affraid of your gentilmens ydill seruing men, onles it be suche as be not of body or stature correspondent to theyr strenghte and currage; orels whose bolde stomackes be dyscourraged thoroughe pouertye. Thus yowe maye see, that yt ys not to be feared leaste they shoulde be effemynatede they yfª were broughte vppe in good craftes and laborsome wourkes, whereby to gett theyre lyuynge; whose stowte and sturdye bodyes (for gentlemen vouchesauffe to corrupte and spill none but picked and chosen men) nowe, other by reason of rest and ydilnes, be brought to weakenes, orels by to easy and womanlye exercises be made feble and vnable to endure hardenes. Trewly howe soeuer the case stondeth, thys me thinketh is nothyng

ª *Leg.* yf they.

quid dicam amplius, ne praesentibus uidear adblandiri uobis. Sed nec uestri illi uel opifices urbici, uel rudes atque agrestes agricolae ociosos generosorum stipatores creduntur ualde pertimescere, nisi aut hi quibus ad uires atque audaciam corpus contigit ineptius, aut quorum animi uis | inopia rei familiaris infringitur. adeo periculum nullum 39 est, ne quorum ualida et robusta corpora (neque enim nisi selectos dignantur generosi corrumpere) nunc uel elanguescitª ocio, uel negociis prope muliebribus emolliuntur, iidem bonis artibus instructi ad uitam, et uirilibus exercitati laboribus effoeminentur. Certe utcunque sese haec habet res, illud mihi nequaquam uidetur publicae rei conducere,

ª elanguescunt, B., *recte.*

---

¹ More is here using the language of a patriot. During the first half of the fifteenth century, at any rate, the English army, unlike the national levies of other countries, was 'an enlisted, picked, drilled, and highly effective service.'— See p. xxi of Professor J. E. Thorold Rogers' edition of Gascoigne's *Liber Veritatum*, 1881. For More's epigrams in a like strain, on the taking of Tournai in 1513, and in answer to Germain de Brie, see J. H. Marsden's *Philomorus*, 1878, pp. 73–78.

a veyleable to the weale publique, for warre sacke[1],
whyche yowe neuer haue but when yow wyll your selfes,
to kepe and mainteyn an vnnumerable flocke of that sort
of men, that be so troblesome and noyous in peace;
wherof yow owght to haue a thowsande times more
regard then of warre.

'" But yet this is not onlye the [2] necessary cause of stealing. There is an other which as I suppose is proper and
peculiare to yow Englishe men alone." "What is that?"
quod the Cardenall. "Forsoth[a]" (quod I), "your shepe[3],
that were wont to be so mylke and tame, and so smal
eaters, now, as I heare saie, be become so greate deuow-
erers, and so wylde, that they eate vp and swallow down
the very men them selfes. They consume, destroy, and
deuoure hole fieldes, howses, and cities. For looke in

[a] forsoth, my lorde.

in euentum belli, quod nunquam habetis, nisi quum uultis, infinitam
eius generis turbam alere, quod infestat pacem, cuius tanto maior
haberi ratio quam belli debeat.

Neque haec tamen sola est furandi necessitas. Est alia magis,
quantum credo, peculiaris uobis. Quaenam est ea? inquit Cardinalis.
Oues, inquam, uestrae, quae tam mites esse, tamque exiguo solent ali,
nunc (uti fertur) tam edaces atque indomitae esse coeperunt, ut
homines deuorent ipsos; agros, domos, oppida uastent ac depopu-
lentur. Nempe quibus cunque regni partibus nascitur lana tenuior,

---

[1] 'For the sake of war;' on account of war.

[2] That is, 'not the only.'

[3] Complaints of the injury done to agriculture in England by the increase of sheep-farming were no new thing in More's day, and continued for many years after. In a tract, of which the date is set down to 1550–3, entitled *The Decaye of England by the great multitude of shepe*, edited by J. Meadows Cowper, six 'prouerbes' are adduced by way of reasons to show that 'shepe and shepemasters doeth cause skantyte of corne.' The six refer to the increased price of (1) wool itself, from the great exportation, (2) mutton, (3) beef, (4) corn, (5) white meat, (6) eggs. In the *Epistolae Obscurorum Virorum*, which appeared in the same year as the *Utopia*, the number of sheep in England is referred to as proverbial (ed. 1557, leaf N. 6).

'Salutes vobis plures
Quam sunt in Polonia fures

. . .

Oues in terra Angliae.'

See more in the Introduction, § 2.

Sheep.
running
nobles
&
abbots

what partes of the realme doth growe the fynyst, and therfore dearist woll, there noble men and gentlemen, yea, and certeyn Abbottes, holy men god wote [a], not contenting them selfes with the yearely reuennues and profyttes that were wont to grow to theyr forefathers and predecessours of their landes, nor beynge content that they liue in rest and pleasure, nothyng profytyng, ye, muche noyinge the weale publique, leaue no grounde for tyllage; they enclose all in [b] pastures; they throw downe houses; they plucke downe townes; and leaue nothing stondynge but only the churche, to make of it [c] a shepehowse[1]. And, as thoughe yow loste no small [2] quantity of grounde by forestes, chases, laundes, and parkes; those good holy[3] men turne all dwellinge places and all glebe lande into desolation and wildernes.

     [a] no doubt.   [b] into.   [c] to be made.

atque ideo preciosior, ibi nobiles et generosi, atque adeo Abbates aliquot, sancti uiri, non his contenti reditibus fructibusque annuis, qui maioribus suis solebant ex praediis crescere ; nec habentes satis, quod ociose ac laute uiuentes nihil in publicum prosint, nisi etiam obsint ; aruo nihil relinquunt, omnia claudunt pascuis, demoliuntur domos, diruunt oppida, templo duntaxat stabulandis suibus relicto et tanquam parum soli perderent apud uos ferarum saltus ac uiuaria, illi | 40 boni uiri habitationes omnes, et quicquid usquam est culti, uertunt in solitudinem.

---

[1] See the Introduction, § 2. A passage in one of the *Ballads from Manuscripts*, ed. by Furnivall (E. E. T. S.), i. p. 97, furnishes a close parallel to the text :—

   'The townes go down, the land decayes;

Off cornefeyldes, playne layes;

Gret men makithe now a dayes

  A shepecott in the churche.'

[2] This does not give the force of *parum* : 'as if Forests and Parks had swallowed up *too little* of the Land' (Burnet). Robynson appears to have

used 'laundes' in the French meaning of the word. The Latin should perhaps be simply rendered ' preserves and deer parks.'

[3] The uncalled-for addition of this epithet by the translator seems intended to point the reproach chiefly against the heads of religious houses, the *Abbates aliquot*, who were called *sancti viri* just above. But there is nothing to show that they were more to blame in this respect than other great landlords. It is easy to understand that, after the civil wars of the

' "Therfore, that one couetous and vnsatiable cormaraunte and verye plage of his natyue contrey may compasse abowte and inclose many thousand acres of grounde to gether within one pale or hedge, the husbandmen be thrust owte of their owne ; orels other by coueyne or fraude, or by vyolent oppression, they be put besydes it, or by wronges and iniuries they be so weried that they be compelled to sell all. By one meanes therfore or by other, other by howke or crooke, they must nedes departe awaye, pore, sylie, wretched soules ; men, women, husbandes, wyues, fatherles chyldren, widdowes, wofull mothers with their yonge babes, and their hole housholde smal in substaunce, and much in nombre, as husbandrie requireth many handes. Awaye they trudge, I say, out of their knowen and accustomed howses, fyndyng no places to rest in. All their housholde stuffe, whiche is verye lytle worth, though it myght well abyde the sale [1], yet bcyng sodeynelye thrust out, they be constrayned to sell it for a thyng of nought. And when they haue, wanderynge about, sone

Ergo ut unus helluo, inexplebilis ac dira pestis patriae, continuatis agris, aliquot millia iugerum uno circumdet septo, eiiciuntur coloni quidam. suis etiam aut circumscripti fraude aut ui oppressi exuuntur, aut fatigati iniuriis adiguntur ad uenditionem. Itaque quoquo pacto emigrant miseri, uiri, mulieres, mariti, uxores, orbi, uiduae, parentes cum paruis liberis, et numerosa magis quam diuite familia, ut multis opus habet manibus res rustica; emigrant, inquam, e notis atque assuetis laribus, nec inueniunt quo se recipiant ; supellectilem omnem, haud magno uendibilem etiam si manere possit emptorem, quum extrudi necesse est, minimo uonundant. id quum breui ciiando

---

last century their lands might in many cases have become less productive, for want of proper cultivation, and themselves embarrassed with debt; anxious, therefore, to find some way of making their estates more profitable. —See Gasquet's *Henry VIII and the*

English Monasteries, 1888, vol. i. ch. 1.
   [1] This appears to mean, ' though it would bear keeping ; ' but the sense of the Latin is, as Burnet gives it : ' which could not bring them much Money, even tho' they might stay for a Buyer.'

spent that[a], what can they[b] els do but steale, and then
iustelye, God wote[c], behanged, or els go about a beggyng?
And yet then also they be cast in prison as vagaboundes,
because they go about and worke not; whom no man
will set a worke, though they neuer so willingly offer[d]
them selfes therto. For[1] one shepherde or heard man is
ynough to eate vp that grounde with cattel, to the occupying wherof about husbandrye many handes were requysyte.

    ' "And this is also the cause that[e] victualles be nowe in
many places dearer. Yea, besydes this the pryce of wolle
is so rysen that poore folkes, whiche were wont to worke
it and make cloth of it[f], be nowe able to bye none at all[2].
And by thys meanes verye manye be fayne[g] to forsake
worke, and to gyue them selfes to ydelnes. For after

<table>
<tr><td>[a] wandered abrode tyll that be spent.</td><td>[b] they then.</td><td>[c] pardy.</td></tr>
<tr><td>[d] proffer.</td><td>[e] why.</td><td>[f] therof.</td><td>[g] forced.</td></tr>
</table>

insumpserint, quid restat aliud denique quam uti furentur, et pendeant
iuste scilicet, aut uagentur atque mendicent? Quanquam tum quoque
uelut errones coniiciuntur in carcerem, quod ociosi obambulent, quorum operam nemo est qui conducat, quum illi cupidissime offerant.
Nam rusticae rei, cui assueuerunt, nihil est quod agatur, ubi nihil
seritur. Si quidem unus opilio atque bubulcus sufficit ei terrae
depascendae pecoribus, in cuius cultum, ut sementi faciendae suffi-
ceret, multae poscebantur manus.

    Atque hac ratione fit ut multis in locis annona multo sit carior.
Quin lanarum quoque adeo increuit precium, ut a tenuioribus, qui
pannos inde solent apud uos conficere, prorsus emi non possint,
atque ea ratione | plures ab opere ablegantur in ocium. Nam post 41

---

[1] Before this sentence Robynson
has entirely left out one, which Burnet
translates: 'For there is no more
Occasion for Country Labour, to which
they have been bred, when there is
no Arable Ground left.'

[2] To the authorities on this subject
quoted in the Introduction, § 2, add
Becon's *Jewel of Joy*, quoted by the

editor of Starkey's *Life and Letters*,
as before, p. lxxvi: 'Those beastes
which were created of God for the
nouryshment of man do nowe deuoure man . . . Since they ['gredy gentylmen'] began to be shepe-maysters
and feders of cattell, we neyther had
vyttayle nor cloth of any resonable
pryce.'

that so muche grounde was inclosed for pasture, an infinite
multitude of shepe died of the rotte[1], suche vengaunce
God toke of their inordinate and vnsaciable couetuousnes,
sendyng amonge the shepe that pestiferous morreyn,
which much more iustely should haue fallen on the shepemasters owne heades. And though the numbre of shepe
increase neuer so fast, yet the pryce falleth not one myte,
because there be so fewe sellers[2]. For they be almoste
all commen into a fewe riche mens handes, whome no
neade driueth to sell before they lust; and they luste not
before they may sell as deare as they lust. Now the
same cause bryngeth in licke dearth of the other kindes
of cattell; yea, and that so much the more, bycause that
after farmes pluckyd downe, and husbandry decayed, ther
is no man that passyth for the breadyng of yonge stoore.
For thees ryche men brynge not vp the yonge ones of
greate cattell as they do lambes. But first they bye them

aucta pascua infinitam ouium uim absumpsit tabes, uelut eorum cupi-
ditatem ulciscente deo, immissa In oues lue, quam in ipsorum capita
contortam esse fuerat iustius. Quod si maxime increscat ouium
numerus, precio nihil decrescit tamen; quod earum, si monopolium
appellari non potest, quod non unus uendit, certe oligopolium est.
Reciderunt enim fere in manus paucorum, eorundemque diuitum,
quos nulla necessitas urget ante uendendi quam libet, nec ante libet
quam liceat quanti libet. Iam caetera quoque pecorum genera, ut
aeque cara sint, eadem ratio est, atque hoc etiam amplius, quod dirutis
uillis, atque imminuta re rustica, non sunt qui foeturam curent. Neque
enim diuites illi, ut ouium, sic etiam armentorum foetus educant: sed

---

[1] I am not sure to what year in particular More here refers. The extreme wetness of 1506 must have been injurious to cattle. About that time we read of a great murrain among cattle in Germany and France. See Hecker's *Epidemics*, tr. by Babington, p. 204.

[2] Here again Robynson curtails his rendering of the Latin. More makes an antithesis between *monopolium* and *oligopolium*. We have 'monopoly,' but not 'oligopoly' (the sale by a few), and so cannot preserve the point of the sentence. Burnet renders: 'Tho' they [the sheep] cannot be called a Monopoly, because they are not engrossed by one Person, yet they are in so few Hands, and these are so rich, that,' &c.

abrode very chepe, and afterward, when they be fattede in their pastures, they sell them agayne excedyng deare. And therfor (as I suppose) the hole incommoditie herof is not yet felte. For yet they make dearth only in those places where they sell. But when they shall fetche them awaye from thens wheare they be bredde, faster then they can be brought vp, then shall there also be felte great dearth, when stoore begynnyth to fayle their ^a whear the ware ys bought.

'"Thus the vnreasonable couetousnes of a fewe hath turned that thyng to the vtter vndoying of your Ilande, in the whiche thyng the chiefe felicitie of your realme dyd consist. For this great dearth of victualles causeth euery man ^b to kepe as lytle houses and as small hospitalitie as he ^c possible maye, and to put awaye their seruauntes : whether, I praye you, but a beggynge? or els, whiche thies gentle bloodis and stoute stomakes wyll soner set theyr myndes vnto, a stealinge ?

'"Nowe, to amende the matters, to this wretched beggerye and myserable pouertie is ioyned great wantonnes, importunate superfluytie, and excessiue ryote [1]. For not only

^a stoore beginning there to faile.   ^b causeth men.   ^c they.

aliunde macra empta uili, posteaquam suis pascuis pinguerint, magno reuendunt. Ideoque, sicuti reor, nondum sentitur totum huius rei incommodum. Nempe adhuc his modo locis reddunt cara, ubi uendunt. caeterum ubi aliquandiu celerius extulerint illinc quam nasci possint, tum demum ibi quoque paulatim decrescente copia, ubi coemuntur, necesse est hic insigni laboretur inopia.

Ita qua re uel maxime felix haec uestra uidebatur insula, iam ipsam paucorum improba cupiditas uertit in perniciem. Nam haec annonae caritas in causa est, cur quisque quam possit plurimos e familia dimittat ; quo, quaeso, nisi mendicatum, aut, quod generosis animis 42 persuadeas facilius, latrocinatum ?

Quid quod ad miseram hanc egestatem atque inopiam adiungitur importuna luxuries. Nam et ministris nobilium, et opificibus, et ipsis

---

[1] These three phrases are all used to render *importuna luxuries.*

Raphael asks for reforms:

gently mens seruauntes, but also hand y craft men, yea, *Vices*
and almoste the ploughemen of the countrey, with all
other sortes of people, vse muche straunge and prowde
newe fanglenes in their apparrell, and to muche prodigal
riotte and sumptuous fare at their table. Nowe bawdes,
qweynes, hoores, harlottes, strumpettes, brothelhouses,
stewes, and yet an other stewes, wine tauernes, ale houses,
and tipling houses, with so many noughty lewde and
vnlawfull games, as dice, cardes, tables[1] tennyes, bolles, *gambling*
coytes, do not al thys sende the haunters of them streyght
a stealynge when theyr money is gone ? *Exhortation*

"Caste out thies pernycious abomynacyons; make a lawe *Laws*
that they whyche plucked downe fermes and townes of *needed:*
husbandrye, shall buylde them vp agayne[a] or els yelde
and vprender the possessyon of them[b] to suche as wyll
goo to the coste of buyldynge them anewe[2]. Suffer not
thies ryche men to bye vp all, to ingrosse and forstalle, *ingrosse:*

forstalle:

[a] reedifie them.   [b] therof.

propemodum rusticis, et omnibus denique ordinibus, multum est in-
solentis apparatus in uestibus, nimius in uictu luxus. Iam ganea,
lustra, lupanar, et aliud lupanar[3], tabernae uinariae, ceruisiariae, postremo tot improbi ludi, alea, charta, fritillus, pila, sphaera, discus, an
non haec celeriter exhausta pecunia recta suos mystas mittunt aliquo
latrocinatum ?
Has perniciosas pestes eiicite, statuite ut uillas atque oppida rustica
aut hi restituant qui diruere, aut ea cedant reposituris atque aedificare
uolentibus. Refrenate coemptiones istas diuitum, ac uelut monopolii

---

[1] Lat. *fritillus*, which properly meant a dice-box, but seems sometimes to have been applied to the board, or 'table.' Of some of the games here mentioned More once spoke less harshly. 'To cast a coyte, a cokstele, and a ball' was one of the child's accomplishments in his pageant. See the *English Works*, leaf iii, and, for the subject of early English games, Brand's *Popular Antiquities*, 1841, ii pp. 233 sqq.

[2] See the Introduction, § 9, p. lxxxvi.

[3] If there be no error in the text, the repetition may be meant to convey the thought of Prov. xxiii. 35, 'I will seek it yet again.' Burnet's idea seems to be, that the 'tabernae,' &c., which follow, are in fact the 'aliud lupanar': 'You have also many infamous Houses, and, *besides those that are known*, the Taverns and Ale-houses are no better.'

and with theyr monopolye to kepe the market alone as
please them.   Let not so manye be brought vp in ydlenes;
lett husbandrye and tyllage be restored agayne[a]; let
clothe workynge be renewed; that there maye be honest
labours for thys ydell sorte to passe theyre tyme in pro-
fytablye, whyche hytherto other pouertye hathe caused to
be theues, or elles nowe be other vagabondes, or ydell
seruynge men, and shortelye wylbe theues.   Dowteles,
oneles yowe fynde a remedye for thyes enormytyes, yowe
shall in vayne auuance your selfes of executinge iustice
vpon fellones. ⌊For this iustice is more beautyfull then
iuste[b] or profytable[1].⌉   For by sufferynge your youthe
wantonlye and viciouslye to be brought vp, and to be
infected euen from theyr tender age by lytle and lytle
wyth vyce; than a goddes name to be punyshed, when
they commytte the same faultes after they be commen[c]
to mannes state, whiche frome ther youthe they were euer
lyke to doo: in thys pointe, I praye yowe, what other
thynge doo yowe, then make theues, and then punyshe
them?"

[a] agayne *omitted*.   [b] is more beautiful in apperaunce, and more florish-
ynge to the shewe, then either iuste.   [c] after being come.

exercendi licentiam.   Pauciores alantur ocio, reddatur agricolatio,
lanificium instauretur, ut sit honestum negocium, quo se utiliter
exerceat ociosa ista turba, uel quos hactenus inopia fures fecit, uel qui
nunc errones aut ociosi sunt ministri, fures nimirum utrique futuri.
Certe nisi his malis medemini, frustra iactetis exercitam in uindicanda
furta iusticiam, ⌈nempe speciosam magis quam aut iustam aut utilem.⌉
Siquidem quum pessime sinitis educari, et mores paulatim ab teneris
annis corrumpi, puniendos uidelicet tum demum quum ea flagitia
uiri designent[2], quorum spem de se perpetuam a pueritia usque
praebuerant, quid aliud, quaeso, quam facitis fures, et iidem plectitis?

---

[1] Robynson (see his later version)
struggles with this sentence. Burnet,
more neatly: 'which tho' it may have
the Appearance of Justice, yet in
itself is neither just nor convenient.'

[2] This use of the verb, for 'to
commit,' is found in the comedians.
Comp. Ter. *Adelphi*, i. 2. 7, 'modo
quid designavit,' and the commentators
there.

'Nowe as I was thus speakynge, the Lawier beganne to make hym selfe readye to aunswere, and was determyned wyth hym selfe to vse the common fassyon and trade of disputers, whyche be more dylygent in rehersynge then aunswerynge, as thynking the memorye worthye of the chiefe prayse. "In dede syr" (quod he) "yow haue sayd well, beinge but a straunger, and one that myght rather here somme thynge of thyes matters, then haue anye exacte or perfecte knowledge of the same, as I will incontinent by open proffe make manifest and playn. For firste I wyll reherse in ordre all that yow haue sayde; then I wyll declare in what thynge ᵃ yowe he deceaued, through lacke of knowledge, in all our fassions, maners and customes; and laste of all I wyll aunswere to ᵇ your argumentes, and confute them euery one. Fyrste therfore I wyll begynne where I promysed. Foure thynges yowe semed to me"—"Hold your peace" (quod the Cardynall ¹), "for by lyke ᶜ yowe wyll make no shorte aunswere, whiche make such a begynning; wherfore at thys tyme yowe shall not take the paynes to make youre aunswere, but

ᵃ wherin.　　ᵇ to *omitted*.　　ᶜ it appeareth that.

43　Iam me haec loquente iuris ille consultus inten|tus interim se ad dicendum composuerat, ac statuerat secum modo illo solenni disputantium uti, qui diligentius repetunt quam respondent; adeo bonam partem laudis ponunt in memoria. Belle, inquit, dixisti profecto, quum sis uidelicet hospes, qui magis audire his de rebus aliquid potueris, quam exacte quicquam cognoscere: id quod ego paucis efficiam perspicuum. Nam primum ordine recensebo quae tu dixisti; deinde ostendam quibus in rebus imposuit tibi nostrarum rerum ignoratio; postremo rationes tuas omnes diluam atque dissoluam. Igitur, ut a primo quod sum pollicitus exordiar, quatuor mihi uisus es—Tace, inquit Cardinalis: nam haud responsurus paucis uideris, qui sic incipias. Quamobrem leuabimus in praesenti te hac respondendi molestia, seruaturi tamen integrum id munus tibi in

Expressit morem ei Cardinali familiarem, interpellandi si quis loquacius ageret.

¹ The marginal note in the Latin calls attention to this habit of Cardinal　Morton, of interrupting too talkative persons.

kepe it to youre nexte meatynge, whiche I would be ryght
gladde that it myght be euen to morrowe nexte (onles
other yowe or mayster Raphaell haue any earnest lette).

Morton asks of better Lows

' " But now, maister Raphaell, I woulde very gladly heare
of yow, whie yow thynke thefte not worthy to be punished
with death : or what other punyshment yow can deuyse
more expedient to the weale publique. For I am sewer
yowe are not of that mynde, that yowe woulde haue thefte
escape vnpunyshed. For if now the extreme punishment
of death cannot cause them to leaue stealynge, then if
ruffians and rubbers shoulde be sewer of their lyues, what
violence, what feare were able to holde their handes from
robbynge, whiche would take the mitigacion of the punishment as a verye peruocation to the mischiefe ? "

Raphael:

' " Suerly my lorde" (quod I) "I thynke it no[a] right nor
iustice that the losse of money should cause the losse of
mans lyfe. For myne opinion is that all the goodes in the
worlde are not able to counteruayle mans lyfe. But if they
wold thus say : that the breaking of iustice, and the trans-
gression of the lawes is recompensed with this punishment, and not the losse of the money ; then why maye
not thys extreame[b] iustice wel bc called extreme[c] iniurie ?

[a] not.   [b] extreme and rigorous.   [c] plaine.

proximum congressum uestrum, quem (nisi quid impediat aut te aut
Raphalem hunc) crastinus dies uelim referat.

Sed interim abs te, mi Raphael, perquam libenter audierim, quare
tu furtum putes ultimo supplicio non puniendum ; quamue aliam
poenam ipse statuas, quae magis conducat in publicum. Nam tole-
randum ne tu quidem sentis. At si nunc per mortem quoque tamen
in furtum ruitur, proposita semel uitae securitate, quae uis, quis
metus potest absterrere maleficos ; qui mitigatione supplicii uelut
praemio quodam ad maleficium se inuitatos interpretarentur ?

Omnino mihi uidetur, inquam, | pater benignissime, homini uitam 44
eripi propter ereptam pecuniam prorsus iniquum esse. Siquidem
cum humana uita ne omnibus quidem fortunae possessionibus paria
fieri posse arbitror. Quod si laesam iustitiam, si leges uiolatas, hac
rependi poena dicant, haud pecuniam : quidni merito summum illud

For neither so[a] cruel gouernaunce, so streyte rules,
and vnmercyfull lawes[1] be allowable, that if a small
offence be commytted, by and by the sworde shoulde
be drawen; nor so stoycall[2] ordinaunces are to be
borne wythall, as to counte all offences of suche equa-
litie, that the kyllynge of a man, or the takynge of hys
money from hym, were bothe a[3] matter; and the one no
more heynous offence then the other : betwene the whyche
two, yf we haue annye respecte to equitie, no symylytude
or equalytie consysteth. God commaundeth vs that we
shall not kyll. And be we then so hastie to kyll a man
for takynge a lytle money? And yf annye man woulde
vnderstande kyllynge, by this commaundement of God, to
bee forbydden after no larger wyse then mans constitucions defyneth[b] kyllynge to be lawfull, then whye maye
it not lykewyse, by mannes constitutions, be determyned
after what sorte hooredome, fornication, and periurye maye
be lawfull? For where as by the permission of God no

stoical

capital

on

man's law
vs.
God's

punishment

[a] For so cruell . . . be not.   [b] defyne.

ius summa uocetur iniuria? Nam neque legum probanda sunt tam
Manliana imperia, ut sicubi in leuissimis parum ob-
temperetur, illico stringant gladium ; neque tam Stoica
scita, ut omnia peccata adeo existiment paria, uti nihil
iudicent interesse, occidatne aliquis hominem, an nummum ei surri-
piat, inter quae (si quicquam aequitas ualet) nihil omnino simile aut
affine. Deus uetuit occidi quenquam ; et nos tam facile occidimus ob
ademptam pecuniolam? Quod si quis interpretetur, illo dei iussu
interdictam necis potestatem, nisi quatenus humana lex declaret occi-
dendum, quid obstat quo minus homines eodem modo constituant inter
se, quatenus stuprum admittendum sit, adulterandum, peierandum?

Manliana im-
peria, ex Liuio.

---

[1] This is a paraphrase of the Latin,
legum . . . Manliana imperia; an expression borrowed from Livy, iv. 29,
where inexorable decrees are called
Manliana imperia. For L. Manlius,
who gained the surname of Imperiosus,
see Livy, vii. 3.

[2] For this oft-quoted paradox of the
Stoics, *omnia peccata esse paria*, with
which Cicero makes merry in the *Pro
Murena*, see Dissert. xxi. in Justus
Lipsius' *Manuductio ad Stoicam Philo-
sophiam*, 1644.

[3] Like the Scotch *ae*, ' one.'

man hathe power to kyll nother hym selfe, nor yet annye
other man[1]; then yf a lawe made by the consente of men
concernynge slaughter of men oughte to be of suche
strengthe, force, and vertue, that they whyche contrarye
to the commaundement of God haue kylled those, whome
thys constitucion of man commaunded to be kylled, be
cleane quyte and exempte owte of the bondes and daunger
of Goddes commaundemente; shall it not then by thys
reason followe that the powre of Goddes commaundement
shall extende no further then mannes lawe dothe defyne
and permytte? And so shall it come to passe, that in lyke
manner mans constitucions in al thynges shal determyne
howe farre the obseruation of all Goddes commaundementes shall extende. To be shorte, Moyses lawe, thoughe
it were vngentle and sharpe, as a lawe that was gyuen to
bondmen[2]; yea, and them verye obstinate, stubborne, and
styf necked; yet it punnyshed thefte by the purse, and not
wyth deathe. And let vs not thynke that God in the newe

NB.

Mozaic law on theft

Siquidem quum deus non alienae modo, uerum etiam suae cuique
mortis ius ademerit, si hominum inter se consensus de mutua cede,
certis placitis consentientium, adeo debet ualere, ut illius praecepti
uinculis eximat suos satellites, qui sine ullo exemplo dei eos intere-
merint quos humana sanctio iussit occidi : an non hoc pacto praeceptum
illud dei tantum iuris est habiturum, quantum humana iura permi-
serint? | ac fiet nimirum ut ad eundem modum omnibus in rebus 45
statuant homines, quatenus diuina mandata conueniat obseruari.
Denique lex Mosaica, quanquam inclemens et aspera (nempe in
seruos, et quidem obstinatos, lata), tamen pecunia furtum haud morte

---

[1] Hythloday is made to argue here
against the infliction of capital punishment, as under no circumstances
justifiable. But he afterwards cites,
apparently without disapproval, cases
in which the Utopians inflicted it.
See below, p. 230.

[2] Compare what Colet says, in his
Letters to Radulphus, about Moses

having adapted his language to ' the
uncultivated nature of those poor
people, but lately occupied among the
bricks and clay.' His tone is yet more
striking in the original Latin, where
he says : ' Sed crassiter et pingue
docenda fuit stulta illa et macra multitudo.' See the *Letters on the Mosaic
Account of the Creation,* 1876, p. 12.

lawe of clemencie and mercie, vnder the whiche he ruleth vs with fatherlie gentlenesse, as his dere chyldren, hath geuen vs greater scoupe and license to execute[a] crueltie one vpon an other.

'"Now ye haue hard the reasons, whereby I am perswaded that this punishment is vnlawful. Furthermore I thinke there is no body that knoweth not, how vnreasonable, yea how pernitious a thynge it is to the weale publique, that a thefe, and a homicide or morderer, shuld suffer equall and lyke punyshment. For the thefe, seing that man that is condempned for thefte in no lesse ieoperdie, nor iudged to no lesse punishment, then hym that is conuict of manslaughter; through thys cogitacion onlye he is stronglye and forcybly prouoked, and in a maner constreyned, to kyl him, whom els he would haue but robbed. For, the murder ones[b] done, he is in lesse care[c], and in more hope that the dede shall not be bewrayed or knowen, seynge the partye is now deade and rydde out of the waye, whyche onely myght haue vttered and disclosed it. But if he chaunce to be taken and discriued, yet he is in no more daunger and ieopardie then yf he had commytted but single fellonye. Therfore whyles we goo about wyth suche crueltye to make theues aferd, we prouoke them to kyll good men.

> [a] to the execution of.   [b] beynge ones.   [c] feare.

mulctauit. Ne putemus deum in noua lege clementiae, qua pater imperat filiis, maiorem indulsisse nobis inuicem saeuiendi licentiam.

Haec sunt cur non licere putem. Quam[a] uero sit absurdum, atque etiam periculosum reipublicae, furem atque homicidam ex aequo puniri, nemo est, opinor, qui nesciat. Nempe quum latro conspiciat non minus imminere discriminis duntaxat furti damnato, quam si praeterea conuincatur homicidii, hac una cogitatione impellitur in caedem eius, quem alioqui fuerat tantum spoliaturus; quippe praeterquam quod deprehenso nihil sit plus periculi, est etiam in caede securitas maior, et maior caelandi spes sublato facinoris indice. Itaque, dum fures nimis atrociter studemus perterrefacere, in bonorum incitamus perniciem.

> [a] quantum, A.

' " Now as touchyng this question, what punysshemente were more commodyous and better ; that trulye in my iudgement is easyer to be founde, than what punysshement were [a] wurse.　For whie should we dowt that to be a good and a profytable waye for the punysshemente of offendours, whyche we knowe dydde in tymes paste so longe please the Romaynes ; men in thadmynystratyon of a weale publyque moste experte, polytyque, and cunnyng ?　Such as amonge them weare conuycte of great and heynous trespaces, them they condempned into ston quarris, and in to myenes to dygge mettalle, there to be kepte in cheynes all the dayes of theyr lyfe[1].

' " But as concernyng this matter, I allow the ordenaunce of no nation so well as that [b] I sawe (whyles I trauayled a brode abowt the wordle) vsed in Persia, amonge the

[a] might be.　　　　　　　　　　[b] that which.

Iam quod quaeri solet, quae punitio possit esse commodior; hoc meo iudicio haud paulo facilius est repertu, quam quae possit esse deterior.　Cur enim dubitemus eam uiam utilem esse castigandis sceleribus, quam scimus olim tam diu placuisse Romanis administrandae reipublicae peritissimis ?　Nempe hi magnorum facinorum conuictos in lapidicinas atque fodienda metalla damnabant, perpctuis adseruandos uinculis.

Quanquam ego quod ad hanc | rem attinet nullius institutum gentis 46 probo quam id quod interea dum peregrinabar in Perside obser-

---

[1] What the state of things was in these penal stone-quarries and mines, may be inferred from a passage of Plautus, where Tyndarus, a character who has gone through them, says that pandaemonium is nothing to them :—

'Vidi ego multa saepe picta, quae
　　Acherunti fierent
Cruciamenta ; verum enim vero nulla
　　adaeque est Acheruns,
Atque ubi ego fui in lapicidinis.'
　　　　　　　　　　Capt. v. 4.
For the subject of condemnation to the mines, which corresponded in some degree to our penal servitude, see the Digest, Lib. xlviii, Tit. xix, §§ 4-6. Pole, in the *Dialogue* before quoted (p. 196) is of much the same opinion as Hythloday.　In case of incorrigible wrongdoers, ' I wold thynke hyt gud,' he says, ' that the felon schold be take and put in some commyn worke as to labur in byldyng the wallys of cytcs and townys, or els in some other magnyfycal work of the prynce of the reame.'

people that commenlye be called the polylerytes[1]; whose
lande is bothe large and ample, and also well and wyttelye gouerned; and the people in all conditions free and
ruled by their owne lawes, sauing that they paye a yerely
content with their owne
tribute to the great king of Persia. But bicause they be
farre from the sea, compassed and closed in [a] almoste
rounde abowte wyth hygh mountaynes, and do content
them selfes wyth the frutes of theyr owne lande, whyche
is of yt selfe verye fertyle and frutefull: for thys cause
nother they goo to other cowntreys, nor other comme to
them. And accordynge to the olde custome of the lande,
isolated
they desyre not to enlarge the bowndes of theyr domy-
nyons; and those that they haue by reason of the hyghe
hylles be easelye defended; and the trybute whyche they
paye to the myghtyc Kynge [b] settethe them quyete and free
from warfare. Thus theyre lyffe ys commodyous rather
then gallawnte, and maye better be callede happye or
luckye, then notable or famous. For they be not knowne
asmuche as by name, I suppose, sauynge onlye to thcyr
nexte neyghbours and borderours.

[a] inclosed.   [b] to their chiefe lord and kinge.

natum apud uulgo dictos Polyleritas adnotaui; populum neque exiguum neque imprudenter institutum, et nisi quod tri-
butum quotannis Persarum pendit regi, caetera liberum   Respublica
ac suis permissum legibus. Caeterum quoniam longe ab   Polyleritarum
                                                             apud Persas.
mari, montibus fere circumdati, et suae terrae nulla in re
maligne [a] contenti fructibus, neque adeunt alios saepe, neque adeuntur,
tamen ex uetusto more gentis neque fines prorogare student, et quos
habent ab omni facile iniuria et montes tuentur, et pensio quam
rerum potienti persoluunt. immunes prorsus ab militia, haud perinde
splendide atque commode, felicesque magis quam nobiles aut clari,
degunt; quippe ne nomine quidem, opinor, praeter quam conterminis,
admodum satis noti.

[a] *i. q* malignae.

[1] Described as a sort of people of
Laish. The name (πολὺs λῆρos, 'much
nonsense') is not, however, meant to
express their character, but to hint
that the assumption of their existence
was nonsense.

F

The Polylerites

' " They that in thys lande be attayntede and conuycte of felonye, make restitutyon of that [a] they stoole to the ryghte owner, and not (as they doo in other landes) to the Kynge ; whome they thynke to haue no more ryghte to the thefe stolen thynge than the thieffe himselfe hath. But if the thynge be loste or made awaye, then the value of yt is paide of the goodes of such offendours, whyche elles remayneth all hole to theire wyffes and chyldrene. And they them selfes be condempned to be common laborers ; and, onles the thefte be verye heynous, they be nother locked in pryson, nor fettered in gyues, but be vntyed and goo at large, laborynge in the common workes. They that refuse labour, or goo slowly and slacly to there woorke, be not only [1] tied in cheynes, but also pricked forward with stripes. They that be [b] diligent about their woorke liue without checke or rebuke. Euery nyghte they be called in by name, and be locked in theyr chambers. Besyde their dayly labour, their lyffe is nothyng harde or incommodyous. Their fare is indyfferent good, borne at the chardges of the weale publyque, bycause they be commen seruauntes to the commen wealth. But their

labor for crime

        [a] that which.   [b] But being.

Ergo apud hos furti qui peraguntur, quod sustulere domino reddunt ; non, quod alibi fieri solet, principi ; utpote cui tantum iuris esse censent in rem furtiuam quantum ipsi furi. Sin res perierit, precio ex bonis furum confecto, ac persoluto tum reliquo uxoribus eorum atque liberis integro, ipsi damnantur in opera. ac nisi atrociter commissum furtum est, neque clauduntur ergastulo, neque gestant compedes, sed liberi ac soluti in publicis occupantur operibus. detrectantes ac languidius gerentes sese, non tam uinculis cohercent quam excitant uerberibus. strenuam nauantes operam, absunt a contumeliis, noctu tantum nominatim censiti cubiculis | includuntur. praeter assiduum 47 laborem nihil incommodi est in uita. Aluntur enim haud duriter, qui publicae rei seruiunt, e publico : alibi aliter. Siquidem alicubi quod

Annotandum nobis, qui secus facimus.

---

[1] This is not the sense of the Latin, which is ' they do not so much imprison as flog them ' : that is, they prefer flogging to imprisonment.

charges in all places of the land is not borne a lyke. For in some partes that [a] is bestowed vpon them is gathered of almes. And though that waye be vncerteyn, yet the people be so full of mercye and pytie, that none is fownde more profytable or plentyfull. In some places certeyn landis [1] be appoynted here vnto ; of the reuenewes wherof they be fownde [b]. And in some places euery man geuyth a certeyne trybute for the same vse and purpose. Agayne in some partes of the lande thies seruyng men (for so be thies damned persons called [2]), do no common worke; but, as euery priuate man nedeth labourours, so he cometh into the markette place [3], and there hiereth some of them for meate and drynke, and a certeyne limityd wayges by the daye, sumwhat cheper then he shoulde hire a free man. It is also lawfull for them to chastyce the slowth of thies seruynge men wyth strypes.

' " By thys meanes they neuer lacke woorke; and besydes their meate and dryncke euery one of them bryngeth dayly sum thynge into the common treasoury [4]. All and

[a] that which.   [b] mainteined.

impenditur in eos ex eleemosyna colligitur : atque ea uia quanquam incerta, tamen ut est ille populus misericors, nulla reperitur uberior. alibi reditus quidam publici ad id destinantur. Est ubi certum in eos usus tributum uiritim conferunt. Quin aliquot in locis nullum publicum opus faciunt, sed ut priuatus quisque eget mercenariis, ita illorum cuiuspiam in eum diem operam, stata mercede, conducit apud forum ; paulo minoris quam quanti liberam fuerat conducturus. praeterea fas est seruilem ignauiam flagris corripere.

Sic fit uti nunquam opere careant ; et praeter uictum aliquid quoque

---

[1] Nothing is said about *lands* in the Latin. The English here is diffuse.

[2] For some reason Robynson has inserted here the explanation that in the Latin comes afterwards, p. 68.

[3] This ancient custom may still be seen practised in some country towns. For the compulsory hiring prevalent in the Tudor times (as by Statute 5 Eliz. cap. 4) see Jacob's *Law Dictionary*, under the heading ' Servants.'

[4] That is, in addition to the advantage gained to the state by these criminals being supported by private employers, the money they receive as wages is paid into the common fund. As is explained just after, the convicts themselves may not keep any.

euery one of them be apparrayled in one colour. Their heddys be not polled or shauen, but rownded a lytle aboue the eeres; and the typpe of the one eare is cut of. Euery one of them may take meat and drincke of their frindes, and also a cote of their owne collour; but to receyve monye is deathe, as well to the geuer as to the receyuour. And no lesse ieopardie it is for a free man to receyue moneye of a seruynge man, for any manner of cause; and lykewyse for seruynge men to touche weapons. The seruyng men of euery seuerall shyere be dystyncte and knowen from other by their seuerall and dystyncte badges; whyche to caste away is death: as it is also to be seene owte of the precyncte of their owne sheire, or to talke wyth a seruynge man of another shyere. And it is no lesse daunger to them for to intende to runne awaye, then to do yt in dede. Yea, and to concele suche an enterpryes in a seruynge man yt is deathe; in a free man seruytude. Of the contrarye parte, to hym that openeth and vttereth suche cownselles be decreyde large giftes: to a free man a great somme of moneye; to a seruynge man freedome; and to them bothe forgeuynes and pardone of that they were of councell in that pretence. So that[1]

die ab singulis publico inferatur aerario. Vno quodam colore uestiuntur et omnes et soli, capillo non abraso, uerum paulo

At idem hodie famuli nobilium pulchrum sibi ducunt.

supra auriculas attonso, e quarum altera paululum praescinditur. Cibum cuique ab amicis dari potumque, ac sui coloris uestem, licet: pecuniam datam esse danti pariter atque accipienti capitale; neque minus periculosum etiam homini libero quacunque de causa nummum a damnato recepisse, et seruos item (sic enim damnatos uocant[2]) arma contingere. Suos quaeque regio propria distinguit nota, quam abiecisse capitale est, ut uel extra suos conspici fines, uel cum alterius regionis seruo quicquam esse collocutum. At neque tutior fugae meditatio quam ipsa est fuga. Quin conscium | talis fuisse consilii in seruo nex est; 48 in libero seruitus. Contra indici praemia decreta sunt; libero pecunia,

---

[1] Rather 'that it may never,' &c.; purpose, not consequence.

[2] See note above, p. 67.

Margin notes (handwritten):

Polyleites

{ Details here become illogical βγωμαντιω

Prisoners' clothing & marks

death? penalty

death penalty

rewards

yt can neuer be so good for them to goo forwarde in
theyre euyll purpose, as by repentaunce to turne backe.

' " Thys is the lawe and ordre in thys behalfe, as I haue
shewed yow. Wherin what humanytye is vsede, howe
farre yt is frome crueltye, and howe commodyous yt is,
yow doo playnlye perceue: for asmuche as the ende of
their wrath and punyshemente intendeth nothyng elles
but the distructyon of vyces and sauynge of men; wyth
so vsynge and orderynge them, that theye can not chuse
but be good; and what harme so euer theye dyd before,
in tho resydewe of theyre lyffe to make amendys for
the same.

' " Moreouer yt is so lytle feared, that they shoulde torne
agayne to theyre vycyous condytyons, that wayefarynge
men wyll for theyre sauegarde chuse them to theyre
guydes before annye other, in euerye sheyre chaungynge
and takynge newe. For yf they wolde commytte robberye,
theye haue nothynge abowte them meate for that purpose.
They maye towche no weapons: moneye fownde abowte
them shoulde betraye the robberye. They shoulde be no
soner taken wyth the maner, but furthwyth they shoulde
be punysshed. Nother theye can haue annye hoope at all
to skape awaye by flycnge. For howe shoulde a man,

seruo libertas. utrique uero uenia atque impunitas conscientiae, ne
quando persequi malum consilium quam poenitere sit tutius.

Huius rei haec lex atque hic ordo est, quem dixi. qui quantum
habeat humanitatis et commodi, facile patet; quando sic irascitur ut
uitia perimat, seruatis hominibus, atque ita tractatis ut bonos esse
necesse sit, et quantum ante damni dederunt, tantum reliqua uita
resartiant.

Porro ne ad pristinos relabantur mores, adeo nullus est metus, ut
uiatores quoque, quibus iter aliquo institutum est, non aliis uix duci-
bus sese tutioreis arbitrentur, quam seruis illis, ad quamque regionem
subinde commutatis. Nempe ad perpetrandum latrocinium nihil
habent usquam non importunum : manus inermes ; pecunia tantum
sceleris index ; deprehenso parata uindicta, neque spes ulla prorsus
fugiendi quoquam. Quo enim pacto falleret ac tegeret fugam, homo

that in no parte of hys apparrell is lyke other men, flye
preuelye and vnknowen, oneles he wolde runne awaye
naked? Howe be yt, so also flyinge, he shoulde be
dyscryued by hys rounding and his eare marke[1]. But
yt is a thynge to be dowted, that they will lay their heddes
togither, and conspire agaynst the weale publyque. No,
no, I warraunte you. For the seruyng men of one shere
alone could neuer hoope to brynge to passe suche an
enterpryse, wythowte sollycytynge, entysynge, and allur-
ynge the seruynge men of many other shyeres to take
their partes. Whych thynge is to them so impossyble,
that they may not asmuche as speake or talke togethers,
or salute one an other. No, it is not to be thought that
they wold make their owne countrey men and companyons
of their cownsell[2] in such a matter, whych they knowe
well shoulde be ieopardye to the conceolour therof, and
greate commodytye and goodnes to the openner of[a] the
same: where as on the other parte, ther is none of them
al hoopeles or in dyspayre to recouer agayne hys[b] freedome, by humble obedience, by pacyent suffrynge, and by
geanyng good tokens and lyklyhode of hymself, that he
wyll euer after that liue lyke a trewe and an honeste

[a] and detectour of.   [b] hys former estate of.

nulla uestium parte populo similis, nisi abeat nudus? quin sic quoque
fugientem proderet auricula. At ne inito saltem consilio coniurent in
rempublicam, id demum scilicet periculum est. quasi in tantam
uenire spem ulla possit uicinia, non tentatis ac sollicitatis ante multarum regionum seruitiis. quae tantum absunt a facultate conspirandi,
ut ne conuenire quidem et colloqui aut salutare se mutuo liceat: ut
credantur interim id consilium intrepide credituri suis, quod | reticen- 49
tibus periculosum, prodentibus maximo esse bono sciant. Quum
contra nemo sit prorsus exspes, obediendo ac perferendo, bonamque
de se prebendo spem emendatioris in posterum uitae, posse his modis

---

[1] Burnet: 'their crop'd Ear.'
[2] 'Of their cownsell,' that is, their confidants.

(handwritten marginal note: { Raphael sees no reason why such a system cannot be instituted in England.)

(handwritten marginal note, right: 71)

man. For euery yeare dyuers be[a] restoryd agayne to their freedome, throughe the commendatyon of their patience[1]."

'Whan I had thus spoken, saynge moreouer that I coulde see no cause whie this ordre might not be had in England, with much more proffyte then the Justyce which the lawier so highly praised: "Naye" (quod the lawier), "this could neuer be so stablished in England, but that it must neades bringe the weale publique into great ieopardie and hasarde." And as he was thus saying, he shaked his heade, and made a wrie mouth, and so[b] held his peace. And all that were ther present, with one assent agreid to his saying.

(handwritten marginal note, right: Lawyer & others disagree.)

'"Well" (quod the Cardinall), "yet it were hard to iudge withowte a proffe whether this order wold doo well here or no. But when the sentence of deathe is geuen, if than the king should commaunde execution to be differryd and

(handwritten marginal note, right: Cardinal Morton: NB hedges)

[a] of them be.   [b] so he.

fieri ut libertatem aliquando recuperet, quippe nullo non anno resti-
tutis aliquot commendatione patientiae.

Haec quum dixissem, atque adiecissem nihil mihi uideri causae,
quare non hic modus haberi uel in Anglia possit[2], multo maiore cum
fructu quam illa iusticia, quam iuris ille peritus tantopere laudauerat:
sub haec ille, nempe iuris consultus: Nunquam, inquit, istud sic
stabiliri queat in Anglia, ut non in summum discrimen adducat rempublicam. et simul haec dicens commouit caput, ac distorsit labrum,
atque ita conticuit. Et omnes qui aderant pedibus in eius ibant sententiam.

Tum Cardinalis, non est, inquit, procliue diuinare, commode ne an
secus res cessura sit, nullo prorsus facto periculo. Verum si, pro-
nuntiata mortis sententia, differri executionem[3] iubeat princeps, atque

---

[1] This is an anticipation of our 'ticket of leave' system. By the Penal Servitude Act of 1853, power was given 'to release convicts in the United Kingdom conditionally on ticket of leave,' instead of releasing them, as formerly, on 'free pardon.'

See Sir F. du Cane's article on Prisons in Chambers's *Encyclopaedia*. The principle, as we here see, had been enunciated long before in the *Utopia*.

[2] This should in strict syntax be *posset*.

[3] This is a late Latin use of the word.

Morton:
it's
worth
trying.

spared, and wold proue this order and fassion; taking away
the priuileges of all saintuaries; if then the proffe wold[a]
declare the thing to be good and profitable, than it were
well done that it were stablisshed. Els the condempned
and repriued parsons may aswell and as iustly be put to
death after this proffe, as when they were first cast.
Nother any ioperdye can in the meane space growe here
of. Yea, and me thinketh that thies vagaboundes may
very well be ordered after the same fassion, against whome
we haue hitherto made so many lawes, and so litle pre-
uailed."

Then they
agree:

'When the Cardinal had thus said, than euery man gaue
greate praise to my sayinges, which a litle before they
had disallowed. But most of all was estemed that which
was spoken of vagaboundes, bicause it was the cardinalles
owne addition.

'I can not tell whether it were best to reherse the communication that followed, for it was not very sad[1]. But

[a] shoulde.

hunc experiatur morem, cohibitis asylorum priuilegiis, tum uero si
res comprobetur euentu esse utilis, rectum fuerit eam stabiliri. alioqui tunc quoque afficere supplicio eos qui sunt ante damnati, neque
minus e republica fuerit, neque magis iniustum, quam si nunc idem
fieret; nec ullum interea nasci ex ea re potest periculum. Quin mihi
certe uidentur errones quoque ad eundem posse modum non pessime
tractari, in quos hactenus tam multis aeditis legibus, nihil | promouimus 50
tamen.

Haec ubi dixit Cardinalis, quae me narrante contempserant omnes,
eadem nemo non certatim laudibus est prosequutus; maxime tamen
illud de erronibus, quoniam hoc ab ipso adiectum est.

Nescio an quae sunt secuta silere prestiterit; erant enim ridicula :

[1] More seems to have had some
little misgiving about introducing the
story that follows. If so, his discernment has been justified by the result.
In one edition of the *Utopia*, printed
at Cologne, 1629, in 24°, and described
on the title-page as 'juxta Indicem
librorum expurgatorum Cardinalis et
Archiepiscopi Toletani correcta,' a
great part of the anecdote is omitted.
From 'Subrisit Cardinalis, et approbat
ioco, caeteri etiam serio,' the text

Raphael continues his report of Morton's table talk:

the Parasite Fool: cf. Erasmus on Folly

yet you shal here it: for ther was no euell in it; and partly it parteined to the matter before said.

'Ther chaunsed to stond by a certein iesting parasite, or scoffer, which wold seme to resemble and cownterfeit the foole. But he did in such wise counterfeyt, that he was almost the very same in dead that he labored to represent. He so studied with wordes and saynges, brought furth so out of time and place, to make sporte and moue laughter, that he himself was oftener laughed at then his iestes were. Yet the foolish fellow brought out now and then such indifferent and reasonable stuffe, that he made the prouerbe trew, which sayeth: he that shoteth oft, at the last shal hit the marke [1]. So that when one of the company said that thorough my communication a good ordre was found for theues, and that the Cardinall also had wel prouided for vagaboundes; so that only remained some good prouision to be made for them that through siknes and age were fallen into pouerty, and were become so impotente and vnweldye, that they were not

The issue of poverty:

sed narrabo tamen: nam non erant mala, et aliquid ad hanc rem pertinebant.

Adstabat forte parasitus quidam, qui uideri uolebat imitari morionem, sed ita simulabat, ut propior uero esset, tam frigidis dictis captans risum, ut ipse saepius quam *Festiuus dialogus fratris et* dicta sua riderentur. Excidebant homini tamen in- *morionis.* terdiu quaedam, adeo non absurda, ut fidem adagio facerent, crebro iactu iaci aliquando Venerem. Is ergo, dicente quodam e conuiuis: Iam meo sermone bene prouisum esse furibus, atque a Cardinale etiam cautum de erronibus, restare nunc uti his praeterea consuleretur publicitus, quos ad egestatem morbus aut senectus im-

passes on to 'En, mi More, quam longo,' &c., leaving out all the section beginning 'Caeterum theologus quidam.' That, in the judgment of some ecclesiastical censors, the *Utopia* should have been declared to need expurgation, is a noticeable fact.

[1] The Latin proverb, taken from the throw of dice, is given by Erasmus in his *Adagia* (1629), p. 99 b, in the form 'Si saepe iacies, aliquando Venerem iacies'; Robynson alters the comparison. Burnet, more correctly: 'He who throws the Dice often, will sometimes have a lucky Hit.'

The
Fool's
cure for
poverty:

able to woorke for their living: "Tush "(quod he) " let me alon with them; you shall see me do well ynough with them. For I had rather then anye good that this kind of people were dreuen sumwhether out of my sighte: they haue so sore troubled me many times and oft, when they haue with their lamentable teares[1] begged money of me; and yet thei could neuer to mi mind so tune theire song, that therby they euer got of me one farthynge. For euer more the one of thies two chaunced: eyther that I wolde not, or elles that I could not, bicause I had it not. Therefore nowe they be waxed wyse. When[a] they see me goo bye, bycause they wyll not leese theyr laboure, they lette me go[b], and saye not one worde to me. So they looke for nothing of me; no, in good sothe, no more then if I were a priest[c]. But I will make a law, that all thies beggers shalbe distribute and bestowed into houses of religion. The men shalbe made laye bretherne, as they call them, and the women nunnes." Here at the Cardenall

Morton.

smiled, and allowed it in iest; yea, and all the residue in good earnest.

    [a] for when.   [b] passe.   [c] priest or a monke.

pulisset, atque ad labores unde uiui possit reddidisset impotes : Sine, inquit, me : nam ego et hoc recte ut fiat uidero. Etenim hoc genus hominum misere cupio aliquo e conspectu amoliri meo; ita me male uexarunt saepe, cum querulis illis opplorationibus flagitarent pecuniam, quas nunquam tamen tam commode potuerunt occinere, ut nummum a me extorquerent. Quippe semper alterum euenit, ut aut non libeat dare, aut ne liceat quidem, quando nihil est quod detur. Itaque nunc coeperunt sapere. nam ne perdant operam, ubi me praeterire ui|dent, 51

Prouerbium uulgo iactatum apud mendicos. praetermittunt taciti: ita nihil a me sperant amplius, non hercle magis quam si essem sacerdos. Sed illos ego mendicos omnes lata lege distribui ac dispartiri iubeo in Benedictinorum caenobia, et fieri laicos ut uocant monachos : mulieres moniales esse impero. Subrisit Cardinalis et approbat ioco, caeteri etiam serio.

---

[1] The Latin is more expressive than this. 'Their pitiful importunities' would come a little nearer, or 'those doleful applications they beset you with.'

The Friar vs. Priests & Monks.

'But a certeyne freare, graduate in diuinitie, toke such pleasur and delite in this ieste of priestes and monkes, that he also, beinge elles a man of grislye and sterne grauitye, beganne merilye and wantonlye to ieste and taunt. "Nay" (quod he), "you shal not so be ridde and dispatched of beggers, oneles you make some prouision also for us frears." "Whie" (quod the iester) "that is doon all redy. For mi lord him selfe set a very good ordre for yow, when he decreed that vagaboundes should be kept strayt, and set to worke; for yow be the greatest and veriest vagaboundes that be."

Fool: calls friars vagabonds.

'This iest also, when they saw the Cardinal not disproue it, euery man tooke it gladly, sauing only the Frear. For he (and that no marueil) when he was thus[a] towchyd one the quicke, and hit on the gawl, so fret, so fumed and chafid at it, and was in such a rage, that he could not refrayn himselfe from chiding, skolding, railing, and reuiling[1]. He called the fellow ribbald, villayn, iauell, back-

[a] beynge thus.

Cacterum Theologus quidam frater hoc dicto in sacerdotes ac monachos adeo est exhilaratus, ut iam ipse quoque coeperit ludere, homo alioqui prope ad toruitatem grauis. At ne sic quidem, inquit, extricaberis a mendicis, nisi nobis quoque prospexeris fratribus. Atqui, inquit Parasitus, hoc iam curatum est. Nam Cardinalis egregie prospexit uobis, quum statueret de cohercendis atque opere exercendis erronibus; nam uos estis errones maximi.

Hoc quoque dictum, quum coniectis in Cardinalem oculis eum uiderent non abnuere, coeperunt omnes non illibenter arripere, excepto fratre. Nam is (neque equidem miror) tali perfusus aceto[2], sic indignatus est atque incanduit, ut nec a conuiciis quidem potuerit temperare: hominem uocauit nebulonem, detractorem, susurronem,

Allusit ad illud Horatianum, italo perfusus aceto.

---

[1] A long rendering of *conuiciis*. Burnet: 'he could not forbear railing at the Fool.'

[2] The reference is indicated in the marginal note: Hor. *Sat.* i. vii. 32, 'At Graecus, postquam est Italo per-fusus aceto,' &c. Pace in his *De Fructu*, which appeared the year after the first edition of the *Utopia*, speaking of More, says that he too, when occasion demands, imitates good cooks, and 'omnia acri perfundit aceto' (p. 82).

The Friar attacks the Fool:

biter, sclaunderer, and the sonne[a] of perdition; citing therwith terrible threatening out of holy scriptur. Then the iesting skoffer began to play the scoffer indede, and verily he was good at yt, for he could play a part in that play, no man better[1]. "Patient iourself, good maister Freare" (quod he), "and be not angry; for scriptur saith:

The Fool

in your patience you shal saue your sowles[2]." Then the Freare (for I wil rehearse his oune very woordes): "No, gallous wretche, I am not angry" (quod he); "or at the leaste wise I do not synne: for the psalmiste saith, *be you angry and sinne not*[3]."

Morton asks for peace:

'Then the Cardinal spake gently to the Freare, and desiered him to quyete hymself. "No, my lord" (quod he), "I speake not but of a good zeal as I ought; for holly men had a good zeale. Wherfor it is said; *the zeale of thy*

Friar.

house hath eaten me[4]. And it is song in the church: *The skorners of Helizeus, whiles he went vp into the house of god,*

[a] childe.

et filium perditionis; minas interim terribiles citans e scriptura sacra. Iam scurra serio scurrari coepit, et erat plane in sua palaestra. Noli, inquit, irasci, bone frater: scriptum est, *in patientia uestra possidebitis animas uestras.* Rursum frater (referam

Vt seruat decorum in narratione.

enim ipsius uerba) non irascor, | inquit, furcifer, uel 52 saltem non pecco. Nam Psalmista dicit, *Irascimini et nolite peccare.*

Admonitus deinde frater a Cardinale suauiter, ut suos affectus compesceret, Non, domine, inquit, ego loquor nisi ex bono zelo, sicut debeo. Nam uiri sancti habuerunt bonum zelum, unde dicitur, *Zelus domus tuae comedit me,* et canitur in ecclesiis: *Irrisores Helizei, dum*

---

[1] The spirit of the idiomatic English here rivals that of the original.

[2] St. Luke xxi. 19. The Revised Version agrees with the Vulgate in using the future tense here: 'ye shall win.'

[3] Ps. iv. 4. The R. V. gives 'be ye angry' as a marginal reading, in place of 'stand in awe.' The former has the support of the LXX and Vulgate, which here agree, and also of St. Paul's citation in Eph. iv. 26.

[4] Ps. lxix. 9 (Vulg. lxviii. 10).

bald friars (handwritten)

felt the zeale of the bald[1]; as peraduentur this skorning
villain ribauld shal feel." "You do it" (quod the cardinall)
"perchaunce of a good mind and affection. But me
thinketh you should do, I can not tel whether more holily,
certes more wisely, if you wold not set your wit to
a fooles witte, and with a foole take in hand a foolish contention." "No, forsoeth, my lorde" (quod he), "I should
not doo more wiselye. For Salomon the wise sayeth[2]:
Answer a foole according to his folishnes[a]; like as I do
now, and do shew him the pit that he shall fall into, if he
take not hede. For if many skorners of Helizeus, which
was but one bald man, felt the zeal of the balde, howe
much more shall one skorner of many frears feele, amonge
whom be many bald men? And we haue also the popes
bulles, wherby all that mock and skorne us be excommunicate, suspended, and acursed[3]." The cardinal seing that
none end wold be made, sent away the iester by a preuy

Morton. (handwritten, right margin)

Friar rages (handwritten, right margin)

Pope's bulls: (handwritten, right margin)

Morton sends the fool away: (handwritten, right margin)

[a] folye.

conscendit domum dei, zelus calui sentiunt[4]; sicut fortasse sentiet iste
derisor, scurra, ribaldus. Facis, inquit Cardinalis,
bono fortassis affectu, sed mihi uideris facturus,
nescio an sanctius, certe sapientius, si te ita compares,
ne cum homine stulto et ridiculo ridiculum tibi certamen
instituas. Non, domine, inquit, non facerem sapientius.
Nam Solomon ipse sapientissimus dicit: *Responde
stulto secundum stultitiam eius*, sicut ego nunc facio, et demonstro ei
foueam in quam cadet, nisi bene praecaueat. Nam si multi irrisores
Helizei, qui erat tantum unus caluus, senserunt zelus calui, quanto
magis sentiet unus derisor multorum fratrum, in quibus sunt multi
calui? et etiam habemus bullam Papalem, per quam omnes qui
derident nos sunt excommunicati. Cardinalis, ubi uidit nullum fieri

> Apparet fratrem
> ob imperitiam
> zelus abusum
> neutro genere,
> sicut hoc scelus.

---

[1] 2 Kings ii. 24. See note 4 below.
[2] Proverbs xxvi. 4.
[3] This addition to 'excommunicate'
is the translator's own.
[4] The lines are from the Hymn of
Adam of St. Victor, *De Resurrectione
Domini* : —

Irrisores Helisaei,
Dum conscendit domum Dei,
Zelum calvi sentiunt.
The marginal note points out the
skit in making the friar use *zelus*, as if
it were a neuter noun declined like
scelus.

beck, and turned the communication to an other matter.
Shortly after, when he was risen from the table, he went
to heare his sueters, and so dismissed vs.

Raphael to More:

'Loke, mayster More with how long and tedious a tale
I haue kept you, which suerly I wolde haue bene ashamed
to haue done, but that you so earnestly desiered me, and
did after suche a sort geue eare vnto hit, as though you
wolde not that any parcell of that communication should

his point is that

be left out; which though I haue doone sumwhat briefely,
yet coulde I not chuse but rehearse it, for the iudgement

good counsel cannot work in court situations.

of them [1], which, when they had improued and disallowed
my sayinges, yet incontinent hearinge the Cardinall allowe
them, dyd themselfes also approue the same; so impu-
dently flattering him, that they were nothinge ashamed
to admit, yea, almost in good earnest, his iesters folish
inuentions; bicause that he him selfe, by smylynge at
them, did seme not to disproue them. So that hereby

Issue of counsel

you may right well perceaue, how litle the courtiers wold
regard and esteme me and my sayinges.'

finem, nutu ablegato parasito, ac aliam in rem commodum [2] uerso sermone, paulo post surgit e mensa, atque audiendis clientum negotiis
dedit se, nosque dimisit.

En, mi More, quam longo te sermone oneraui; quod tam diu facere
plane puduisset me, nisi tu et | cupide flagitasses, et sic uidereris 53
audire, tanquam nolles quicquam eius confabulationis omitti; quae,
quanquam aliquanto perstrictius, narranda tamen mihi fuit omnino
propter eorum iudicium, qui quae me dicente spreuerant, eadem
rursus euestigio non improbante Cardinale, etiam ipsi comprobarunt;
usque adeo assentantes ei, ut parasiti quoque eius inuentis, quae
dominus per iocum non aspernabatur, adblandirentur [3], et serio propemodum admitterent: ut hinc possis aestimare quanti me ac mea
consilia aulici forent aestimaturi.

---

[1] That is 'for the sake of showing
what the judgment of those persons
was worth, who,' &c. Burnet takes it
to imply the enabling a hearer to form
his judgment *of them*.

[2] Both Robynson and Burnet ignore
this word in their translations. It is
common in the sense of 'opportunely,'
'seasonably.'

[3] For this compound there is, I think,
no authority.

'I ensure you, maister Raphael' (quod I), 'I toke great
delectation in hearing you: all thinges that yow sayde
were spoken so wittily and so pleasauntly. And me
thought my self to be in the meane time not only at home
in my countrey, but also, throughe the pleasaunt remembraunce of the Cardinall, in whose housse I was brought
vp of a child[1], to waxe a childe agayne. And, frend
Raphaell, though I did beare verye greate loue towardes
you before, yet seynge yow do so earnestly fauour thys
man, yow wyll not beleue howe muche my loue towardes
yow is nowe increased. But yet, all this notwithstanding,
I can by no meanes chaunge my mind, but that I must
needys beleue that you, if you be disposed, and can find in
youre harte to followe some pryncens courte, shall with
your good cownselles greatly healpe and further the commen wealthe. Wherefore there is nothynge more apper-
teynynge to your dewty; that is to say, to the dewty of
a good man. For where as youre Plato[2] Judgethe that

Profecto, mi Raphael, inquam, magna me affecisti uoluptate, ita
sunt abs te dicta prudenter simul et lepide omnia. praeterea uisus
mihi interim sum, non solum in patria uersari, uerum etiam re-
puerascere quodammodo iucunda recordatione Cardinalis illius, in
cuius aula puer sum educatus. cuius uiri memoriae quod tu tam
impense faues, non credas, mi Raphael, quanto mihi sis effectus hoc
nomine charior, cum esses alioqui charissimus. Caeterum non possum adhuc ullo pacto meam demutare sententiam, quin te plane
putem, si animum inducas tuum, uti ne ab aulis principum abhorreas,
in publicum posse te tuis consiliis plurimum boni conferre. quare
nihil magis incumbit tuo, hoc est boni uiri, officio. Si quidem cum
tuus censeat Plato, respublicas ita demum futuras esse felices, si aut

---

[1] See the Introduction, § 1.
[2] Here, as below, p. 104, More gives
the sense, not the exact words of
Plato, as would be only natural, when
the quotation is supposed to be made
from memory. The passage is in the
Republic, Book v. § 473. In Ficino's
Latin version it runs :—' Si non, inquam ego, aut philosophi regnabunt
in ciuitatibus, aut reges qui nunc
dicuntur et potentes legitime et iuste
philosophabuntur ... non est malorum
requies, chare Glauco, ciuitatibus.'

More: on counsel.

weale publyques shall by this meanes attayne perfecte
felicitie, other if phylosophers be kynges, or els if kynges
giue them selfes to the study of Philosophie; how farre,
I praye yowe, shall commen wealthes then be from thys
felicitie, if phylosophers wyll, $_{\wedge}^{not}$ vouchesaufe to instructe
kynges with their good counsell[1]?' ' 'They be not so
vnkind' (quod he), 'but they would gladlye do it; yea,

Raphael.

manye haue done it all readie in bookes that they haue
put furth, if kynges and princes would be wyllyng and
readie to folowe good counsell. But Plato doubteles dyd
well forsee, oneles kynges themselfes would applye their
myndes to the studye of philosophie, that elles they would
neuer thoroughlye allowe the counsell of philosophers;
beyng themselfes before euen from their tender age
infectyd and corrupt with peruerse and euyll opinions.
Whiche thynge Plato hymselfe prouyd trewe in kynge
Dionise[2]. If I should propose to any kynge holsome
decrees, doinge my endeuour to pluck out of hys mynde

Plato &
Dionysias
{ R. Edwardes,
cf. Damon
& Pythias

regnent philosophi, aut reges philosophentur; quam procul aberit
felicitas, si philosophi regibus nec dignentur saltem suam im|partiri 54
consilium? Non sunt, inquit ille, tam ingrati, quin id libenter facerent; imo multi libris aeditis iam fecerunt; si hii qui rerum patiuntur
essent parati bene consultis parere. Sed bene haud dubie praeuidit
Plato, nisi reges philosophentur ipsi, nunquam futurum ut peruersis
opinionibus a pueris imbuti atque infecti penitus philosophantium
comprobent consilia: quod ipse quoque experiebatur apud Dionysium.
An non me putas, si apud aliquem regem decreta sana proponerem,

---

[1] The answer to the question thus
put, would be ' Not far'; and this may
have been what the translator meant.
But the form of the sentence which
follows makes it more likely that he
wrote 'wyll not vouchesaufe,' corre-
sponding to the *nec dignentur* of the
Latin.

[2] Plutarch, in his *Life of Numa*
quotes the saying of Plato (*Rep.* v. 473)
to the effect that ' the only sure pro-

spect of deliverance from the evils of
life will be, when the divine Providence
shall so order it, that the regal power,
invested in a prince who has the sentiments of a philosopher, shall render
virtue triumphant over vice.' Lang-
horne's transl., 1805, i. p. 191. For
the change in the demeanour of Dionysius the younger, tyrant of Syracuse,
towards Plato, see Plutarch's *Dion*,
ib., v. p. 243.

Raphael cites French Court as example

the pernitious originall causes of vice and noughtenes, thynke you not that I shoulde furthe with other be dryuen awaye, or elles made a laughynge stocke?

French King

'Goo to, suppose that I were [a] with the Frenche kynge, and there syttynge in hys counsell, whyles that in [b] that moste secrete consultation, the kyng hym self there beynge present in hys owne persone, they beat their braynes, and serche the verye bottomes of theyr wittes to discusse by what crafte and meanes the kyng maye styll kepe Myllayne and drawe to hym agayne fugatyue Naples [1]; and then howe to conquere the Venetians [2], and howe to bryng vnder his Iurisdiction all Italye [3]; then

Evil councillors

Milan. Naples. Venice Italy

  [a] Well, suppose I were.   [b] whyles in.

et perniciosa malorum semina conarer illi euellere, protinus aut eiiciendum aut habendum ludibrio?

Age, finge me apud regem esse Gallorum, atque in eius considere consilio, dum in secretissimo secessu, praesidente rege ipso in corona prudentissimorum hominum, magnis agitur studiis, quibus artibus ac machinamentis Mediolanum retineat, ac fugitiuam illam Neapolim ad se retrahat: postea uero euertat Venetos, ac totam Italiam subiiciat

dehortatur ab Italia paranda.

---

[1] 'Louis the Twelfth, on ascending the throne (1498), assumed the titles of Duke of Milan and King of Naples, thus unequivocally announcing his intention of asserting his claims, derived through the Visconti family, to the former, and, through the Angevin dynasty, to the latter state.'—Prescott: *Ferdinand and Isabella*, ch. x. Prescott then relates how, after securing the neutrality of Spain by the treaty of Marcoussis, Aug. 5, 1498, Louis 'effected the conquest of the entire duchy in little more than a fortnight.' Its duke, Lodovico Sforza, was sent captive into France, and the French king then turned his arms against Frederick, king of Naples, whose dominions he soon afterwards shared between himself and Ferdinand of Spain.

Naples is called by More *fugitiva*, 'that has so oft slip'd out of their Hands' (Burnet), to imply that the French kings had laid claim to it before. For the attempts upon it of Charles VIII, see Prescott, as above, p. 380.

[2] The partition of Venice between Louis XII, Ferdinand of Spain, the emperor Maximilian, and the Pope, was settled by the treaty of Cambray, in December, 1508. Louis had planned this six years before.

[3] 'If the French get possession of Rome, the liberties of all Italy, and of every state in Europe, are in peril.'— Letter of Peter Martyr, *Epist.* 465, quoted by Prescott.

Flaunders

howe to wynne the dominion of Flaunders, Brabant, and of all Burgundie, with dyuers other landes, whose kyngdomes he hath longe a goo in mynde and purpose inuaded. Here [1], whyles one counselleth to conclude a leage of peace with the Venetians, whiche shal so longe endure [a], as shalbe thought mete and expedient for theire purpose, and to make them also of their counsell, yea, and besydes that to gyue them parte of the praye, whyche afterwarde, when they haue brought theyr purpose abowte after theyr owne myndes they maye requyre and claym agayne. An other thynketh beste to hyere the Germaneynes [2]. An

mercenaries.

other would haue the fauoure of the Swychers [3] wonne with money. An others aduyse is to appease the puyssaunte powre of the emperours maiestie with golde, as with a moste pleasaunt and acceptable sacrifice [4]. Whyles an other gyueth counsell to make peace wyth the kynge

[a] so longe to endure.

sibi; deinde Flandros, Brabantos, totam postremo Burgundiam suae faciat ditionis, atque alias praeterea gentes, quarum regnum iam olim animo inuasit. Hic dum alius suadet feriendum cum Venetis foedus, tantisper duraturum, dum ipsius fuerit commodum; cum illis communicandum consilium ; quin deponendam quoque apud eosdem aliquam praedae partem, quam rebus
Eluetii con-
ducticii.
ex sententia peractis repetat; dum alius consulit conducendos Germanos, alius pecunia demulcendos Eluetios ; alius aduersus numen imperatoriae maiestatis auro uelut

---

[1] At this point begins an almost interminable sentence in the Latin, of which the conditional member comes at p. 84, *si ego homuncio*, and the conclusion not till p. 87 ; the episode of the Achorians being worked into it.

[2] The allusion is, as the marginal note in later editions has it, to the ' Lance-knights,' the German Lanz-knechte, who served as mercenaries in the French army on some occasions. In the great battle fought under the

walls of Ravenna, April 11, 1512, Count Pedro Navarro led the Spanish Infautry against a formidable body of these, who were fighting on the side of the French under Gaston de Foix.

[3] On the Swiss as mercenaries, see note below, p. 252.

[4] A hit at the cupidity of the ' penniless and shifty' Maximilian, who actually took pay and served in the English camp at Tournay. — See Brewer : *Reign of Henry VIII*, i. p. 11.

of Arragone[1], and to restore vnto hym hys owne kyngdome of Nauarra[2], as a full assurance of peace. An other
cummeth in wyth his .v. egges[3], and aduyseth to howke   5 egges.
in the kynge of Castell[4] with somme hope of affynytie or
allyaunce, and to brynge to theyr parte certeyne peers of
hys courte for greate pensions: whyles they all staye at
the chyefeste dowte of all, what to doo in the meane tyme
with England, and yet agree al in this to make peace with   England.
the englishmen, and with moste suere and strong bondes
to bind that weake and feable frendshyppe, so that they
must be called frendes, and hadde in suspicion as enemies;   use of
and that therfore the skottes must be hadde in a reddines,   Scots
                                                              vs.
                                                              England

55 anathemate | propitiandum; dum alii uidetur cum Arragonum rege
componendas esse res, et alieno Nauariae regno, uelut pacis authora-
mento, cedendum; alius interim censet Castelliae principem aliqua
spe affinitatis irretiendum, atque aulicos nobiles aliquot in suam factionem certa pensione esse pertrahendos; dum maximus omnium
nodus occurrit, quid statuendum interim de Anglia sit; caeterum de
pace tractandum tamen, et constrigenda firmissimis uinculis semper
infirma societas, amici uocentur, suspiciantur ut inimici; habendus
igitur paratos uelut in statione Scotos, ad omnem intentos occasionem,

---

[1] Ferdinand, the husband of Isabella
of Castile.

[2] When the petty states previously
in dispute between France and Spain
had been absorbed by one or the
other, it became evident that the little
kingdom of Navarre, on the border
of the two countries, must share the
same fate. The proceedings connected
with it are related in Prescott, ch. xxiii.
They ended by the estates of Navarre
taking an oath of allegiance to Ferdinand, March 23, 1513; and 'on the 15th
of June, 1515, the Catholic monarch, by
a solemn act in Cortes, held at Burgos,
incorporated his new conquests into
the kingdom of Castile.'—Prescott, as
before, p. 680.

[3] Mr. C. E. Doble points out to me
that this proverb for officious intrusion

often occurs in Swift's *Journal to Stella*,
but in the form ' comes in with his *two*
eggs a penny' (*Works*, 1824, II. pp. 392,
412, 468). Ray, *English Proverbs*, 1737,
p. 187, gives it in full: 'You come in
with your five eggs a penny, and four
of them be rotten.' See also the *New
English Dict.* under ' egg.' When it
was a complaint that eggs were but
' fower a penny,' (*Roque of England*,
p. 98), one who ' came in with his five'
might stand for a pushing dealer.

[4] This may refer to some fresh
negociation for a marriage between
the Princess Claude and Charles, who,
just about the time when More was
writing, after the death of his grandfather Ferdinand (Jan. 23, 1516), had
caused himself to be proclaimed afresh
King of Castile. See above, p. xxxii, *n*.

as it were in a standing reddie at all occasions, in aunters [1] the Englyshe men should sturre neuer so litle, incontinent to set vpon them ; and moreouer preuilie and secretly, for openly it maye not be doone by the truce that is taken ;

use of exiled peers pryuelyc therfore, I saye, to make muche of some peere of Englande, that is bannyshed his countrey, whiche must cleyme title to the crown of the realme, and affirme hym

Perkin Warb. selfe iuste inheritoure therof [2]; that by thys subtyll meanes they maye holde to them the kynge, in whom elles they haue but small truste and affiaunce.

'Here, I saye, where so greate and high matters be in consultation, where so manye noble and wyse men coun-

Example of good counsel. sell their kyng only to warre ; here, if I [3], sely man, should ryse vp and wylle them to turne ouer the leafe [4], and learne a newe lesson ; sayng that my counsell is not to medle with Italy, but to tarrye styll at home, and that the kyngdome of fraunce alone is all moste greater, then that it maye well be gouerned of one man ; so that the kyng

si quid se commoueant Angli protinus immittendus ; ad haec fouendum exulem nobilem aliquem occulte (namque id aperte ne fiat prohibent foedera) qui id regnum sibi deberi contendat, ut ea uelut ansa contineat suspectum sibi principem :—hic, inquam, in tanto rerum molimine, tot egregiis uiris ad bellum sua certatim consilia conferentibus, si ego homuncio surgam, ac uerti iubeam uela, omittendam Italiam censeam, et domi dicam esse manendum, unum Galliae regnum fere maius esse quam ut commode possit ab uno administrari,

---

[1] That is, in case that. See the Glossary.

[2] The reference is probably to Perkin Warbeck, who, in his assumption of the title of Duke of York, might be regarded, from the point of view taken in the text, as a 'peere of Englande, that is bannyshed his countrey.' 'It is well known,' says Tytler, 'that the conspiracy was encouraged by Charles VIII of France, who invited Perkin into his kingdom, and received him with high distinction.' It was part of the plan for the rising in Warbeck's favour, that 'the Scottish monarch was to break at the head of his army across the Borders, and compel Henry to divide his forces.'—*Hist. of Scotland,* 1864, ii. pp. 259, 260.

[3] See below, p. 87, n. 2.

[4] This does not rightly convey the metaphor in *verti vela,* 'that there should be a shifting of sail,' 'that they should go on another tack.'

Utopia mentioned; cf. pp. 34, 95:

{Raphael's example of good counsel:

The Achorians —

Utopia} Island

cf. claim to France

shoulde not nede to studye howe to gett more : and then
shoulde propose vnto them the decrees of the people that
be called the Achoriens[1], whiche be situate ouer agaynst
the Ilande of Vtopia on the sowtheaste syde. Thies Achoriens ones made warre in their kinges quarrel, for to gette
him an other kyngdom, whiche he layde clayme vnto, and
auaunced hymself righte inheritoure to the crowne therof,
by the title of an olde aliaunce[2]. At the last, when they
had gotten it, an sawe that they hadde euen as muche
vexation and trouble in keping it, as they had in gettyng
it ; and that[3] other there newe conquered subiectes by
sondrye occasions were makynge dayly insurrections to
rebell agaynste them, or els that other countreys were
contynually with diuers inrodes and forraginges inuad-
inge them ; so that they were euer fyghtinge other for
them, or agaynste them, and neuer coulde breke vp their
campes : seynge them selfes in the meane season pylled

ne sibi putet rex de aliis adiiciendis esse cogitandum : tum si illis
proponerem decreta Achoriorum populi, Vtopiensium
insulae ad Euronotum[4] oppositi ; qui quum olim bellum
gessissent, ut regi suo aliud obtinerent regnum, quod
56 affinitatis antiquae causa sibi contendebat haereditate | deberi, conse-
quuti tandem id, ubi uiderunt nihilo sibi minus esse molestiae in
retinendo, quam in quaerendo pertulerunt, uerum assidua pullulare
semina uel internae rebellionis uel externae incursionis ; in deditos
ita semper aut pro illis aut contra pugnandum ; nunquam dari facultatem dimittendi exercitus ; compilari interim se ; efferri foras pecu-

Exemplum annotandum.

---

[1] The name is formed like that of
the Utopians, from α and χώρα, 'those
who have no room, or place' on the
earth. ἄχωρος is found in Aelian in
the sense of 'homeless,' 'with no
resting-place.'

[2] That is, marriage alliance, *affinitas.*
More may perhaps have been thinking
of the ancient claim of England to the
throne of France, as Shakspeare states
it in the beginning of *Henry V.*

[3] The translation is here rather
lax. More literally it is : 'but that
the seed-plots were ever ripening of
insurrection from within or invasion from without ; and that they
must be so incessantly at war, either
for or against their new subjects,
that,' &c.

[4] Euronotus, Εὐρόνοτος, a word found
in Pliny and Columella for the South-
east wind.

and impoueryshed ; their money carryed owt of the Realme ;
theyr owne men kylled to mayntayne the glory of an other
nation ; when they had no warre, peace nothynge better
then warre [1], by reason that their people in warre had
inured themsclfes to corrupte and wycked maners ; that
they hadde taken a delycte and pleasure in robbynge and
stealyng ; that through manslaughter they had gathered
boldenes to mischiefe ; that their lawes were hadde in contempte, and nothynge set by or regarded ; that their kynge,
beynge troubled with the chardge and gouernaunce of two
kingdomes, coulde not nor was not able perfectly to discharge his office towardes them bothe ; seynge agayne
that all thies euelles and troubles were endeles : at the
last laid there heades together ; and, lyke faithful and
louinge subiectes, gaue to their kynge free choyse and
libertie to kepe still the one of this .ii. kingdomes, whether
he would ; allegyng that he was not able to kepe both,
and that they were mo then might wel be gouerned of
half a king ; for asmuche as no man would be content to
take hym for his mulettour [2] that kepeth an other mans

King made to choose

niam ; alienae gloriolac suum impendi sanguinem ; pacem nihilo
tutiorem ; domi corruptos bello mores ; imbibitam latrocinandi libi-
dinem ; confirmatam caedibus audaciam ; leges esse contemptui ;
quod rex in duorum curam regnorum distractus minus in utrumuis
animum posset intendere : cum uiderent alioqui tantis malis nullum
finem fore, inito tandem consilio, regi suo humanissime fecerunt
optionem retinendi utrius [3] regni uellet, nam utriusque non fore
potestatem, se plures esse quam qui a dimidiato possint rege guber-
nari, quum nemo sit libenter admissurus mulionem sibi cum alio

---

[1] That is, the state of things in time
of peace being no better (*lit.* safer) than
in time of war. The clause which follows, 'by reason that,' &c., is diffuse.

[2] I have not met with any proverb
in this exact form. Equivalent ones
will be found at p. 292 a of Erasmus's
Adagia, ed. 1629, under the general
heading of ' Impossibilia.'

'Moyle,' for mule, is found in a
proclamation of the Lord Mayor of
London, Aug. 5, 1554, quoted in
Dr. W. Sparrow Simpson's *S. Paul's
Cathedral and old City Life,* 1894,
p. 85.

[3] The construction is by ' attraction.'

More concedes: also on 97:

The Prince constrained:

moyles besides his. So this good prince was constreyned
to be content with his olde kyngdome, and to gyue ouer
the newe to one of his frendes; whiche shortelie after
was violentlie drcuen out. Furthermore if I should
declare vnto them, that all this busy preparaunce to warre,
wherby so many nations for hys[1] sake shuld be brought
into a troublesom hurley-burley, when all hys coffers were
emptied, his treasures wasted and his people destroyed,
should at the length through som mischaunce be in vaine
and to none effect; and that therfore it were best for him
to content him selfe with his owne kingdome of fraunce,
as his forfathers and predecessours did before him; to
make much of it, to enriche it, and to make it as flourissh-
ing as he could; to endeauoure himself to loue his sub-
iects, and again to be beloued of them; willingly to liue
with them, peaceably to gouerne them; and with other
kyngdomes not to medle, seinge that whiche he hath all
reddy is euen ynough for hym, yea, and more then he
can well turne hym to; thys myne aduyse, maister More,
how thynke you it would be harde and taken?' 'So God
helpe me, not very thankefully' (quod I).

The question

Raphael challenges More:

More concedes once: cf. p. 77

communem: ita coactus est ille bonus princeps, nouo regno cuipiam
ex amicis relicto (qui breui etiam post eiectus est) antiquo esse contentus;—praeterea si ostenderem omnes hos conatus bellorum, quibus
tot nationes eius causa tumultuarentur, quum thesauros eius ex-
hauoissent, ac destruxissent populum, aliqua tandem fortuna frustra
cessuros tamen; proinde auitum regnum coleret, ornaret quantum
posset, et faceret quam florentissimum; amet suos et ametur a suis;
57 cum his una uiuat, imperetque suauiter | atque alia regna ualere
sinat, quando id quod nunc ei contigisset satis amplum superque
esset:—hanc orationem quibus auribus, mi More, putas[2] excipien-
dam? Profecto non ualde pronis, inquam.

[1] That is, the French king's.
[2] This is the conclusion of the long
sentence begun above, p. 82. It is followed, or rather resumed after a short
break, by another and still more
lengthy one, beginning with *Si consiliariis* . . . and not ending till we
reach the words *quam surdis essem
narraturus fabulam*, p. 97.

Raphaeli on money raising

revaluing the coinage

'Wel, let vs procede then' (quod he). 'Suppose that some kyng and his counsell were together whettinge their wittes, and deuisinge what subtell crafte they myght inuente to enryche the king with greate treasures of money. First one councelleth to rayse and enhaunce the valuacion of money, when the king must paye any ; and agayne to calle downe the value of coyne to lesse then it is worthe, when he must receiue or gather any : for thus great sommes shalbe payde with a lytyll money, and where lytle is due muche shalbe receaued [1]. An other coun-

feigning war

selleth to fayne warre, that when vnder this coloure and pretence the kyng hath gathered great aboundaunce of money, he maye, when it shall please hym, make peace wyth great solempnitie and holye ceremonies, to blynde the eyes of the poore communaltie, as taking pitie and

Pergamus ergo, inquit. Si consiliariis cum rege quopiam tractantibus [2], et comminiscentibus quibus technis ei queant coaceruare thesauros, dum unus intendendam consulit aestimationem monetae, quum ipsi sit eroganda pecunia, deiiciendam rursus infra iustum, quum fuerit corroganda, uti et multum aeris paruo dissoluat, et pro paruo multum recipiat : dum alius suadet ut bellum simulet, atque eo praetextu coacta pecunia, cum uisum erit, faciat pacem sanctis ceremoniis, quo plebeculae oculis fiat praestigium, miseratus uidelicet

---

[1] One instance of the practice described is furnished by Edward IV, who brought in two new coins, termed the angel and angelot, in place of the noble and half-noble. Though considerably inferior in weight to the former pieces, they were ordered to pass for the same value, namely, 6s. 8d. and 3s. 4d. (Eccleston : *Introd. to English Antiquities*, 1847, p. 206). Henry VII is said never to have debased his coinage ; but by calling in all 'minished or impaired coins' and receiving them at the Mint by weight, without any allowance made, he secured a great profit (Bacon's *Works*, ed. Spedding, vi. p. 223 ; Traill's *Social*

England, ii. p. 558). An American writer says that Henry VIII and Edward VI so debased their coinage, that 'it is impossible to learn or estimate their weight, fineness or value.' See A. M. Smith's *Encyclopaedia of Gold and Silver Coins*, 1886, pp. 252, 254. The proverb 'Testers are gone to Oxford to study at Brasenose' (testers, or shillings, being first coined in 1504), will occur to the reader. It might itself have been coined by More.

[2] In this intransitive sense of 'debate,' 'discuss,' the word is found in Suetonius and Tacitus. Comp. Tac. *Ann.* i. 13, 'Augustus ... cum tractaret, quinam,' &c.

compassion Gode wote[a] vpon mans bloude, lyke a louing
and a mercifull prince [1].

'An other putteth the kyng in remembraunce of certeyn
olde and moughte-eaten lawes [2], that of long tyme haue
not bene put in execution ; whiche, because no man can
remember that they were made, euerie man hath trans-
gressed. The fynes of thies lawes he counselleth the
kynge to require : for there is no waye so proffytable, nor
more honorable ; as the whiche hath a shewe and coloure
of iustice. An other aduyseth hym to forbidde manye
thynges vnder great penalties and fines, specially suche
thynges as is for the peoples profit not be vsed [3] ; and

[a] forsothe.

humanum sanguinem princeps pius : dum alius ei suggerit in mentem antiquas quasdam et tineis adesas leges, longa desuetudine
antiquatas ; quas quod nemo latas meminisset, omnes sint trans-
gressi ; earum ergo mulctas iubeat exigi ; nullum uberiorem prouen-
tum esse, nullum magis honorificum, utpote qui iustitiae prae se
personam ferat : dum ab alio admonetur, uti sub magnis mulctis
multa prohibeat, maxime talia, quae ne fiant in rem sit populi ; post

[1] For the subsidies demanded as
each parliament met in Henry VII's
reign, see the caustic remarks of
Bishop Stubbs : *Lectures on Medieval
and Modern History*, 1887, p. 409.
The special instance More had in his
mind may have been that of 1492,
when two-tenths and two-fifteenths
were being raised 'for the defence of
Brittany against France.' The result
was the expedition to Boulogne in
October, 1492, after which the king
made peace.

[2] Hallam, speaking of the insatiable
avarice of Henry VII, mentions his
having recourse to statutes passed in
previous reigns, 'the pecuniary penalties of which, though exceedingly
severe, were so little enforced as to
have lost their terror.' ' These,' he
adds, 'his ministers raked out from
oblivion ; and prosecuting such as
could afford to endure the law's
severity, filled his treasury with the
dishonourable produce of amercements
and forfeitures.'—*Constitutional History*, ch. i.

The names of Empson and Dudley
are notorious in this association. But
Morton himself, though it would not
have been pleasing to More to admit
it, was an agent in the same exac-
tions.—See Bacon's *Hist. of Hen. VII*
(*Works*, ed. 1730, iii. pp. 442, 487).

[3] We should have expected 'not
to be used.' Burnet gives the sense
more perspicuously : 'especially such
as were against the Interest of the
People.'

afterward to dispence for money with them, which by this prohibicion susteyne losse and dammage. For by this meanes the fauour of the people is wonne, and proffite riseth two wayes : first by takyng forfaytes of them whom couetousnes of gaynes hath brought in daunger of thys statute ; and also by sellynge preuyleges and licences ; whiche the better that the prynce is forsothe, the deerer he selleth them ; as one that is lothe to graunte to any pryuate persone any thyng that is agaynste the proffyt of hys people ; and therfore maye sell none but at an ex-ceding dere pryce.

pressure on the judges:

' An other giueth the kynge counsell to endaunger vnto hys grace the iudges of the Reyalme, that he maye haue them euer on hys syde ; whyche muste [a] in euerye matter despute and reason for the kynges rygth. And they muste be called into the kynges palace, and be desired to argue [b] and discusse his matters in his owne presence. So there shalbe no matter of his, so openlye wronge and uniuste, wherin one or other of them, other because he wyll haue sumthyng to allege and obiecte, or that he is ashamed to saye that whiche is sayde already, or else to pike a thanke [1] with his prince, wyll not fynde some hole open to set

[a] and that they maye.   [b] Yea and further to call them into his palace, and to require them there to argue.

pecunia cum illis dispenset, quorum commodis obstat interdictum ; sic et a populo gratiam iniri, et duplex adferri compendium ; uel dum hii mulctantur, quos quaestus cupiditas pellexit in casses, uel dum aliis uendit priuilegia tanto pluris quanto scilicet fuerit me|lior 58 princeps, utpote qui grauatim quicquam contra populi commodum priuato cuique indulgeat, et ob id non nisi magno precio : dum alius ei persuadet obstringendos sibi iudices, qui quauis in re pro regio iure disceptent ; accersendos praeterea in palatium, atque inuitandos uti coram se de suis rebus disserant ; ita nullam causam eius tam aperte iniquam fore, in qua non aliquis eorum uel contradicendi studio, uel pudore dicendi eadem, uel quo gratiam ineant, apud eam

---

[1] That is, to be a pick-thanks, or fawning parasite. See the Glossary.

a snare in, wherewith to take the contrarie parte in a trippe [1].
Thus whiles the iudges cannot agree amonges themselfes,
reasoning and arguing of that which is playne enough,
and bringing the manifest trewthe in dowte, in the meane
season the king may take a fyt occasion to vnderstand the
lawe as shal most make for his aduauntage ; wher vnto al
other for shame or for feare wil agree. Then the Judges
maye be bolde to pronounce of the kynges side. For he
that geueth sentence for the kyng cannot be without
a good excuse. For it shalbe sufficient for hym to haue
equitie of[a] his part, or the bare wordes of the lawe, or
a wrythen and wrested vnderstandynge of the same, or
els, whiche with good and iust Judges is of greater force
then all lawes be, the kynges indisputable prerogatiue.
To conclude, al the counsellours agre and consent together
with the riche Crassus [2], that no abundance of gold can be
sufficient for a prince, which muste kepe and maynteyne
an armie : furthermore that a kynge, thoughe he would,

[a] on.

aliquam reperiant rimam, qua possit intendi calumnia ; sic dum
iudicibus diuersa sentientibus res per se clarissima disputatur, et
ueritas in quaestionem uenit, ansam commodum [3] regi dari pro suo
commodo ius interpretandi ; caeteros aut pudore accessuros aut
metu ; sic intrepide fertur postea pro tribunali sententia ; neque
enim deesse praetextus potest pronuncianti pro principe : nempe
cui satis est aut aequitatem a sua parte esse, aut uerba legis, aut
contortum scripti sensum, aut quae legibus denique omnibus prae-
ponderat apud religiosos iudices, principis indisputa-
bilem praerogatiuam ; dum omnes in Crassiano illo   Crassi diuitis
consentiunt atque conspirant, Nullam auri uim satis esse   dictum.
principi, cui sit alendus exercitus ; praeterea nihil inuste regem facere,

---

[1] Lit. 'whereby a false accusation
may be directed.' I do not remember
to have seen the phrase *calumniam
intendere* used.

[2] The saying here attributed to the
'riche Crassus' (M. Licinius Crassus
Dives, the contemporary of Cicero),
seems to be a reminiscence of what

is told in Pliny, *Hist. Nat* xxxiii. 10,
that ' M. Crassus negabat locupletem
esse, nisi qui reditu annuo legionem
tueri posset.'

[3] Robynson seems to have taken
this as if meant for *commodam* ; but it
is the adverb, 'opportunely.'

King can
do no
wrong.

cf.
Machiavelli

Raphael
again
challenges
on Kings:
cf. p. 97

commonalty
choose
King.

can do nothynge uniustly; for all that men haue, yea
also the men them selfes, be all his; and that euery man
hath so much of his owne as the kynges gentilnes hath
not taken from hym; and that it shalbe moste for the
kynges aduauntage that his subiectes haue very lytle or
nothing in their possession; as whose sauegarde dothe
herein consiste, that his people do not waxe wanton and
wealthie through riches and libertie; because, where thies
thinges be, there men be not wonte patientlye to obeye
harde, vniuste, and vnlawfull commaundementes; where
as, on the other part, neade and pouertie doth holde downe
and kepe vnder stowte courages, and maketh them patient
perforce, takyng from them bolde and rebellynge stomakes.

More' Here agayne if I should ryse vp, and boldelye affirme
that all thies counselles be to the kyng dishonoure and
reproche, whoes honoure and sauitie is more and rather
supported and vpholden by the wealth and ryches of his
people, then by hys owne treasures; and if I shuld declare
that the comminaltie chueseth their king for their owne
sake and not for his sake [1]; for this [a] intent that through

[a] to the.

ut maxime etiam uelit posse, quippe omnia omnium eius esse, ut
homines etiam ipsos, tantum uero cuique esse proprium quantum
regis benignitas ei non ademerit, quod ipsum ut quam minimum sit
principis multum referre, ut cuius tutamen tum in eo situm sit, ne
populus diuitiis ac libertate lasciuiat, | quod hae res minus patienter 59
ferant dura atque iniusta imperia; quum contra egestas atque inopia
retundat animos ac patientes reddat, adimatque pressis generosos
rebellandi spiritus :—hic si ego rursus adsurgens contendam haec
consilia omnia regi et inhonesta esse et perniciosa, cuius non honor
modo sed securitas quoque in populi magis opibus sita sit quam suis;
quos si ostendam regem sibi deligere sua causa, non regis, uidelicet

---

[1] This thesis, under different forms, was made the subject of several epigrams by More. The very titles of some of them have a bold look, to be written under a Tudor dynasty; for instance, 'Populus consentiens regnum dat et aufert':—

Quicumque multis uir uiris unus praeest,
Hoc debet his quibus praeest:
Praeesse debet neutiquam diutius,
Hi quam uolent quibus praeest.

Raphael loses the syntax in his anger!

his labour and studie they might al liue wealthily, sauffe
from wronges and iniuries; and that therfore the kynge
ought to take more care for the wealthe of his people,
then for his owne wealthe, euen as the office and dewtie of
a shephearde is, in that he is a shepherd, to feade his shepe
rather then hymself[1]. For as towchynge this, that they
thinke the defence and mayntenaunce of peace to consiste
in the pouertie of the people, the thyng it self sheweth
that they be farre owt of the way. For where shall a man
finde more wrangling, quarelling, brawling, and chiding,
then among beggers? Who be more disiorous of newe
mutations and alterations, then they that be not content
with the present state of their lyfe? Or, finally, who be
bolder stomaked to brynge all in hurlieburlie (therby
trustyng to get sum wyndfall), then they that haue nowe
nothing to leese? And if so be that there were any kyng,
that were[a] so smallye regarded, or so[b] behated of his subiectes, that other wayes he coulde not kepe them in awe,
but onlie by open wronges, by pollinge and shauinge, and
by brynginge them to beggerie; sewerly it were better for

King as Shepherd:

uti eius labore ac studio ipsi commode uiuant tutique ab iniuriis;
eoque magis ad principem eam pertinere curam, ut populo bene sit
suo, quam ut sibi; non aliter ac pastoris officium est oues potius
quam semet pascere, quatenus opilio est: nam quod populi egestatem
censeant pacis praesidium esse, longissime aberrare eos ipsa res
docet: nempe ubi plus rixarum comperias quam inter mendicos?
quis intentius mutationi rerum studet, quam cui minime placet praesens uitae status? aut cui denique audacior impetus ad conturbanda
omnia, spe alicunde lucrandi, quam cui iam nihil est quod possit
perdere? quod si rex aliquis adeo aut contemptus esset aut inuisus
suis, ut aliter eos continere in officio non possit, nisi contumeliis,
compilatione et sectione grassetur[2], eosque redigat ad mendicitatem,

---

[1] Comp. Ezek. xxxiv. 2, and Plato's
Repub. (Jowett's translation), i. § 343,
'You fancy that the shepherd or
neatherd fattens or tends the sheep or
oxen with a view to their own good,
and not to the good of himself or his
master.'

[2] Lit. 'Unless he were to proceed

Fabricius

hym to forsake hys kyngdome, then to holde it by this
meanes ; whereby, though the name of a kyng be kept,
yet the maiestie is lost. For it is against the dignitie of
a kynge to haue rule ouer beggers, but rather ouer ryche
and welthie men. Of thys mynde was the hardie and
couragius [1] Fabrice, when he sayde that he had rather be
a ruler of ryche men then be ryche hymselfe [2]. And
verelye one man to lyue [3] in pleasure and wealth, whyles
all other wepe and smarte for it, that is the parte not
of a kynge but of a iayler.

Raphael sums up evil & good princes:

'To be shorte, as he is a folyshe phisition, that cannot
cure his patientes disease, onles he caste hym in an other
syckenes; so he that cannot amend the liues of his subiectes, but be taking from them the wealth and commoditie
of lyfe, he must nedes graunte that he knoweth not the

praestiterit illi profecto regno abdicare, quam his retinere artibus,
quibus quanquam imperii nomen retineat, certe amittit maiestatem :
neque enim regiae dignitatis est. imperium in mendicos exercere,
sed in opulentos potius atque felices ; quod ipsum sensit certe uir
erecti ac sublimis animi Fabricius, cum responderet malle se im|-
perare diuitibus quam diuitem esse : et profecto unum aliquem 60
uoluptate ac deliciis fluere, gementibus undique ac lamentantibus
aliis, hoc non est regni, sed carceris, esse custodem : denique ut
imperitissimus medicus est, qui morbum nescit nisi morbo curare,
ita qui uitam ciuium non nouit alia uia corrigere, quam ademptis
uitae commodis, is se nescire fateatur imperare liberis : quin aut

---

by way of,' &c. *Sectio* is quite classical
in the sense of parcelling out con-
fiscated goods.

[1] These epithets are a little wide of
the Latin. 'A Man of a noble and
exalted Temper' (Burnet).

[2] The anecdote is found in Valerius
Maximus, iv. 5, only the saying is
there ascribed to M. Curius Dentatus,
who defeated Pyrrhus in B. C. 275.
The envoys of the Samnites were
bidden to report that Curius ' malle

locupletibus imperare, quam ipsum
fieri locupletem.' Fabricius is mentioned in the same chapter, as having
gone as an ambassador to Pyrrhus,
and as having prayed (on hearing
a description of Epicurus's doctrines
from Cineas) that Pyrrhus and the
Samnites might embrace that philosophy.

[3] Lat. *fluere*, 'to abound,' 'to be in
affluence.'

feate howe to gouerne fre[a] men. But let hym rather
amende hys owne lyfe, renounce vnhonest pleasures, and
forsake pride. For thies be the chiefe vices that cause
hym to runne in the contempt or hatered of his people.
Let him lyue of hys owne, hurtinge no man. Let him
do coste not aboue his power. Let hym restreyne wycked-
nes. Let hym preuente vices, and take a waye the occasions of offences be well orderyng his subiectes, and not
by sufferyng wickednes to increase, afterward to be
punyshed. Let hym not be to hastie in callynge agayne[1]
lawes, whiche a custome hathe abrogated ; speciallye suche
as haue bene long forgotten and neuer lacked nor neaded.
And let hym neuer vnder the cloke and pretence of trans-
gression take suche fynes and forfaytes, as no Iudge wyll
suffre a priuate persone to take, as uniuste and ful of gile[2].
   'Here if I should brynge furth before them the lawe of
the Macariens[3], whiche be not farre distaunt from Vtopia ;

[a] fre *omitted*[4].

inertiam potius mutet suam, aut superbiam : nam his fere ulltis
accidit, ut populus sum uel contemnat uel habeat odio : uiuat inno-
cuus de suo ; sumptus ad reditus accommodet ; refrenet maleficia,
et recta institutione suorum praeueniat potius, quam sinat increscere
quae deinde puniat ; leges abrogatas consuetudine haud temere
reuocet, praesertim quae diu desitae nunquam desyderatae sunt ;
neque unquam commissi nomine eiusmodi quicquam capiat, quale
priuatum quempiam iudex, uelut iniquum ac uafrum,
non pateretur accipere : hic si proponerem illis Maca-   *Mira lex
rensium legem, qui et ipsi non longe admodum absunt   Macarensium.*
ab Vtopia, quorum rex quo primum die auspicatur imperium,

[1] That is, recalling, or reviving.
[2] The case of alderman Sir William Capel is an example in point, who ' was condemned in the sum of £2,700 under certain obsolete penal laws, though he was allowed to compound with the king (Henry VII) for £1,600.' Gairdner, as before, p. 151.
[3] Τῶν Μακαρίων, 'of the Blessed;'

perhaps with a reference to the *Fortunatae Insulae*, or Islands of the Blessed, with which Utopia, or at least Eutopia, would naturally be associated. Budé wrote concerning this latter that ' it is in fact one of the Fortunate Isles, perhaps very close to the Elysian Fields.'—See above, p. lxxxix.
[4] This omission must have been

King
bound
to
limited
wealth:

whose kynge, the daye of hys coronacion, is bounde by
a solempne othe, that he shall neuer at anye tyme haue in
hys treasure aboue a thousande pounde of golde or syluer[1].
They saye a verye good kynge, whiche toke more care for
the wealthe and commoditie of hys countrey, then for
thenrychinge of himself, made this lawe to be a stop and
a barre to kynges for heaping and hording vp so muche
money as might impoueryshe their people. For he for-
sawe that this som of treasure woulde suffice to supporte
the kynge in battail against his owne people, if they shuld
chaunce to rebell; and also to maintein his warres against
the inuasions of hys forreyn enemies. Againe he perceiued
the same stocke of money to be to litel, and vnsufficient
to encourage and able[a] hym wrongfullye to take a waye
other mens goodes[2]; whyche was the chiefe cause whie

[a] enable.

magnis adhibitis sacrificiis iurijurando astringitur, nunquam se uno
tempore supra mille auri pondo in thesauris habiturum, aut argenti,
quantum eius auri precium aequet: hanc legem ferunt ab optimo
quodam rege institutam, cui maiori curae fuit patriae commodum,
quam diuitiae suae, uelut obicem aceruandae pecuniae tantae, quanta
faceret inopiam eius in populo : nempe eum thesaurum uide bat 6r
suffecturum, siue regi aduersus rebelleis, siue regno aduersus hostium incursiones esset confligendum ; caeterum minorem esse quam
ut animos faciat inuadendi aliena : quae potissima condendae legis

accidental, as the Latin is *liberis*,
'freemen.' In More's epigram 'Quid
inter Tyrannum et Principem,'

Legitimus immanissimis
Rex hoc tyrannis interest :
Seruos tyrannus quos regit,
Rex liberos putat suos,

it is doubtful whether by *liberos*, as
the antithesis of *seruos*, was meant
'freemen' or 'children.'

[1] Compare with this the £1,800,000
which Henry VII is said to have left in
his coffers at his decease ; a sum to be
multiplied by 10, at least, to bring it

to a modern equivalent. See Stubbs,
Medieval and Modern History, p. 411 ;
and Gairdner, as before, p. 209.

[2] The rendering is here a little
clumsy. Burnet : 'He thought that
moderate Sum might be sufficient for
any Accident ; if either the King had
occasion for it against Rebels, or
the Kingdom against the Invasion
of an Enemy ; but that it was not
enough to encourage a Prince to in-
vade other Men's Rights.' The last
words perhaps point rather to 'foreign
invasion.'

the lawe was made. An other cause was this. He
thought that by thys prouision his people shuld not lacke
money, wherewith to maynteyne their dayly occupieng
and chaffayre. And seynge the kynge coulde not chewse
but laye owt and bestowe all that came in aboue the
prescript some of his stocke, he thought he woulde seke
no occasions to doo hys subiectes iniurie. Suche a kynge
shalbe feared of euell men, and loued of good men. [Thies
and suche other informatyons (yf I) should vse emonge
men holy enclined and geuen to the contrarye part, how
deaffe hearers, thyncke you, should I haue ¹?'

'Deaffe hearers douteles' (quod I), 'and in good faith
no marueyle. And to speake as I thynke, truelye I can
not a lowe that such communicatyon shall be vsed, or
suche cownsell geuen, as you be suere shall neuer be
regarded nor receaued. For how can so straunge informa-
tions be profitable, or how can they be beaten into their
headdes, whose myndes be all reddye preuented with
cleane contrarye persuasyons? Thys schole ² philosophie
is not vnpleasaunte emonge fryndes in famylier communication; but in the counselles of kynges, where greate

causa fuit: proxima, quod sic prospectum putauit, ne desit pecunia,
quae in quotidiana ciuium commutatione uersetur, et quum regi
necesse est erogare, quicquid thesauro supra legitimum accreuit
modum, non quaesiturum censuit occasionem iniuriae: talis rex et
malis erit formidini, et a bonis amabitur,—haec ergo atque huiusmodi
si ingererem apud homines in contrariam partem uehementer inclina-
tos, quam surdis essem narraturus fabulam?
Surdissimis, inquam, haud dubie; neque hercule miror, neque
mihi uidentur (ut uere dicam) huiusmodi sermones ingerendi, aut
talia danda consilia, quae certus sis nunquam admissum iri. Quid
enim prodesse possit, aut quomodo in illorum pectus influere sermo
tam insolens, quorum praeoccupauit animos atque insedit penitus

---

¹ See note above, p. 87.
² Lat. *scholastica*. We might now
say 'academic;' or, as Burnet puts
it, 'this philosophical Way of Speculation.'

H

[margin: More's civil philosophy:]

matters be debated and reasoned wyth great aucthorytye, thies thynges haue no place.'

[margin: Rapael:]

'That is yt whyche I mente' (quod he), 'when I said phylosophye hadde no place amonge kinges.' 'In dede'

[margin: More:]

(quod I) 'this schole philosophie hath not; whiche thinketh all thynges mete for euery place. But ther is an other philosophye more cyuyle, whyche knoweth as ye wolde saye her owne stage, and thereafter orderynge

[margin: analogy of stage]

and behauynge herselfe in the playe that she hathe in hande, playethe her parte accordynglye wyth comlynes, vtteringe nothynge owte of dewe ordre and fassyon. And thys ys the phylosophye that yowe muste vse. Orels, whyles a commodye [1] of Plautus is playinge, and the vyle bondemen skoffynge and tryfelynge amonge them selfes, yf yowe shoulde sodenlye come vpon the stage in a philosophers apparrell, and reherse owte of Octauia the place

[margin: Seneca in The Octavia.]

wherin Seneca dysputeth with Nero [2]; had it not bene

[margin: Philosophia scholastica.]

diuersa persuasio? Apud amiculos in familiari colloquio non insuauis est haec philosophia scholastica.

Hoc est, inquit ille, quod dicebam, non esse apud principes locum philosophiae. Imo, inquam, est uerum, non huic scholasticae, quae quiduis putet ubiuis conuenire; sed est alia philosophia ciuilior, quae suam nouit scenam, eique sese [a] accommodans in ea fabula, quae in manibus est, suas | partes concinne et cum 62 decoro tutatur. Hac utendum est tibi. Alioquin dum agitur quae-

[margin: ὁμοίωσις mira.]

piam Plauti comoedia, nugantibus inter se uernulis, si tu in proscenium prodeas habitu philosophico, et recenseas ex Octauia locum in quo Seneca disputat cum Nerone, nonne

[a] sit, A.

---

[1] This way of spelling *comedy* may be due to the Greek κωμῳδία, but is more likely the result of unconscious assimilation of the vowels.

[2] The passage referred to is in the second act of Seneca's *Octavia*. The following lines will serve as a sample:—

Ner. Inertis est, nescire quid liceat sibi.
Sen. Id facere, laus est, quod decet, non. quod licet.
Ner. Calcat iacentem vulgus. *Ner.* Invisum opprimet.

More could speak from his own experience of 'sodenly coming upon the stage;' as Roper tells us that, in his

muta persona

better for yowe to haue played the domme persone[1], then
by rehersynge that, which serued nother for the tyme nor
place, to haue made suche a tragycall comedye or gally-
malfrcye[2]? For by bryngynge in other stuffe that nothynge apperteyneth to the presente matter, yowe must
nedys marre and peruert the play that ys in hande,
thoughe the stuffe that yowe brynge be muche better.
What parte soeuer yowe haue taken vpon yowe, playe
that as well as yowe canne, and make the beste of yt; and
doo not therefore dysturbe and brynge owt of ordre the
hole matter, bycause that an othere, whyche is meryere
and bettere, cummethe to yowre remembraunce.

'So the case stondethe in a common wealthe; and so yt
ys in the consultatyons of Kynges and prynces. Yf euell
opynyons and noughty persuasions can not be vtterly and
quyte pluckede owte of their hartes; if you can not euen
as you wold remedye vyces, whiche vse and custome hath
confirmed; yet for this cause yow must not leaue and
forsake the common wealth; yow must not forsake the
shippe in a tempeste, bycause yowe can not rule and kepe

duty to face evil

praestiterit egisse mutam personam, quam aliena reci-
tando talem fecisse tragicomoediam? Corruperis enim   κωφὸν πρόσωπον.
peruerterisque praesentem fabulam, dum diuersa permisces etiam si
ea quae tu affers meliora fuerint. Quaecunque fabula in manu est,
eam age quam potes optime; neque ideo totam perturbes, quod tibi
in mentem uenit alterius quae sit lepidior.

Sic est in Republica, sic in consultationibus principum. Si radicitus euelli non possint opiniones prauae, nec receptis usu uitiis
mederi queas ex animi tui sententia, non ideo tamen deserenda
Respublica est, et in tempestate nauis destituenda est, quoniam

---

youthful days, 'at Christmas tyd (he
would) sodenly sometymes stepp in
among the players, and, never study-
inge for the matter, make a parte of
his owne there presently amonge
them, which made the lookers on more
sport than all the players besid.'

[1] The *muta persona*. See the marginal note to the Latin.

[2] *Gallimawfrey* is properly a dish
made up of various meats minced
together; then metaphorically for a
confused jumble of things. See the
Glossary.

indirect mitigation of evil.

downe the wyndes. No, nor yow muste not laboure to dryue into their heades newe and straunge informatyons[1], whyche yow knowe well shalbe nothynge regarded wyth them that be of cleane contrary mindes. But you must with a crafty wile and a subtell trayne studye and endeuoure your selfe, asmuch as in yow lyethe, to handle the matter wyttelye and handsomelye for the purpose; and that whyche yowe can not turne to good, so to order it that it be not very badde. For it is not possible for all thynges to be well, onles all men were good: which I thynke wil not be yet thys good many yeares.'

cf. end of BK. II

Raphael replies:

verbal difficulty.

'By thys meanes' (quod he) 'nothynge elles wyll be broughte to passe, but, whyles that I goo abowte to remedy the madnes of others, I should be euen as madde as they. For if I wolde speake thynges[a] that be trewe, I muste neades speake suche thinges. But as for to speake false thynges, whether that be a philosophers part, or no, I can not tell; truely it is not my part. Howebeit thys communicatyon of myne, thoughe peraduenture it maye seme vnplesaunte to them, yett can I not see whie it should seme straunge, or foolisshelye newfangled. If so be that

---

     [a] suche thynges.

---

uentos inhibere non possis. at neque insuetus et insolens sermo inculcandus, quem scias apud diuersa persuasos pondus non habiturum; sed obliquo ductu conandum est atque adnitendum tibi, uti pro tua uirili omnia tractes commode, et quod in bonum nequis uertere, efficias saltem ut sit quam minime malum. Nam ut omnia bene sint fieri non potest, nisi omnes boni sint : quod ad aliquot abhinc annos adhuc non expecto.

Hac, inquit, arte nihil fieret aliud, quam ne dum aliorum furori mederi studeo, ipse cum illis insaniam. Nam si uera loqui uolo, talia loquar necesse est. Caeterum falsa loqui, sit ne philo|sophi, nescio : 63 certe non est meum. Quanquam ille meus sermo ut fuerit fortasse ingratus illis atque molestus, ita non uideo cur uideri debeat usque

---

     [1] 'Discourses' (Burnet).

[handwritten marginalia: Raphael argues for the good sense of his Ideas!]

[handwritten marginalia: Plato Utopians]

I shoulde speake those thynges that Plato fayneth in hys weale publique, or that the vtopians do in theires ; thies thinges thoughe they were (as they be in dede) better, yet they myghte some spoken owt of place; for a smuch[a] as here amonges us, euerye man hath hys possessyons seuerall to hymselfe, and there all thinges be common.

[handwritten marginalia: example of Utopian Communism]

'But what was in my communication conteyned, that mighte not and oughte not in anye place to be spoken ? sauynge that to them whyche haue throughlye decreed and determined with them selfes to rome [b] *[correction above: ronne]* hedlonges the contrary waye, it can not be acceptable and plesaunt; bicause it calleth them backe, and sheweth them the ieopardies. Verilye yf all thynges that euell and vitiouse maners haue caused to seme inconueniente and noughte should be refused, as thinges vnmete and reprochefull, then we must emong Christen people wyncke at[1] the moste parte of all those thynges whyche Christe taughte vs, and so streytlye forbadde them to be wyncked at, that those thinges also whyche he whispered in the eares of

[handwritten marginalia: Raphael sees no hope for Christian principle by More's policy:]

[a] as much.   [b] runne.

ad incptias insolens. Quod si aut ea dicerem, quae fingit Plato in sua Republica, aut ea quae faciunt Vtopienses in sua, haec quanquam essent, ut certe sunt, meliora, tamen aliena uideri possint, quod hic singulorum priuatae sunt possessiones, illic omnia sunt communia.

[side note: Vtopiensium instituta.]

Mea uero oratio[2], nisi quod ad eos qui statuissent secum ruere diuersa uia praecipites iucundus esse non potest, qui reuocet ac praemonstret pericula, alioquin quid habuit, quod non ubiuis dici uel conueniat uel oporteat ? Equidem si omittenda sunt omnia tanquam insolentia atque absurda, quaecunque peruersi mores hominum fecerunt ut uideri possint aliena, dissimulemus oportet apud Christianos pleraque omnia quae CHRISTVS docuit, ac dissimulari usqueadeo uetuit, ut ea quoque quae ipse in aures insusurrasset suis, palam in tectis

---

[1] That is, connive at the neglect of; or, as Burnet puts it, 'give over pressing.'

[2] There is here a confusion of two constructions, *oratio . . . iucunda,* and *meus uero sermo* (the reading of ed. 1563) *iucundus.*

hys dyscyples, he commaunded to be proclaymed in open
howses [1]. And yet the most parte of them is moore dissident from the maners of the worlde nowe a dayes then my
communicatyon was. But preachers, slye and wilie men,
followynge your cownsell (as I suppose), bicause they
saw men euel willing to frame theyr manners to Christes
rule, they haue wrested and wriede hys doctryne, and lyke
a rule of leade haue applyed yt to mennys maners [2]; that
by some meanes at the leaste waye they myghte agree to
gether. Wherby I can not see what good they haue
doone, but that men may more sickerlye be euell. And
I truelye shoulde preuaile euen asmuche[a] in kinges counselles. For other I muste saye other wayes then they
saye, and then I were as good to saye nothynge; or els
I muste saye thesame that they saye, and (as Mitio saieth
in Terence [3]) helpe to further their madnes. For that
craftye wyle and subtill traine of yours, I can not perceaue

in Terence
as Mitio says

                          [a] as little.

iusserit praedicari. Quorum maxima pars ab istis moribus longe est
alienior quam mea fuit oratio : nisi quod concionatores, homines
callidi, tuum illud consilium secuti, puto, quando mores suos homines
ad CHRISTI normam grauatim paterentur aptari, doctrinam eius uelut
regulam plumbeam accommodauerunt ad mores, ut aliquo saltem
pacto coniungerentur scilicet [4]. qua re nihil uideo quid profecerint,
nisi ut securius liceat esse malos ; atque ipse profecto tantundem
pro|ficiam in consiliis principum. Nam aut diuersa sentiam, quod 64
perinde fuerit ac si nihil sentiam ; aut eadem, et ipsorum adiutor sim,
ut inquit Mitio Terentianus, insaniae. Nam obliquus ille ductus non
uideo quid sibi uelit, quo censes adnitendum, si non possint omnia

---

[1] Lat. *palam in tectis,* ' openly on the
house-tops.' Comp. St. Luke xii. 3.

[2] Compare what Dr. Richard Sibbes
wrote of the *rule of faith,* that ' it is
a fixt and unchangeable rule, and
therefore we must bring all to it, not
it to all.' *Exposition of Phil. III.,* 1639,
p. 170.

[3] Ter. *Adelphi,* i. 2. 65 :--' Verum si

augeam, Aut etiam adiutor sim eius
iracundiae, Insaniam profecto cum
illo.' Burnet omits the reference to
Terence altogether.

[4] The position of *scilicet* at the end
of a sentence is not uncommon in
Plautus. Comp. *Captivi,* ii. 2. 33, ' Nunc
vivatne, necne, id Orcum scire oportet
scilicet.'

to what purpose it serueth; wherewyth yow wolde haue
me to studdy and endeuoure my selfe, yf all thynges can
not be made good, yet to handle them wittily and hand-
somely for the purpose; that, as farre furth as is possible,
they maye not be very euell. For there [1] is no place to
dissemble in nor to wincke in. Noughtye cownselles
must be openlye allowed, and verye pestylent decrees
muste be approued. He shalbe cowntede worse then a
spye, yea almoste as euell as a traytoure, that wyth a faynte
harte doth prayse euell and noyesome decrees. [2]

'Moreouer a man canne haue no occasyon too doo good,
chauncynge into the companye of them, whyche wyll sonere
make noughte [a] a good man, then be made good themselfes; throughe whose euell companye he shalbe marred,
or els yf he remayne good and innocent, yett the wycked-
nes and folysshenes [b] of others shalbe imputed to hym,
and layde in hys necke [3]. So that yt is impossyble wyth

[a] peruerte.   [b] folye.

reddi bona, tamen ut tractentur commode, fiantque quoad licet quam
minime mala. Quippe non est ibi dissimulandi locus, nec licet
conniuere: approbanda sunt aperte pessima consilia, et decretis
pestilentissimis subscribendum est. Speculatoris uice fuerit, ac pene
proditoris etiam, qui improbe consulta maligne laudauerit.

Porro nihil occurrit in quo prodesse quicquam possis, in eos delatus
collegas, qui uel optimum uirum facilius corruperint quam ipsi corri-
gantur; quorum peruersa consuetudine uel deprauaberis, uel ipse
integer atque innocens alienae malitiae stultitiaeque praetexeris;

---

[1] The word 'there' is emphatic,
answering to the Latin *ibi*. Burnet
brings out the sense more clearly:
'For *in Courts* they will not bear
with a Man's holding his Peace, or
conniving at what others do.'

[2] Lat *maligne*. Compare the *sub
luce maligna* of Virgil. The expression
means 'to give a stinting approval to,'
or 'damn with faint praise.'

[3] To lay in one's neck, or (as below,
p. 251) to *set* in one's neck, seems to
imply fastening on, or imputing;
the metaphor being derived from setting on dogs to the neck of a hunted
animal. The Romans had a similar usage: 'Cogitabat legiones ad
Urbem adducere, et in cervicibus
nostris collocare.'—Cic. *Ad Fam.*
xii. 23.

that craftye wyele and subtell trayne to turne anny thing to better.

Plato

Republic

VI

'Wherfore Plato by a goodly simylitude declareth whie wise men refreyn to medle in the common wealth [1]. For when they see the people swarm in to the stretes, and dailie wett to the skin wyth rayne, and yet can not persuade them to goo owt of the rayne, and to take their houses; knowynge well that if they shoulde goo owte to them, they shoulde nothynge preuayle, nor wynne ought by it, but be[a] wett also in the rain; they do kepe them selfes within their howses; beynge content that they be saffe them selfes, seynge they can not remedye the follye of the people. Direct thesis for communism:

His thesis for private property causes Injustice.

'Howe be it dowteles, mayster Moore (to speke truelye as my mynde geueth [2] me), where soeuer[b] possessyons be pryuate, where moneye beareth all the stroke [3], it is hard

[a] but with them be.   [b] soeuer *omitted.*

tantum abest ut aliquid possit in melius obliquo illo ductu conuertere.

Quam ob rem pulcherrima similitudine declarat Plato, cur merito sapientes abstineant a capessenda Republica. Quippe quum populum uideant in plateas effusum assiduis imbribus perfundi, nec persuadere queant illis ut se subducant pluuiae, tectaque subeant; gnari nihil profuturos sese si exeant, quam ut una compluantur, semet intra tecta continent; habentes satis, quando alienae stultitiae non possunt mederi, si ipsi saltem sint in tuto.

Quanquam profecto, mi More (ut ea uere dicam, quae meus animus fert) mihi uidetur, | ubicunque priuatae sunt possessiones, ubi omnes 65

---

[1] More gives the gist of the passage, which is found in the *Republic*, Bk. vi. § 496: 'Such a man keeps quiet and confines himself to his own concerns, like one who takes shelter behind a wall on a stormy day, when the wind is driving before it a hurricane of dust and rain; and when from his retreat he sees the infection of lawlessness spreading over the rest of mankind, he is well content, if he can in any way live his life here untainted in his own person by unrighteousness and unholy deeds' (Davies and Vaughan's Translation).

[2] We retain this idiom in the use of *misgive*: 'my mind misgave me.'

[3] That is, 'has all the influence.' Halliwell illustrates this use of the word from Stanihurst's *Description of*

Raphael cites Utopian communism.

and almoste impossyble that there the weale publyque maye iustelye be gouerned and prosperouslye floryshe. Onles you thynke thus: that Iustyce is there executed, wher all thynges come into the handes of euell men; or that prosperytye their floryssheth, where all is deuyded amonge a fewe; whyche fewe neuerthelesse do not leade their lyues very wealthely, and the resydewe lyue myser-ablye, wretchedlye, and beggerlye.

'Wherefore when I consyder wyth my selfe, and weye in my mynde, the wyse and godlye ordynaunces of the Vtopyans, amonge whome wyth verye fewe lawes all thynges be so well and wealthelye ordered, that vertue is had in pryce and estimatyon; and, yet, all thynges beynge ther common[1], euery man ha(t)h abundaunce of euery thynge: agayne, on the other part, when I compare wyth them so manye natyons euer makyng new lawes, yet none of them all well and suffycyentlye furnysshed wyth lawes; where euery man calleth that he hath gotten hys owne proper and pryuate goodes; where so many newe

Utopians.

2 for 1 Latin

omnia pecuniis metiuntur, ibi uix unquam posse fieri ut cum Republica iuste agatur aut prospere, nisi uel ibi sentias agi iuste, ubi optima quaeque peruenium ad pessimos, uel ibi feliciter, ubi omnia diuiduntur in paucissimos; nec illos habitos undecunque commode, caeteris uero plane miseris.

Quam ob rem quum apud animum meum reputo prudentissima atque sanctissima instituta Vtopiensium, apud quos tam paucis legibus tam commode res administrantur, ut et uirtuti precium sit, et tamen aequatis rebus omnia abundent omnibus; tum ubi his eorum moribus ex aduerso comparo tot nationes alias, semper ordinantes, nec ullam satis ordinatam unquam earum omnium, in quibus quod quisque nactus fuerit suum uocat priuatum; quorum tam multae indies con-

---

Ireland, p. 38—'This house, as well for antiquitie as for the number of worshipful gentlemen that be of the surname, beareth no small stroke in the English pale of Ireland.'

[1] On this, the basis of the Utopian commonwealth, see the Introduction, p. xxxvi, n. 3. In addition to what is there said, the reader may be referred to some sensible remarks by Dr. W. Cunningham, in his *Growth of English Industry*, 1890, p. 94 n.

Laws complicated by property

lawes daylye made be not suffycyente for euerye man to
enioye, defend, and knowe from an other mans that whych
he calleth his owne; which thyng the infinyte contro-
uersies in the lawe, that daylye ryse ᵃ neuer to be ended,
playnly dcclare to be trewe : thies thynges (I say) when
I consider with me selfe, I holde well with Plato, and doo

Plato: insisted on a Communism in Arcadia.

no thynge marueyll that he wolde make no lawes for them
that refused those lawes, wherby all men shoulde haue
and enioye equall portions of welthes and commodities ¹.
For the wise man dyd easely forsee, that thys is the one
and onlye waye to the wealthe of a communaltye, yf
equaltye of all thynges sholde be broughte in and sta-
blyshed. Whyche I thynke is not possible to be obserued,
where euerye mans gooddes be proper and peculyare to
him selfe. For where euerye man vnder certeyne tytles
and pretences draweth and plucketh to himselfe asmuch
as he can, and so ᵇ a fewe deuide amonge themselfes all

       ᵃ dayle rysynge.   ᵇ so that.

ditae leges non sufficiunt uel ut consequatur quisquam, uel ut tueatur,
uel ut satis internoscat ab alieno illud quod suum inuicem quisque
priuatum nominat: id quod facile indicant infinita illa tam assidue
nascentia quam nunquam finienda litigia :—haec, inquam, dum apud
me consydero, aequior Platoni fio, minusque demiror dedignatum
illis leges ferre ullas, qui recusabant eas quibus ex aequo omnes
omnia partirentur commoda. Siquidem facile praeuidit homo pru-
dentissimus, unam atque unicam illam esse uiam ad salutem publicam, si rerum indicatur aequalitas ; quae nescio an unquam possit
obseruari, ubi sua sunt singulorum | propria. Nam quum certis 66
titulis quisque quantum potest ad se conuertit, quantacunque fuerit
rerum copia, eam omnem pauci inter se partiti reliquis relinquunt

---

¹ The story is told by Diog. Laertius,
De Vitis Philosoph., ed. 1594, p. 200 C.
' Refert Pamphila in vigesimo quinto
Commentariorum, Arcadas ac Theba-
nos, condita ciuitate ingentis magni-
tudinis, rogasse illum vt eam rempublicam instrueret : quos quum ille
didicisset aequalitatem sectari nolle,
profectum non esse' (Lat. tr.). More
may, however, have taken the anecdote from Aelian, *Var. Hist.* ii. 42.
Neither author mentions that the state
in question was the newly-founded
Megalopolis in Arcadia, though Laertius
hints as much, by calling it μεγάλην
πόλιν.

the riches that there is ᵃ, be there neuer so muche abundaunce and stoore, there to the resydewe is lefte lacke and
pouertye [1]. And for the moste parte yt chaunceth that
thys latter sort is more worthye to enioye that state of
wealth, then the other be ; bycause the rych men be
couetous, craftye, and vnprofytable [2] : on the other parte,
the poore be lowlye, symple, and by their daily labour
more profytable to the common welthe then to them selfes.

'Thus I doo fullye persuade me selfe, that no equall and
iuste distrybutyon of thynges can be made ; nor that perfecte wealthe shall euer be among men ; onles this propriety be exiled and bannished. But so long as it shal

Rollins & Baker selection

ᵃ all the whole riches [3].

inopiam ; fereque accidit ut alteri sint alterorum sorte dignissimi ;
quum illi sint rapaces, improbi atque inutiles ; contra hi modesti
uiri ac simplices, et cotidiana industria in publicum quam in semet
benigniores.

Adeo mihi certe persuadeo, res aequabili ac iusta aliqua ratione
distribui, aut feliciter agi cum rebus mortalium, nisi sublata prorsus
proprietate, non posse ; sed manente illa, mansuram semper apud

---

[1] Latimer repeats More's complaint, but he will not admit the cause of the evil to be the same. 'And here,' he says, 'I have occasion to speak of the proprieties of things : for I fear, if I should leave it so, some of you would report me wrongfully, and affirm that all things should be common. I say not so. Certain it is that God hath ordained proprieties of things, so that that which is mine is not thine ; and what thou hast I cannot take from thee. If all things were common, there could be no theft, and so this commandment, *Non facies furtum*, "Thou shalt not steal," were in vain.' The true communism, he continues, is that taught us by St. Paul : *Sitis necessitatibus sanctorum communicantes*; 'Help the necessity of those which be poor.' 'Our good is not so ours that

we may do with it what us listeth ; but we ought to distribute it to them which have need.'—*Sermons*, ed. 1844, pp. 406–407.

[2] This sounds rather rhetorical. But perhaps More had in mind a passage from the *Menippus* of Lucian, in which the trial of the rich is described. The crimes alleged against them are, in the words of his own translation, 'violentia, superbia, fastus, iniuriae.' Part of the penalty decreed by the Plutonian court is that their souls shall inhabit the bodies of asses on earth for 250,000 years.—See the *Lucubrationes*, ed. 1563, p. 301.

[3] The alteration seems to show that Robynson did not feel it right to make *riches* the subject of *is*. But he elsewhere uses the word as a singular, in the same form as the French *richesse*.

contynew, so long shal remayn among the most and best part of men the heuy and ineuitable burden of pouerty and wretchednes. Which, as I graunt that it may be sumwhat eased, so I vtterly deny that it can holy be taken away. For if ther wer a statute made, that no man should possesse aboue a certein measure of ground[1], and that no man should haue in his stocke aboue a prescripte and appointed some of money; if it were by certein lawes decreed that nother the king should be of to greate powre, nother the people to prowd[a] and wealthye; and that offices shold not be obteined by inordinate suyte or by brybes and giftes; that they should nother be bought nor sold, nor that it sholde be nedeful for the officers to be at any cost or charge in their offices: for so occasion is geuen to the officers[b] by fraud and rauin to gather vp their money again[2], and

[a] haute.　　　　　　　　　[b] geuen theym.

multo maximam multoque optimam hominum partem egestatis et erumnarum anxiam atque ineuitabilem sarcinam. Quam ut fateor leuari aliquantulum posse, sic tolli plane contendo non posse. Nempe si statuatur ne quis supra certum agri modum possideat, et uti sit legitimus cuique census pecuniae; si fuerit legibus quibusdam cautum, ut neque sit princeps nimium potens, neque populus nimis insolens; tum magistratus ne ambiantur, neu dentur uenum, aut sumptus in illis fieri sit necesse: alioquin et occasio datur per fraudem ac rapinas

[1] Some limitation of this kind, as regards the acquisition of fresh farms by landed proprietors, was attempted by a bill of 1548. See the Introduction to the *Discourse of the Common Weal of . . . England*, ed. 1893, pp. xlvi, xlvii.

[2] That is, to recoup themselves for what they have had to lay out. Latimer, in his Fifth Sermon before King Edward VI (April 5, 1549), inveighed against the abuse which More here has in his mind:—'One will say, peradventure, "You speak unseemly and inconveniently, so to

be against the officers for taking of rewards in doing pleasures. Ye consider not the matter to the bottom. Their offices be bought for great sums; now how should they receive their money again but by bribing? Ye would have them undone. Some of them gave two hundred pound, some five hundred pound, some two thousand pound: and how shall they *gather up this money again* [Robynson's phrase], but by helping themselves in their office"'? Still more vigorously, in the Last Sermon before the King, he assails the takers of bribes in office,

[margin handwritten note: Raphael argues for limits on wealth, land & offices: but the only cure is communism.]

by reason of giftes and bribes the offices be geuen to rich men, which shoulde rather haue bene executed of wise men; by such lawes, I say, like as sicke bodies that be desperat and past cure, be wonte with continual good cherissing to be kept vp[a], so thies euelles also might be lightened and mytygated. But that they may be perfectlye cured and brought to a good and vpryght state, it is not to be hoped for, whiles euery man is maister of his owne to hym selfe. Yea, and whyles yow goo abowt to do your cure of one part, yow shall make bygger the sore of an other parte: so the healpe of one causeth anothers harme, for as much as nothynge can be geuen to annye man[b], onles that be taken from an other[1].'

[margin handwritten note: MORE]

'But I am of a contrary opinion' (quod I) 'for me thynketh that men shal neuer there lyue wealthelye, where all thynges be commen. For how can there be abundaunce of gooddes, or of any thing, where euery man with draweth his hande from labour? whome the regarde

[margin handwritten note: More replies: vs. communism. cf. end of BK. II]

a kept and botched vp for a time.　　　　b one.

sarciendae pecuniae, et fit necessitas eis muneribus praeficiendi diuites, quae potius fuerant administranda prudentibus: talibus, inquam, legibus, quemadmodum aegra assiduis solent fomentis fulciri corpora deploratae ualetudinis, ita haec quoque mala leniri queant ac mitigari: ut sanentur uero atque in bonum redeant habitum, nulla omnino
67 spes est, dum | sua cuique sunt propria. Quin dum unius partis curae studes, aliarum uulnus exasperaueris. ita mutuo nascitur ex alterius medela alterius morbus, quando nihil sic adiici cuiquam potest, ut non idem adimatur alii.

At mihi, inquam, contra uidetur, ibi nunquam commode uiui posse, ubi omnia sint communia. Nam quo pacto suppetat copia rerum, unoquoque ab labore subducente se; utpote quem neque sui quaestus

and declares that 'it will never be merry in England, till we have the skins of such.' See pp. 185, 260 of Latimer's *Sermons*, as before.

[1] 'Remembering always the great, palpable, inevitable fact—the rule and root of all economy—that what one person has, another cannot have.' Ruskin: *Unto this last*, ed. 1893, p. 171. Compare also Bacon's dictum: 'whatsoever is somewhere gotten is somewhere lost' (*Essay of Seditions and Troubles*), and the illustrative passages collected there by Mr. Reynolds.

of his owne gaines driueth not to woorke, and[a] the hoope
that he hath in other mens trauayles maketh hym slowth-
full. Then when they be prycked with pouertye, and yet
no man can by any law or right defend that for his owne,
which he hath gotten wyth the laboure of his owne
handes, shall not ther of necessitie be continuall sedition
and bloodshede? specially the authoritie and reuerende of
magistrates being taken away ; which what place it maye
haue wyth suche men, amonge whome is no difference,
I can not deuise.' ⌊ 'I maruell not' (quod he) 'that you

Raphael. be of this opinion. For you conceaue in your mynde
other none at all, or els a very false ymage and symyli-

cites tude of thys thynge[1]. But yf yow hadde bene wyth me

Utopia in Vtopia, and hadde presently sene their fasshions and
lawes, as I dyd, whiche liued ther .v. yeares and moore,

5 yrs. + ⌈and wolde neuer haue commen thence, but only to make⌉
⌊that new lande knowen here ; then dowteles you wold⌋

⌈*motive to*
spread the news:⌋   [a] but.

urget ratio, et alienae industriae fiducia reddit segnem ? At quum et
stimulentur inopia, nec quod quisque fuerit nactus, id pro suo tueri
ulla possit lege, an non necesse est perpetua caede ac seditione laboretur? sublata praesertim autoritate ac reuerentia magistratuum ;
cui quis esse locus possit apud homines taleis, quos inter nullum
discrimen est, ne comminisci quidem queo. ⁄ Non miror, inquit. sic
uideri tibi, quippe cui eius imago rei aut nulla succurrit aut falsa.
Verum si in Vtopia fuisses mecum, moresque eorum atque instituta
uidisses praesens, ut ego feci, qui plus annis quinque ibi uixi, neque
unquam uoluissem inde discedere, nisi ut nouum illum orbem prode-

---

[1] More, speaking in the person of
Hythloday, does not meet the force of
this objection directly. To find an
answer to it, he points to the state of
things prevailing in Utopia. The only
possible answer to it would appear to
be, that work should be done from new
and higher motives, not from mere
considerations of self-interest. So
done, it would bring about the state
of things in the socialist's dream :—
'All work is now pleasurable; either
because of the hope of gain in honor
and wealth, with which the work is
done . . . or else, because it is grown
into a pleasurable habit, as is the case
with what you may call mechanical
work.'—W. Morris : *News from Nowhere*, 1890, p. 127.

graunt, that you neuer sawe people well ordered, but only there.'

'Surely' (quod maister Peter), 'it shalbe harde for you to make me beleue, that ther is better order in that newe lande, then is here in thies countreys that wee knowe. For good wyttes be aswell here as there; and I thynke owr commen wealthes be auncienter than theires: wherin long vse and experience hath fownde owt many thinges commodious for mannes life, besides that many thinges here amonge vs haue bene founde by chaunce, whych no wytte colde euer haue deuysed.'

'As towchynge the auncyetnes' (quod he) 'of common wealthes, than [1] you might better iudge, if you had red the histories and chronicles of that lande; which if wee may beleue, cities were there, before there were men [a] here. Now what thinge soeuer hitherto by witte hath bene deuised, or found by chaunce, that myghte be aswell there as here. But I thinke verily, though it were so that we did passe them in witte, yet in studye and [b] laboursome endeuoure they farre passe vs. For (as there Cronicles

[a] men were.   [b] in trauaile and in.

rem; tum plane faterere populum recte institutum nusquam alibi te uidisse quam illic.

Atqui profecto, inquit Petrus Aegidius, aegre persuadeas mihi, melius institutum populum in nouo illo quam in hoc noto nobis orbe reperiri; ut in quo neque deteriora ingenia et uetustiores opinor esse quam in illo Republicas, et in quibus plurima ad uitam commoda longus inuenit usus; ut ne adiiciam apud | nos casu reperta quaedam, quibus excogitandis nullum potuisset ingenium sufficere.

Quod ad uetustatem, inquit ille, rerum attinet publicarum, tum pronunciare posses rectius, si historias illius orbis perlegisses; quibus si fides haberi debet, prius apud eos erant urbes quam homines apud nos. Iam uero quicquid hactenus uel ingenium inuenit, uel casus repperit, hoc utrobique potuit extitisse . Caeterum ego certe puto, ut illis praestemus ingenio, studio tamen atque industria longe a tergo relinquimur. Nam (ut ipsorum habent annales) ante appulsum illuc

66
[68]

---

[1] That is, *then*.   [2] More correctly, *exsistere*.

(marginal notes, left:) cf. Dante

(marginal notes:) Raphael notes antiquity of Utopia

(left margin:) hence below Equator (apud)

testifie) before our arriuall ther they neuer harde any thinge of vs, whome they call the ultraequinoctialles; sauinge that ones about .M.CC. yeares ago, a certein shyppe was loste by the Ile of Vtopia whiche was driuen thither by tempest. Certeyn Romayns and Egyptyans[1] were caste on lande, whyche after that neuer wente thence.

(left margin:) Romans & Egyptians.

'Marke nowe what profite they tooke of thys one occasion, through delygence and earneste trauaile. There was no craft nor scyence within the impery[2] of Rome, wher of any proffite could rise, but they other lerned it of thies straungers, or els, of them taking occasion to searche for yt, fownde it owte. So great proffyte was it to them that euer annye wente thyther from hence[3]. But yf annye lyke chaunce before thys hath brought any man from thence hether, that is as quyte out of remembraunce, as this also perchaunce in time to come shalbe forgotten that euer I was there. And like as they quickelye, almoste at the first

(left margin:) Utopians learned from the Romans

nostrum de rebus nostris (quos illi uocant Vltraequinoctialeis) nihil unquam quicquam audierant, nisi quod olim annis abhinc ducentis supra mille, nauis quaedam apud insulam Vtopiam naufragio periit, quam tempestas eo detulerat. Eiecti sunt in littus Romani quidam, atque Aegyptii, qui postea nunquam inde discessere. Hanc unam occasionem uide quam commodam illis sua fecit industria. Nihil artis erat intra Romanum imperium, unde possit aliquis esse usus, quod non illi aut ab expositis hospitibus didicerint, aut acceptis quaerendi seminibus adinuenerint. tanto bono fuit illis aliquos hinc semel illuc esse delatos. At siqua similis fortuna quempiam antehac illinc huc perpulerit, tam penitus hoc obliteratum est, quam istud quoque forsan excidet posteris, me aliquando illic fuisse. Et ut

---

[1] The joining of these two seems to point to a ship of Alexandria, such as conveyed St. Paul to Rome. 'About 1200 years' before the *Utopia* was written would bring us to the end of the reign of Diocletian (*ob.* A.D. 313); but it is not likely that More had any reason beyond mere fancy for naming this particular time.

[2] That is, empire (*imperium*).

[3] This does not express the sense very well. Burnet has: 'So happily did they improve that Accident, of having some of our People cast upon their Shore.'

Their quickness to learn:

meting, made their owne, what so euer is among vs wealthely[1] deuysed; so I suppose it wold be longe befor *We not willing to learn from* we wolde receaue any thing that amonge them is better *Utopians:* instytuted then amonge vs[2]. And thys I suppose is the chiefe cause whie theyr common wealthes be wyselyere gouerned, and do florysh in more wealth then ours; though wee nother in wytte nor in[a] ryches be ther inferiours.'

More asks R. to describe Utopia

'Therfore, gentle maister Raphaell' (quod I) 'I praye you and beseche yow descrybe vnto vs the Iland. And study not to be shorte; but declare largely in order their groundes, there ryuers, their cities, theire people, theire manners, their ordenaunces, ther lawes, and, to be short, al thinges that you shal thinke vs desierous to knowe. And you shal thinke vs desierous to know what soeuer we knowe not yet.' 'There is nothing' (quod he) 'that I will

Raphael:

[a] in *omitted*.

illi uno statim congressu quicquid a nobis commode inuentum est fecerunt suum; sic diu | futurum puto, priusquam nos accipiamus quicquam, quod apud illos melius quam nobis est institutum. Quod unum maxime esse reor in causa, cur quum neque ingenio neque opibus inferiores simus eis, ipsorum tamen res quam nostra prudentius administretur, et felicius efflorescat.

Ergo, mi Raphael, inquam, quaeso te atque obsecro, describe nobis insulam; nec uelis esse breuis, sed explices ordine agros, fluuios, urbes, homines, mores, instituta, leges, ac denique omnia quae nos putes uelle cognoscere: putabis autem uelle quicquid adhuc nescimus.

67
[69]

[1] That is, 'well.' See the Glossary.

[2] The slowness of our countrymen to adopt new ideas, or to admit improvements discovered by foreigners, has often been remarked. It is hard to select instances in so wide a field, but the proverb 'they manage these things better in France' may be readily illustrated—to take but a single example—from Evelyn's *Diary*. Compare his entries under Dec. 24, 1643, where he speaks of the flat stone pavement in the streets of Paris, and contrasts it with ' our pebles in London '; or under Aug. 30 1653, where he describes the recent drainage works in the fens of Lincolnshire, suggested by similar works in Holland, at which the inhabitants, ' consisting of a poore and very lazy sort of people,' were much displeased.

I

do gladlier.   For all these thinges I haue freshe in mind.
But the matter requireth leasure.'   'Let vs go in therfor'
(quod I) 'to dinner : afterward we will bestowe the time at
our pleasure.'   'Content' (quod he) 'be it.'   So we went
in and dyned.

When diner was done, we came into the same place
again, and sate vs downe vpon the same benche[1], com-
maunding oure seruauntes that no man should trowble vs.
Then I and maister Peter Giles desiered maister Raphaell
to performe his promise.   He therefore seinge vs desierous
and willinge to harken to him, when he had sit still and
paused a litle while, musing and bethinkynge hymself,
thus he began to speake.

The ende of the ffyrste boke.

Nihil, inquit, faciam libentius, nam haec in promptu habeo.   Sed res
ocium poscit.   Eamus ergo, inquam, intro pransum : mox tempus
nostro arbitratu sumemus.   Fiat, inquit.   Ita ingressi prandemus.

Pransi, in eundem reuersi locum, in eodem sedili consedimus, ac
iussis ministris ne quis interpellaret, ego et Petrus Aegidius hortamur
Raphaelem ut praestet quod erat pollicitus.   Is ergo ubi nos uidit
intentos atque auidos audiendi, quum paulisper tacitus et cogita-
bundus assedisset, hunc in modum exorsus est.

PRIMI LIBRI

FINIS[a].

^a *Addunt* A. *et* B. sequitur secundus.

---

[1] This may have been suggested by
the way in which Cicero introduces
the discourse, in the early part of his
Brutus, § 24 : 'Sed quo facilius sermo
explicetur, sedentes, si videtur, agamus.
Quum idem placuisset illis, tum in
pratulo propter Platonis statuam consedimus.'

REDUCED FACSIMILE OF THE WOODCUT OF THE ISLAND OF UTOPIA

The second

Boke of the communication

of Raphael Hythlodaye, concernyng
the best state of a common wealthe: con-
teynyng the discription of Vtopia,
with a large declaration of the
Godly[a] gouernement, and of
all the good lawes and
orders of the same
Ilande.

The Ilande of Vtopia conteyneth in breadthe in the myddell part of it (for there it is brodest) CC. miles. Whiche bredthe continueth through the moste parte of the lande, sauyng that by lytle and lytle it commeth in and

[a] politike.

200 miles

SERMONIS QVEM

RAPHAEL HYTHLODAEVS DE OPTI
MO REIP. STATV HABVIT, LI
BER SECVNDVS, PER THO
MAM MORVM CIVEM
ET VICECOMITEM
LONDINENSEM[1].

*

VTOPIENSIVM INSVLA in media sui parte (nam hac latissima est) millia passuum ducenta porrigitur, magnumque per insulae spatium non multo angustior, fines uersus paulatim utrinque

---

[1] A. and B. have the shorter title: Raphaelis Hythlodei sermo de optimo Reip. statu, per Thomam Morum. Liber secundus.

I 2

waxeth narrower towardes both the endes. Whiche fetch-
ynge about a circuite or compasse of .v.c.[1] myles, do fassion the hole Ilande lyke to the newe mone [2]. Betwene
thys two corners the sea runneth in, diuydyng them a
sonder by the distaunce of .xi. miles or there aboutes, and
there surmounteth into a large and wyde sea [3], which, by
reason that the lande of euery syde compasseth it about,
and shiltreth it from the windes, is not rough nor mountith
not with great waues, but almost floweth quietlye, not
muche vnlike a great standing powle ; and maketh almoste [a]
al the space within the ' bellye ' of the lande in maner of
a hauen ; and to the great commoditie of the Inhabitauntes
receaueth in shyppes towardes euery parte of the lande.
The forefrontes or frontiers of the .ii. corners, what wythe
fordys and shelues, and what with rockes, be very ieoperd-
ous and daungerous [5]. In the middel distaunce betwene

        [a] welnieghe.

tenuatur. hi uelut circunducti circino quingentorum ambitu millium,
              insulam totam in lunae speciem renascentis effigiant [4].
Situs et forma   Cuius cornua fretum interfluens millibus passuum
Vtopiae nouae   plus minus undecim dirimit, ac per ingens inane
   insulae.   diffusum, circumiectu undique terrae prohibitis uentis,
uasti in morem lacus, stagnans magis quam saeuiens, omnem prope
eius terrae aluum pro portu facit, magnoque hominum usu naues
quaqua uersus transmittit. fauces | hinc uadis inde saxis formidolosae. 71

---

[1] That is, five hundred.

[2] The editions of 1516 and 1518
illustrate this description by a woodcut,
giving a bird's-eye view of the island,
which was reproduced, in smaller size,
in the *Lucubrationes* of 1563. See the
Introduction, § 5.

[3] The island is conceived of as
something in the shape of a horse-
shoe, the two ends of it only eleven
miles apart. Between these extremities, as between two projecting moles
of a harbour, the sea flows in, expanding on the concave side of the
crescent into a vast, sheltered bay.

[4] The verb *effigiare* is found in
Prudentius. See also the *Cornucopiae*
(ed. 1513), col. 754.

[5] As a fair specimen of the difference in style between the older
translation and Burnet's, and also
as helping to make the description
clearer, the opening section in Burnet's rendering may be given here :—
' The Island of *Utopia* is in the Middle
two hundred Miles broad, and holds
almost at the same Breadth over a
great Part of it ; but it grows narrower
towards both Ends. Its Figure is not
unlike a Crescent : Between its Horns

them both standeth vp aboue the water a great rocke, which therfore is nothing perillous bicause it is in sight. Vpon the top of this rocke is a faire and a strong towre builded, which thei holde with a garison of men. Other rockes ther be, that lye[a] hidde vnder the water, and[b] therefore be daungerous. The channelles be knowen onely to themselfes. An[1] therfore it seldome chaunceth that any straunger, oneles he be guided by a Vtopian, can come in to this hauen. In so muche that they themselfes could skaselie entre without ieoperdie, but that their way is directed and ruled by certaine lande markes standing on the shore. By turning, translatynge[2], and remouinge this markes into other places, they maye destroye their enemies nauies, be thei neuer so many[3]. | The out side of[c] the lande is also full of hauens ; but the landing is so surely

[a] lyinge.   [b] which.   [c] or vtter circuite of.

In medio ferme interstitio una rupes eminet, eoque innoxia, cui inaedificatam turrim praesidio tenent : caeterae latentes et insidiosae. Canales solis ipsis noti ; atque ideo non temere accidit ut exterus quisquam hunc in sinum, nisi Vtopiano duce, penetret ; ut in quem uix ipsis tutus ingressus est, nisi signis quibusdam e litore uiam regentibus. His in diuersa translatis loca, hostium quamlibet numerosam classem facile in perniciem traherent. Ab altera parte non infrequentes portus. At ubique[a]

Locus natura tutus unico praesidio defenditur.

Stratagema ex mutatis signis.

[a] nusquam . . . non, A.

the Sea comes in eleven Miles broad, and spreads itself into a great Bay, which is environed with Land to the Compass of about five Hundred Miles, and is well secured from Winds : In this Bay there is no great Current ; the whole Coast is, as it were, one continued Harbour, which gives all that live in the Island great Convenience for mutual Commerce : But the Entry into the Bay, occasioned by Rocks on the one hand, and Shallows on the other, is very dangerous.'

[1] Still used provincially for ' and.'

[2] That is, transferring, or changing. The word is still used in its literal sense of changes in episcopal sees. The reader will be inclined to apostrophize the one poor Latin term, *translatis*, in the words of Quince to Bottom, as he marks how Robynson struggles with it.

[3] On this and other repellent features of the Utopian character, as drawn by More, see the Introduction, § 4, p. xlvii.

defenced [a], what by nature and what by workmanshyp of mans hande, that a fewe defenders maye dryue backe many armies.

Howbeit, as they saye, and as the fassion of the place it selfe doth partely shewe, it was not euer compassed about *King Utopus.* with the sea. But kyng Vtopus, whose name as conquerour the Iland beereth (for before that [b] tyme it was *Abraxa.* called Abraxa [1]), which also brought the rude and wild people to that excellent perfection, in al good fassions, *once savages.* humanitie, and ciuile gentilnes, wherin they now go beyond al the people of the world; euen at his first arriuinge and enteringe vpon the lande, furth with obteynynge the victory caused .xv. myles space of vplandyshe grounde, where the sea had no passage, to be cut and dygged vp; and so brought the sea rounde aboute the lande. He set to thys worke not only the inhabitauntes of the Ilande (because they should not thynke it done in contumelye and

       [a] fenced.   [b] his.

---

descensus in terram ita natura munitus, aut arte, ut [a] ingentes copiae paucis inde queant propugnatoribus arceri.

   Caeterum, uti fertur, utique ipsa loci facies prae se fert, ea tellus olim non ambiebatur mari. Sed Vtopus, cuius utpote uictoris nomen refert insula (nam ante id tempus Abraxa dice-

Vtopia insula ab Vtopo duce.   batur) quique rudem atque agrestem turbam ad id, quo nunc caeteros prope mortales antecellit, cultus

Hoc plus erat quam Isthmum perfodere.   humanitatisque perduxit, primo protinus appulsu uictoria potitus, passuum milia quindecim, qua parte

Facile fertur quod omnibus commune est.[b] tellus continenti adhaesit, exscindendum curauit, ac mare circum terram duxit. Quumque ad id operis non incolas modo coegisset (ne contumeliae loco laborem ducerent)

       [a] quin, A.   [b] sit, A.

---

[1] It is not easy to say whether More had any special idea in his mind, when he devised this name. He may have intended to express the notion of roughness or ruggedness, as Strabo did by his derivation of the river-name Araxes. Or possibly, as he calls the name of the river of Amaurote 'Waterless' (Anydrus), he may have meant something of the same kind by Abraxa, as if Ἄβρεκτος, 'not rained upon.'

despyte), but also all hys owne soldiours. Thus the
worke, beyng diuyded into so great a numbre of worke-
men, was with exceding maruelous spede dyspatched. In
so muche that the bordcrers, whiche at the fyrst began
to mocke and to gieste at thys vayne enterpryse, then
turned theyr laughter to marueyle at the successe, and
to feare.

There be in the Ilande .liiii.[1] large and faire cities or
shiere townes, agreyng all together in one tonge, in lyke
maners, institucions, and lawes. They be all set and
situate a lyke, and in all poyntes fashioned a lyke, as
farfurth as the place or plotte suffereth. Of thies cyties
they that be nighest together be xxiiii. myles a sonder.
Again there is none of them distaunt from the next aboue
one dayes iorneye a fote.

There cum yearly to Amaurote out of euery cytie .iii.
olde men, wyse and well experienced, there to entreate and

[right margin handwritten notes:]
54 towns:
London 1
Eng 40
Wales 13
—
54
shires

Amaurote
3 rep. men

sed suos praeterea milites omnes adiungeret, in tantam hominum
multitudinem opere distributo, incredibili cclcritate res perfecta ;
finitimosque [a] (qui initio uanltatem incoepti riserant) admiratione
successus ac terrore perculerit.

70   Insula ciuitates habet | quatuor et quinquaginta,   OppidaVtopiae insulae.
[72] spatiosas omnes ac magnificas, lingua, moribus, in-
stitutis, legibus prorsus iisdem. idem situs omnium,   Similitudo concor-
                                                         diam facit.
eadem ubique quatenus per locum licet rerum facies.
Harum quae proximae inter sunt [b], millia quatuor   Vrbium inter se me-
                                                      diocre interuallum.
ac uiginti separant. Nulla rursus est tam deserta,
e qua non ad aliam urbem pedibus queat unius itinere diei peru>eniri.
Ciues quaque ex urbe terni senes ac rerum periti tractatum de

---

[a] que *om.* A. *Legend.* ut finitimos   [b] inter se sunt, A.

---

[1] In England and Wales together
we now reckon fifty-two shires; but
in Harrison's *England* (ed. by Furnivall, 1877), pp. 96, 97, the number is
given as fifty-three. Monmouthshire
is there classed as a Welsh county,
making thirteen; and the county of
Richemond, in place of it, keeps up the
English number to forty. As under-
sheriff of London, More may have
been often reminded that the City
was a county in itself; and thus,
perhaps, his number of fifty-four was
made up.

Amaurote debate of the common matters of the lande. For thys cytie (because it standeth iust in the myddes of the Ilande, and is therfore moste mete for the embassadours of all partes of the realme) is taken for the chiefe and head cytie. The precinctes and boundes of the shieres be so commodiously appoynted out, and set furth for the cyties, that neuer a one [a] of them all hath of anye syde lesse then xx. myles of grounde, and of som syde also muche more [1], as of that part where the cyties be of farther distaunce a sonder. None of the cities desire to enlarge the boundes and lymites of their shieres [2]. For they count them selfes *not owners:* rather the good husbandes, then the owners of their landes.

farms They haue in the countrey in all partes of the shiere howses or fermes buylded, wel appointed and furnyshed with all sortes of instrumentes and tooles belongyng to husbandrie. Thies houses be inhabited of the cytezens, whiche cum thyther to dwel by course. No howsholde

[a] that none.

rebus insulae communibus quotannis conueniunt Amaurotum. Nam ea urbs (quod tanquam in umbilico terrae sita maxime iacet omnium partium legatis opportuna) prima princepsque habetur. Agri ita commode ciuitatibus assignati sunt, ut ab nulla parte minus soli quam $\overline{xx}$ [a] passuum millia una quaeuis habeat, ab aliqua multo etiam amplius; uidelicet qua parte longius urbes inter se disiunguntur. Nulli urbi cupido promouendorum finium. Quippe quos habent, agricolas magis eorum se, quam dominos, putant. Habent ruri per omnes agros commode dispositas domos, rusticis instrumentis instructas. Hae habitantur ciuibus per uices eo commigrantibus. Nulla familia rus-

Distributio agrorum.

At hinc hodie pestis rerum prope omnium.

Prima cura agricolationis.

[a] $\overline{xii}$., A.

---

[1] But yet, as said before, so as not to exceed a day's journey on foot.
[2] The marginal note in the Latin calls attention to this love of territorial aggrandizement as one of the great plagues of the time. See above, p. 81, for examples.

or ferme in the countrey hath fewer then .xl.[1] persones,   *40 persons.*
men and women, besydes two bonden men, whiche be all
vnder the rule and order of the good man and the good   *2 bondmen.*
wyfe of the house, beynge bothe very sage and discrete[a]
persones.   And euery .xxx. fermes or famelies haue one
heade ruler, whiche is called a Phylarche[2], being as it   *Phylarch =*
were a hed baylyffe.   Out of euery one of thies famelies   *30 familes*
or fermes cummeth euery yeare into the cytie .xx. persones whiche haue contynewed .ii. yeres before in the
countrey.   In their place so manye freshe be sent thither   *50 %*
out of the citie[3], whiche of them that haue bene there   *rotation.*
a yeare all ready, and be therfore expert and conninge in   *{ every 2*
husbandry, shalbe instructed and taught; and they the   *years.*
next yeare shall teache other.   This order is vsed, for
feare that other skarsenes of victualles or some other like   *} ? This*
incommoditie shuld chaunce through lacke of knowledge,   *does*
yf they should be al together newe and fresh and vn-   *not*
experte in husbandrie.   This maner and fassion of yearlye   *explain*
chaunginge and renewinge the occupiers of husbandrie,   *the*

a   discrete and auncientc.

reason for
the
rotation,
which goes
unexplained.

tica in uiris mulieribusque pauciores habet quam quadraginta, praeter
duos asscriptitios seruos, quibus pater materque familias graues ac
maturi praeficiuntur; et singulis tricenis familiis philarchus unus.
E quaque familia uiginti quotannis in urbem remigrant, hi qui biennium ruri compleuere.   In horum locum totidem recentes ex urbe
73 subrogantur, ut ab his qui annum | ibi fuere, atque ideo rusticarum
peritiores rerum, instituantur; alios anno sequente docturi: ne, si
pariter omnes ibi noui agricolationisque[4] rudes essent, aliquid in
annona per imperitiam peccaretur.   Is innouandorum agricolarum
mos etsi solemnis sit, ne quisquam inuitus asperiorem uitam cogatur

---

[1] In Dibdin's edition (Boston reprint, 1878, p. 234) this is for some
reason given as 'fifty persons.'

[2] See the note below, p. 124.   The
description of this officer as a sort of
head bailiff, is inserted by Robynson
from what More says a little later on.

[3] The benefit of such an alternation of town and country life, where
attainable, is obvious.   See W.
Morris's *News from Nowhere*, 1890,
p. 19.

[4] The word *agricolatio* is found in
Columella.

though it be solempne and customablie vsed, to thintent
that no man shall be constrayned against his wil to contynewe longe in that harde and sharpe[1] kynde of lyfe, yet
manye of them haue suche a pleasure and delete in husbandrye, that they obteyne a longer space of yeares.
Thies husbandmen plowe and till the grounde, and bryde[2]
vp cattell, and make[a] readye woode, whiche they carrye
to the cytie, other by lande or by water, as they maye
moste conuenyently. They brynge vp a greate multytude
of pulleyne, and that by a meruelous policie. For the
hennes doo not syt vpon the egges : but by kepynge them
in a certayne equall heate, they brynge lyfe into them,
and hatche them[3]. The chykens, assone as they be come
owte of the shell, followe men and women in steade of the
hennes.

        [a] prouide and make.

continuare diutius; multi tamen, quos rusticae rei studium natura
              delectat, plures sibi annos impetrant. Agricolae ter-
Agricolarum
  officia.   ram colunt, nutriunt animalia, ligna comparant, atque
              in urbem qua commodum est terra mariue conuehunt.
Pullorum infinitam educant multitudinem, mirabili artificio. Neque
              enim incubant oua gallinae ; sed magnum eorum
  Mira ratio
fouendi oua.   numerum calore quodam aequabili fouentes animant
              educantque. Hi simul atque e testa prodiere, homines
uice matrum comitantur et agnoscunt.

[1] Lit. 'the rougher life'—of the
husbandman.

[2] That is, *breed*.

[3] The now familiar process of artificial incubation is alluded to by Bacon
as something which rested only on
hearsay. 'Eggs, as is reported by
some, have been hatched in the warmth
of an oven.' *Nat. Hist.* Cent. ix. § 856.
But Pliny had referred to it long before
as practised in Egypt. *Hist. Nat.* x.
54. There is a curious passage relating to the same subject in *The Voiage
and Travaile* of Sir John Maundeville,
ed. 1883, p. 49, where, speaking of
Cairo, he says : ' There is a comoun

Hows in that Cytee, that is fulle of
smale Furneys; and thidre bryngen
Wommen of the Toun here Eyren of
Hennes, of Gees and of Dokes, for to
ben put in to tho Furneyses. And
thei that kepen that House coueren
hem with Hete of Hors Dong, with
outen Henne, Goos or Doke or any
other Fowl ; and at the ende of
3 Wekes or of a Monethe, thei comen
ayen and taken here chickenes
and norissche hem and bryngen hem
forthe.' Even Sir John, however,
does not cite the additional marvel
with which More concludes his
description.

They bryng vp very fewe horses; nor non, but very
fearce ones[1]; and for none other vse or purpose, but
only to exercyse their youthe in rydynge and feates of
armes[2]. For oxen be put to all the labour of plow-
ynge and drawyng. Whiche they graunte to be not so
good as horses as[a] sodeyne brunt, and (as we saye) at
a dead lifte[3]; but yet they holde opinion, that oxen
wyll abyde and suffre much more laboure and payne[b]
then horses wyl. And they thinke that they[c] be not in
daunger and subiecte vnto so manye dysseases, and that
they bee kepte and maynteyned wyth muche lesse coste
and charge; and fynally that they be good for meate when
they be past labour.

They sowe corne onlye for bread. For their drynke
is other wyne made of grapes, or els of apples or peares[4],

      [a] at a.   [b] payne and hardnes.   [c] oxen.

Equos alunt perquam paucos, nec nisi ferocientes[5], neque alium in
usum quam exercendae rebus equestribus iuuentuti.
Nam omnem seu colendi sed uehendi laborem boues   Vsus equorum.
obeunt; quos, ut fatentur equis impetu cedere, sic   Vsus boum.
patientia uincere, nec tot obnoxios morbis putant; ad
haec minore impendio et operae et sumptus ali, ac denique laboribus emeritos in cibum tandem usui esse.

Semente in solum panem utuntur. Nam aut uuarum   Cibus ac potus.
uinum bibunt, aut pomorum pirorumue, aut denique

---

[1] Burnet's rendering, 'full of mettle,'
is better.

[2] The thought may have been suggested by a passage in the *Republic*,
Bk.V. § 467 (tr. by Davies and Vaughan):
'We must put them [the children] on
horseback at the earliest possible age;
and when we have taught them to ride,
we must take them to see the fighting,
mounted, not on spirited animals, or
good chargers, but on horses selected
for speed and docility.'

[3] 'Sodeyne brunt' and 'dead lifte'
(that is, a lift or pull when there is
no way or momentum on the load to
make it easier) represent the single
word *impetus* in the Latin.

[4] Burnet, more concisely: 'Wine,
Cyder, or Perry.'

[5] A word found in some MSS. of
Quintilian, *Instit.* x. 3. 10, instead of
efferentes se, as an epithet of *equos*.
The *Cornucopiae* gives it.

mead.
licorice.

foreign
distribution
of
surplus:

holiday
visits to
cities:

or els it is cleane water; and many tymes methe made
of honey or liqueresse sodde in water[1], for therof they
haue great store. And though they knowe certeynlye (for
they knowe it perfetly in dede), how much victayles the
cytie with the hole countrey or shiere rounde a boute it
dothe spende; yet they sowe much more corne, and bryed
vp muche more cattell, then serueth for their own vse. And
the ouerplus they parte[a] amonge their borderers. What
soeuer necessary thynges be lackynge in the countrey, all
suche stuffe they fetche out of the citie; where without
anye exchaunge they easelye obteyne it of the magistrates
of the citie. For euerye moneth manye of them goo into
the cytie on the hollye daye. When theyr haruest daye
draweth nere and is at hande, then the Philarches[2], whiche

         [a] partynge the overplus.

aquam nonnunquam meram; saepe etiam qua mel aut glycyrizam
incoxerint, cuius haud exiguam habent copiam. Quum exploratum
habeant (habent | enim certissimum) quantum annonae consumat 74
urbs, et circumiectus urbi conuentus, tamen multo

Modus sementis.   urbs, et circumiectus urbi conuentus, tamen multo
amplius et sementis faciunt et pecudum educant, quam
quod in suos usus sufficiat, reliquum impartituri finitimis. Quibuscun-
que rebus opus est, quae res ruri non habentur, eam supellectilem
omnem ab urbe petunt, et sine ulla rerum commutatione a magistratibus urbanis nullo negocio consequuntur. Nam illo singulo[3] quoque

---

[1] The drink here described as made
by an infusion of honey or liquorice,
may have been a kind of mead, as
Robynson takes it. Harrison, in his
Description of England, Bk. II. (ed.
1877, p. 161), speaks slightingly of
a beverage known by this name, made
by the Essex goodwives 'with honi-
combs and water,' but not to be compared with the true metheglin, with
which mead is sometimes identified.
The word appears, however, to have
been sometimes used in a more general
sense, as by Milton, when he represents Eve as preparing to entertain the

angel guest :—
      'for drink the grape
She crushes, inoffensive must, and
     meaths
From many a berry, and from sweet
     kernels press'd
She tempers dulcet creams.'
[2] The change of spelling (see above,
p. 121) is only capricious, and not
meant to indicate a derivation from
φίλαρχοι instead of φύλαρχοι. For
the officers themselves, see below,
p. 135.
[3] The singular is found in Plautus,
Cist. iv. 2. 36.

be the hed officers and bayliffes of husbandrye, sende
woorde to the magistrates of the citie, what numbre of
haruest men is nedefull to bee sente to them out of the
cytie. The

Harvest day national.

whiche companye of haruest men,
beyng there[a] readye at the daye
appoynted, almoste in one
fayre daye dispatcheth
all the haruest
woorke.

(.·.)

[a] there *omitted.*

mense plerique ad festum diem conueniunt. Quum frumentandi
dies instat, magistratibus urbanis agricolarum phy-
larchi denunciant, quantum ciuum numerum ad se   *Mutua opera*
mitti conueniat ; quae multitudo frumentatorum, quum   *quantum ualeat.*
ad ipsum diem opportune adsit, uno prope sereno die tota frumen-
tatione defunguntur.

Of the cy=

ties and namely of Amaurote.

All cities the same: (handwritten)

AS for their Cyties, he that[a] knoweth one of them
knoweth them all: they be all so lyke one to
an other, as ferfurth as the nature of the place permytteth.
I wyll descrybe therfore to yowe one or other of them,
for it skylleth not greatly whych; but which rather then
Amaurote[1]? Of them all this is the worthiest and of
moste dignitie. For the resydwe knowledge it for the
head cytie, because there is the councell house. Nor to
me any of them al is better beloued, as wherin I lyued
fyue hole yeares together. *Hythloday lived 5 yrs. in* (handwritten)
Amaraute (handwritten)

Amaurote: (handwritten)
'Dark' (handwritten)
'Fogsy' (handwritten)
'Wall-less.' (handwritten)

[a] who so.

DE VRBIBVS, AC NOMINA
TIM DE AMAVROTO.

VRBium qui unam norit, omnes nouerit: ita sunt inter se (quatenus loci natura non obstat) omnino similes. Depingam
igitur unam quampiam (neque enim admodum refert quam)[2].
Sed quam potius quam Amaurotum? qua nec ulla
dignior est, quippe cui senatus gratia reliquae deferunt[3], nec ulla mihi notior, ut in qua annos quinque
perpetuo uixerim.

Amauroti pri-
mariae Vtopien-
sium urbis
descriptio.

---

[1] The name is evidently derived
from ἀμαυρός, 'dim,' whence ἀμαύρωσις,
'obscuration,' &c. Baumstark, in his
Thomas Morus, 1879, p. 90, oddly
interprets the word by 'mauerlos,'
'without walls,' though he adds just
after that 'die Stadt ist mit Thürmen,
Bollwerken und Mauern befestigt.'
A passage in Mr. John Watney's
*Account of the Hospital of St. Thomas
of Acons*, 1892, p. 115, shows that

London in More's time, as now, was
subject to fogs; and possibly there
may have been some thought of this
in the author's mind, as his Amaurotum
is evidently drawn with reminiscences
of London. But most likely the name
was only meant to convey the same
impression of vagueness or non-exist-
ence as Utopia itself.

[2] An anglicism.

[3] *Deferre* in the sense of 'defer to,' is

Hythloday's affectionate picture of the capitol:

The cytie of Amaurote standeth vpon the syde of a low hill, in fashion almoste four square. For the bredeth of it begynneth a litle benethe the toppe of the hyll, and styll contyneweth by the space of twoo miles vntyll it cum to the ryuer of Anyder. The lenghte of it whiche lyeth by the ryuers syde is sumwhat more.

River Anyder:

The ryuere of Anyder[1] rysethe .xxiii. myles aboue Amaurote owte of a lytle sprynge. But beynge increasede by other small floodes[a] and broukes that runne into yt, and amonge othere .ii. sumwhat bygge ons, before the cytye yt ys halfe a myle brode, and farther broder. And lx[b] myles beyonde the citye yt falleth into the Ocean sea. By al that space that lyethe betwene the sea and the cytye, and a good sorte of[c] myles also aboue the cytye, the water ebbethe and flowethe .vi. houres togethere wyth a swyfte tyde. Whan the sea flowethe in for the lenghte of xxx. myles, yt fyllethe all the Anyder wyth salte water,

tides

[a] riuers. [b] fortie. [c] and certen.

Situm est igitur Amaurotum in leni deiectu montis, figura fere quadrata. Nam latitudo cius paulo infra collis incoepta uerticem, 75 milli bus passuum duobus ad flumen Anydrum pertinet, secundum ripam aliquanto longior.

Oritur Anydrus milibus octoginta supra Amaurotum, modico fonte, sed aliorum occursu fluminum, atque in his duorum etiam mediocrium, auctus, ante urbem ipsam quingen- *Anydri fluminis descriptio.* tos in latum passus extenditur. Mox adhuc amplior, sexaginta milia prolapsus, excipitur oceano. Hoc toto spacio, quod urbem ac mare interiacet, ac supra urbcm quoque *Idem fit apud Anglos in flumine Thamysi.* aliquot milia, sex horas perpetuas influens aestus ac refluus alternat celeri flumine. Quum sese pelagus infert, triginta in longum milia, totum Anydri alueum suis occupat

late Latin. The construction probably arose from an ellipse of *honorem*.

[1] Anyder, or rather Anydrus, Ἄνυδρος, 'waterless,' is a name in keeping with the rest. The description of it, in some particulars, would accord with that of the Thames; and this resem-

blance is pointed out in the marginal note which follows. But the measurements would not by any means agree. From London Bridge to the Nore is about 45 miles, not 60; and the length of stream above bridge to its source is about 160 miles, not 24.

Tides:

and dryuethe backe the fresshe water of the ryuer. And sumwhat furthere yt chaungethe the swetenes of the freshe water wyth saltnes. But a letell beyonde that, the ryuer waxeth swet, and runneth forby[1] the city fresh and pleisaunt. And when the sea ebbeth, and goyth backe agayn, the freshe water followeth yt almoste euen to the verye falle in to the sea.

stone bridge.

gorgeous arches.

There goeth a brydge ouer the ryuer made not of pyles or of tymber, but of stonewarke[2], with gorgious and substanciall archeis at that parte of the cytye that is farthest from the sea; to the intent that shyppes maye goo[a] alonge forbie all the syde of the cytie without lette.

(The Fleet)

They haue also an other ryuere, whiche in dede is not very great. But it runneth gentelly and pleasauntlye[3].

[a] passe.

undis, profligato retrorsum fluuio. Tum aliquanto ultra liquorem eius salsugine corrumpit; dehinc paulatim dulcescens amnis syncerus urbem perlabitur, ac refugientem uicissim purus et incorruptus ad ipsas propre fauces insequitur.

Vrbs aduersae fluminis ripae, non pilis ac sublicibus ligneis sed ex opere lapideo egregie arcuato ponte, commissa est, ab ea parte quae longissime distat a mari, quo naues totum id latus urbis possint inoffensae praeteruehi. Habent alium praeterea fluuium[a], haud magnum quidem illum, sed perquam placidum ac iucundum. Nam ex eodem

Et in hoc Londinum cum Amauroto conuenit.

[a] gurgitem, A.

---

[1] The German *vorbei*, 'past.'

[2] According to Maitland, *Hist. of London*, 1739, p. 34, the old London Bridge, of stone, was begun in 22 Hen. II, and finished 10 John (1209).

[3] A reminiscence to some extent of the Flete river. Our barbarous treatment of rivers and streams is of very old standing, and More's description of this tributary of the Anyder sets forth what the Flete, with the other water-courses mingling with it, ought to have been, but never was. A few years before, however, in 1502, scared perhaps by the plague of 1500, which drove the court to Calais, the citizens had done something. 'At this time,' says Maitland (*ubi sup.*), 'Fleet Ditch, being choked with mud and dirt, was render'd intirely useless; wherefore it was now effectually cleans'd, and the navigation thereof restored to Holbourn-Bridge, as formerly.'

For it ryseth euen out of the same hyll that the cytie standeth vpon, and runneth downe a slope through the myddes of the citie into Anyder. And bicause it ryseth a lytle without the citie, the Amaurotians haue inclosed the head sprynge of it with stronge fences and bulwarkes, and so haue ioyned it to the cytie. Thys is done to the intente that the water should not be stopped, nor turned a waye, or poysoned, if their enemyes should chaunce to come vpon them[1]. From thence the water is deryued and brought[a] downe in cannellis of brycke dyuers wayes into the lower partes of the cytie. Where that cannot be done, by reason that the place wyll not suffer it, there they gather the rayne water in greate cisternes[2], which doth them as good seruice.

brick
channels:
conduits

The cytie is compassed aboute wyth a highe and thycke walle[b], full of turrettes and bulwarkes. A drye dyche, but deape and brode and overgrowen with busshes, briers, and thornes[3], goeth about .iii. sydes or quarters of the cytie. To the fowrth syde the ryuer it selfe serueth for a dytche.

walls

 [a] conuoied.   [b] stone walle

scaturiens monte, in quo ciuitas collocatur, mediam illam per deuexa perfluens Anydro miscetur. Eius fluuii caput fontem-
que, quod paulo extra urbem nascitur, munimentis   Vsus aquae
amplexi Amaurotani iunxerunt oppido, ne si qua uis   potabilis.
76 hostium ingruat, intercipi atque auerti aqua, neue corrumpi queat.
Inde canalibus coctilibus diuersim ad inferiores urbis partes aqua diriuatur. id sicubi locus fieri uetat, cisternis capacibus collecta pluuia tantundem usus adfert.

Murus altus ac latus oppidum cingit, turribus ac propugnaculis frequens, arida fossa, sed alta lataque, ac ueprium sepibus impedita, tribus ad lateribus circumdat moenia.   Moenium muni-
quarto flumen ipsum pro fossa est. Plateae cum ad   mentum.

---

[1] Comp. 2 Kings xviii. 17.
[2] For an example of this on a large scale, see Davis: *Carthage and her remains*, 1861, p. 393. We have not yet learnt to husband our rain-water.

[3] The ditch or moat surrounding the Tower of London may have been in More's mind. This was not, however, drained and planted till 1843.

K

why carriages?

streets

carriages.
(gorgeous.

gardens

doors
unlocked

10 yr.
change
of housing.

The stretes be appoynted and set forth verye commodious and handsome, bothe for carriage and also agaynst the wyndes. The houses be of fayre and gorgious buyldyng, and in [a] the streete syde they stonde ioyned together in a longe rowe throughe the hole streate without anye partition or separacion[1]. The stretes be twenty fote brode [2]. On the backe syde of the houses, through the hole lengthe of the strete, lye large gardeynes, whyche be closed in [b] rounde about with the backe parte of the stretes. Euery house hath two doores; one into the strete, and a posternne doore on the backsyde into the gardyne. Thyes doores be made with two leaues, neuer locked nor bolted, so easye to be opened that they wil followe the least drawing of a fynger and shutte agayne by themselfes [c]. Euerye man that[d] wyll maye goo yn, for there is nothynge wythin the howses that ys pryuate, or annye mannes owne[3]. And euerye .x. yeare they chaunge their howses by lotte.

[a] on.   [b] [whyche . . . in] inclosed.
[c] alone.   [d] [Euery . . . that] Whoso.

Plateae cuiusmodi.
Aedificia.
Horti aedibus adhaerent[a].
Haec sapiunt communitatem Platonis.

uecturam, tum aduersus uentos, descriptae commode. aedificia neutiquam sordida, quorum longa et totum per uicum perpetua series aduersa domorum fronte conspicitur. has uicorum frontes uia distinguit pedes uiginti lata. Posterioribus aedium partibus, quanta est uici longitudo, hortus adiacet, latus, et uicorum tergis undique circumseptus. Nulla domus est, quae non, ut hostium in plateam, ita posticum in hortum habeat. Quin bifores quoque facili tractu manus apertiles, ac dein sua sponte coeuntes, quemuis intromittunt. ita nihil usquam priuati est. Nam domos ipsas uno quoque decennio sorte commutant.

[a] adhaerentes.

---

[1] This is a lax rendering. The sense is : ' a long row of buildings, stretching the whole length of the streets, makes a fine spectacle, as the fronts of the houses face you.'

[2] See the Introduction, § 2, p. xxx.

[3] Community of dwelling-houses was included in the general communism of the *Republic*. 'No one,' so it was provided, ' should have a dwelling or storehouse, into which all who please may not enter.'—Davies and Vaughan's translation, p. 116.

They sett great stoore be theyr gardeins. In them they haue vyneyardes[1], all manner of frute, herbes, and flowres, so pleisaunte, so well furnished, and so fynelye kepte, that I neuer sawe thynge more frutefull nor better trymmed in anny place. Their studye and delygence herin cummeth not only of pleasure, but also of a certeyne stryffe and contentyon that is betwene strete and strete, concernynge the trymmynge, husbanding, and furnyshyng of their gardeyns, euery man for hys owne part. And verily yow shall not lyghtly fynde in all the citye annye thynge that is more commodyous, other for the proffyte of the citizins, or for pleasure. And thcrfore it may seme that the first fownder of the city mynded nothynge so muche as he dyd[a] thies gardeyns.

For they say that kyng Vtopus himself, euen at the first begenning, appointed and drew furth the platte fourme of

gardens

competition in gardening

Utopus

[a] he dyd omitted.

Hos hortos magnifaciunt. in his uineas, fruclus, herbas, flores, habent, tanto nitore cultuque, ut nihil fructuosius usquam uiderim, nihil elegantius. qua in re studium horum non ipsa uoluplas modo, sed uicorum quoque inuicem de suo cuiusque horti cultu certamen accendit.
et certe non aliud quicquam temere urbe tota reperias, sine ad usum
77 ciuium, siue ad uoluptatem com|modius. eoque nullius rei, quam huiusmodi hortorum, maiorem habuisse curam uidetur is qui condidit.
Nam totam hanc urbis figuram, iam inde ab initio descriptam ab

Vtilitas hortorum
etiam Maroni
praedicata[2].

---

[1] The London of More's time was not without its vineyards, unlikely as that may now seem. Vine Street, Saffron Hill, took its name from the adjacent vineyard of Ely Place. There was another at Westminster, near St. John's Church. Vinegar-yard, Drury Lane, is the Vinegarth yard. An extensive vineyard, where wine was made and sold, existed near what is now Addison Road Station, till

the latter end of last century. See Faulkner's *Hammersmith*, p. 42.
[2] The reference is to Virg. *Georg.* iv. 118:—

> Forsitan et pingues hortos quae cura
>   colendi
> Ornaret, canerem, &c.

This part of his subject, which Virgil left unfinished, was followed out by Columella, and after him by René Rapin.

K 2

the city into this fasion and figure that it hath nowe ; but
the gallaunt garnishing, and the bewtiful setting furth of
it, wherunto he sawe that one mans age wold not suffice,
that he left to his posterity. For their Cronicles, which
they kepe written with al deligent circumspection, conteining the history of m .viic. lx.[1] years, euen from the fyrste
conquest of the Iland, recorde and witnesse that the
howses in the beginning were verye lowe, and lyke
homelye cotages, or poore shepparde howses, made at all
aduentures of euerye rude pyece of woode[a] that came
fyrste to handes, wyth mudde walles, and rydged rooffes
thatched ouer with straw[2]. But nowe the houses be
curiously builded, after a gorgiouse and gallaunt sort, with
.iii. storries one ouer another[3]. The owte sydes of the

Chronicles of 1760 yrs.

earlier houses were crude.

           [a] tymber.

ipso Vtopo ferunt. Sed ornatum, caeterumque [a] cultum, quibus unius
aetatem hominis haud suffecturam uidit, posteris adiiciendum reliquit.
Itaque scriptum in annalibus habent, quos ab capta usque insula
mille septingentorum ac sexaginta annorum complectentes historiam
diligenter et religiose perscriptos adseruant, aedes initio humiles, ac
veluti casas et tuguria fuisse, e [b] quolibet ligno temere factas, parietes luto obductos, culmina in aciem fastigiata stramentis operue-
rant. At nunc omnis domus uisenda forma tabulatorum trium.

      [a] ornatum caeterumque *om.* A.   [b] *om.* A.

---

[1] That is, 1760.

[2] Even as late as Evelyn's time, this
description would apply to many parts
of England. Salisbury he describes,
in 1653, as a city which at small cost
' might be purg'd and render'd infi-
nitely agreeable, and made one of the
sweetest townes; but now the common
buildings are despicable and the streets
dirty.' Uppingham about the same
time is remarkable for being ' well
builte of stone, which is a rarity in
that part of England, where most of
the rural parishes are but of mud.'—
Diary, ed. 1890, pp. 233, 235.

[3] According to Martin (*Mediaeval
Houses and Castles in England*, 1862,
p. 9) the addition of even a second
storey was of comparatively recent
introduction. ' Late in the fifteenth
and at the beginning of the sixteenth
century the houses of the preceding
period were almost universally altered.
The hall was divided into two stories.
Being no longer required for the entertainment of a feodal retinue, a smaller
height was sufficient; and the altered
customs of the time rendered additional bed-room accommodation necessary. Both purposes were answered

walles be made other of harde Flynte or of plauster, or
elles of brycke ; and the ynner sydes be well strengthened
with tymber woorke [1]. The rooffes be playne and flatte,
couered with a certayne kinde of plaster, that is of no
coste, and yet so tempered that no fyre can hurte or
peryshe it, and withstandeth the violence of the weether
better then anye leade. They kepe the wynde out of their
windowes with glasse [2], for it is there much vsed; and
sumwhere also with fyne lynnen clothe dipped in oyle or

[margin notes: flints, plaster, glass, linen]

parietum facies, aut silice, aut cementis aut latere coctili constructae,
in aluum ª introrsus congesto rudere. Tecta in planum subducta,
quae intritis ᵇ quibusdam insternunt, nullius impendii, sed ea tem-
peratura quae nec igni obnoxia sit, et tolerandis tem-   Vitreae aut
pestatum iniuriis plumbum superet. Ventos e fenestris   linteatae fenes-
uitro (nam eius ibi creberrimus usus est) expellunt ;   trae.
interim [3] etiam lino tenui, quod perlucido oleo aut succino perliunnt,

ª *Loco verborum* aut caementis . . . aluum *exhibet* A. aut lapide duro aut
denique coctile [*sic*] constructae in alueum. *Inserit* B. denique *ante* coctili.
ᵇ sementis (*i. q.* caementis), A.

by inserting a floor at the level of the
bed room. From this to the so-called
Elizabethan house the transition was
almost imperceptible.'
    [1] It is interesting to compare with
this what Harrison wrote in 1577, in
his *Description of England*, Bk. II. c. 10
(pp. 233 sqq. in Dr. Furnivall's reprint,
1877). The houses then were still
mostly of timber. The ' certayne kinde
of plaster' spoken of in the text, is
called plaster of Paris by Harrison,
made of 'fine alabaster burned, whereof
in some places we haue great plentie,
and that verie profitable against the
rage of fire.' A kind of stucco is
also described in Erasmus's Dialogue,
Convivium Religiosum.
    [2] Eden (*State of the Poor*, i. p. 77)
infers from Harrison's description, in
the chapter just referred to, that glass
windows were not introduced into

farm-houses much before the reign
of James I. They are mentioned in
a lease dated 1614. In the houses
of richer people they were probably
introduced in the reign of Henry VIII.
' Of old time,' says Harrison, ' our
countrie houses, in steed of glasse,
did vse much lattise, and that made
either of wicker or fine rifts of oke
in chekerwise.' It is not clear what
period Harrison meant by ' of old
time,' but he mentions a specimen of
glasing with beryl as still extant at
Sudley castle. As for the use of ' panels
of horne,' he says that they are now
' quite laid downe in euerie place,'
and lattices less used, glass being so
plentiful. *Description of England*, as
before, pp. 236, 23.
    [3] *Interim*, in the sense of *inter-
dum*, is found in Seneca and Quintilian.

ambre ; and that for twoo commodities. For by thys
meanes more lyght cummeth in, and the wynde is better
kept out.

gemino nimirum commodo.   Si quidem ad eum modum fit, ut et plus
lucis transmittat, et uentorum minus admittat.

Of the Ma=
gystrates.

Euerye thyrty families or fermes chewse them yearlye
an offycer, whyche in their olde language is called
the Syphograunte[1], and by a newer name the Phylarche.
Euerye tenne Syphoagrauntos, with all their 300[a] families,
bee vnder an offycer whyche was ones called the Tranibore[2], now the chiefe Phylarche.

Moreouer, as concerninge the electyon of the Prynce,

[a] thirtie.

[handwritten margin notes: 30 familes a Syphograunt; 300 f. a Tranibore; election of Prince.]

78   DE MAGISTRATIBVS.

Triginta quaeque familiae magistratum sibi quotannis eligunt,
quem sua prisca lingua Syphograntum uocant,   Traniborus Vtopi-
recentiore phylarchum.   Syphograntis decem   ensium lingua
cum suis familiis Traniborus olim, nunc protophyl- sonat praefectum
archus dictus, praeficitur.   primarium

Syphogranti omnes, qui sunt ducenti, iurati lecturos sese quem

[1] As the old language of the Utopians is here contrasted with the new,
in which the names of the magistrates
are of Greek formation, it might be
natural to suppose that such words as
Syphogranti and *Tranibori* were meant
to be simply unintelligible jargon, like
the specimen of Utopian speech given
above (p. xciv). But as More tells us
later on, that the Utopian language,
though in other respects not unlike
the Persian, 'keepeth dyuers signes
and tokens of the Greke langage in
the names of their cityes and of
theire *magistrates*' (p. 214), we are
encouraged to look for a Greek origin
in the words now before us. And it
must be admitted that while one of
them has a suspicious resemblance
to θρανιβόροι 'bench-eaters,' the first
part, at any rate, of the other recalls
σύφος 'a sty.' Can More have been
thinking of the Benchers and Steward
(Sty-ward) of his old Inn? It mày
seem an idle guessing of riddles. But
it is certain that in his account of the
public meals of the Utopians there are
reminiscences of his old life at an Inn
of Court. See below, p. 164, where
the dining together in 'messes' of four
is described.

[2] See the preceding note.

all the Syphoagrauntes, which be in number 200, first be sworne to chewse him whome they thynke moste mete and expedyente. Then by a secrete electyon they name [handwritten: 4 candidates] prynce[1] one of those .iiii. whome the people before named vnto them. For owte of the .iiii. quarters of the citie there be .iiii. chosen, owte of euerye quarter one, to stande for the election, whiche be put vp to the counsell. The princes office contineweth all his liffe time, onles he be deposed [handwritten: Tyranny.] or put downe for suspition of tirannye. They chewse the tranibores yearlye, but lightlye they chaunge them not. All the other offices be but for one yeare. The Tranibores euerye thyrde daye, and sumtymes, if neade be, oftener, come into the councell howse with the prynce. Theire councell is concernynge the common wealth. Yf there be annye controuersyes amonge the commoners, whyche be very fewe, they dyspatche and ende them by and by[2]. They take euer ii. Siphograntes to them in cowncell, and euerye daye a newe coupel. And that ys prouydede that no thynge towchynge the common wealthe shalbe con-

maxime censent utilem, suffragiis occultis renunciant principem, unum uidelicet ex his quatuor, quos eis populus nominauit. Nam a quaque urbis quarta parte selectus unus commendatur senatui. Principis ma-

Mira ratio creandi magistratus. gistratus perpetuus est in omnem illius uitam, nisi tyrannidis affectatae suspicio impediat. Traniboros

Tyrannis inuisa bene institutae reipublicae. quotannis eligunt. Caeterum haud temere commutant. Reliqui magistratus omnes annui. Tranibori

Cito dirimendae controuersiae, quas nunc data opera in immensum prorogant. tertio quoque die, interdum, si res postulat, saepius, in consilium cum principe ueniunt. De republica consultant, controuersias priuatorum (si quae sunt) quae perquam paucae sunt, mature dirimunt. Syphograntos semper in senatum duos adsciscunt, atque omni die diuersos: cautumque ut ne quid ratum sit quod ad rempu-

---

[1] It is evident from the description that this 'prince' (*princeps*) is the chief magistrate of each city only, and not king of the whole island. See the Introduction, above, p. xlv.

[2] Lat. *mature,* 'quickly.' This is the old sense of 'by and by,' as in Luke xxi. 9, 'but the end is not by and by,' where the Revised Version has 'immediately.'

fyrmed and ratifyed, on les yt haue bene reasonede of and
debatede iii. dayes in the cowncell, before yt be decreed.
It is deathe to haue annye consultatyon for the common
wealthe owte of the cownsell, or the place of the common
electyon. Thys statute, they saye, was made to thentente,
that the prynce and Tranibores myghte not easely conspire together to oppresse the people by tyrannye, and
to chaunge the state of the weale publique. Therfore
matters of greate weyghte and importaunce be brought to
the electyon house of the syphograuntes, whyche open
the matter to their familyes ; and afterwarde, when they
haue consulted among them selfes, they shewe their
deuyse to the cowncell. Sumtyme the matter is brought
before the cowncell of the hole Ilande.

    Furthermore thys custome also the cowncell vseth, to
dyspute or reason of no matter the same daye that it ys
fyrste proposed or putt furthe, but to dyfferre it to the
nexte syttynge of the cownsell. Bycause that no man
when he hathe rasshelye there spoken that cummeth
fyrste [a] to hys tonges ende, shalt then afterwarde rather
studye for reasons wherewyth to defende and confyrme [b]
hys fyrste folyshe sentence, than for the commodytye of

    [a] fyrste *omitted*.   [b] mainteine.

Margin notes: death penalty, for private discussion — {Whole council of-Island}

blicam pertineat, de quo non tribus in senatu diebus ante agitatum
quam decretum sit. Extra senatum aut comitia publica
de rebus communibus inire consilia capitale habetur.   *Nihil subito statuendum.*
Haec eo ferunt instituta, ne procliue esset coniura-
tione principis ac Tranibororum, oppresso per tyrannidem populo,
statum reipublicae mutare. Atque ideo quicquid magni momenti
iudicatur, ad Syphograntorum comitia defertur, qui cum suis familiis
communicata re post inter se consultant, ac suum consilium renun|-
79 ciant senatui. Interdum ad totius insulae consilium res defertur.

    Quin id quoque moris habet senatus, ut nihil, quo
die primum proponitur, eodem disputetur, sed in   *Vtinam idem hodie fiat in*
frequentem senatum differatur ; ne quis ubi quod in   *nostris consiliis.*
buccam primum uenerit temere effutierit, ea potius
excogitet postea, quibus decreta tueatur sua, quam quae ex reipu-

the common wealthe ; as one rather wyllynge the harme
or hynderaunce of the weale publyque, then annye losse
or dymynutyon of hys owne existymatyon ; and as one
that wolde not for shame (which is a verye folyshe shame)
be cowntede ᵃ annye thynge(ouerseen ¹) in the matter at
the fyrste ᵇ; who at the fyrste owghte to haue spoken
rather wysely then hastely or rashelye.

ᵃ wolde be ashamed . . . to be.   ᵇ at the firste ouersene in the matter.

blicae usu sint; malitque salutis publicae quam opinionis de se

Hoc sibi uolebat   iacturam facere, peruerso quodam ac praepostero
uetus prouerbi-   pudore, ne initio parum prospexisse uideatur. Cui
um, ἐν νυκτὶ   prospiciendum initio fuit, ut consulto potius quam
βουλή ².   cito loqueretur.

---

¹ The Latin means literally 'deficient
in foresight.' Halliwell illustrates this
use of ' overseen' in the sense of
' deceived' by a passage from *Terence
in English*, 1614 : ' where if thou be
overseene in anything, be it never so
little, I shall utterly perish.'
² Erasmus gives the proverb under

the heading ' In nocte consilium '
(*Adag.* ed. 1629, p. 199 b). See also
Herod. vii. 12. Erasmus shows the
application of the saying to be against
rashness or precipitancy; so that this
marginal note should rather be attached to the words 'sed infrequentem
senatum differatur.'

[handwritten: Education through play: quasi per ludum]

Of ſcyences
Craftes and Occupatyons.

[handwritten: All farmers]

Husbandrye is a scyence common to them all in-generall, both men and women, wherin they be all experte and cunnynge.   In thys they be all instructe euen from their youth ; partely in ſcholes with traditions and preceptes, and partely in the contrey nighe the cytye, *[handwritten: taken out as in play]* [brought vp[1] as it wer in playing, not onlye beholdynge the vse of it, but by occasyon of exercisinge their bodies practising it also.

Besides husbandry, which (as I sayde) is common to *[handwritten: Each has another craft.]* them all, euery one of them learneth one or other scuerall and particuler science, as hys owne proper crafte.   That is most commonly other clotheworkinge[2] in wolle or flaxe, *[handwritten: wool & flax]* or masonrie, or the smythes crafte, or the carpentes

DE ARTIFICIIS.

Ars una est omnibus uiris mulieribusque promiscua agricultura, cuius nemo est expers. Hac a pueritia erudi- *Agricolatio communis omnium, quam nunc in paucos contemptos rei cimus.* untur omnes, partim in schola traditis prae-ceptis, partim in agros uiciniores urbi, quasi per ludum, educti ; non intuentes modo, sed per exerci-tandi corporis occasionem tractantes etiam.

Praeter agriculturam (quae est omnibus, ut dixi, communis) quilibet unam quampiam, tanquam suam, docetur. ea est fere *Artes ad necessitatem, non ad luxum, discendae.* aut lanificium, aut operandi lini studium, aut cemen-tariorum, aut fabri, seu ferrarii seu materiarii, artifi-

---

[1] Robynson has confused *educti* with *educati.*   What More says is, that all are trained in husbandry from child-hood ; partly by rules taught in school, and partly by being *taken out*, as in play, into the fields adjoining their city, which would serve as the best kind of object lesson.

[2] More probably specifies this in the first place, as the manufacture of

Garments

one dress:

male-
female

married-
unmarried

scyence. For there is none other occupacyon that anye numbre to speke of doth vse there. For their garmentes, whyche through owte all the Ilande be of one fassion, (sauynge that there is a difference betwene the mans garmente and the womans, betwene the maried and the unmaryed), and this one continueth for euer more un-chaunged, semely and comely to the eye, no let to the mouynge and weldynge of the bodie, also fitte bothe for winter and summer: as for thies garmentes (I saye), euery familye maketh theire owne[1]. But of the other foreseyde craftes euerye man learneth one; and not only the men, but also the women. But the women, as the weaker sorte, be put to the easere craftes. They[a] worke wull and flaxe. The other[b] more laborsome sciences be committed to the men. For the moste parte euerye man is brought vp in

[a] as to.   [b] other *omitted.*

cium. Neque enim aliud est opificium ullum, quod numerum aliquem dictu dignum occupet illic. Nam uestes, quarum, nisi quod habitu sexus discernitur, et caelibatus a con-iugio, una per totam insulam forma est, eademque per omne aeuum perpetua, nec ad oculum indecora, et ea corporis motum | habilis, tum ad frigoris aestusque rationem appositas, eas, 80 inquam, quaeque sibi familia conficit. Sed ex aliis illis artibus unus quisque aliquam discit, nec uiri modo, sed mulieres etiam. Caeterum hae, uelut imbecil-liores, leuiora tractant. lanam fere linumque operantur. uiris artes reliquae magis laboriosae mandantur. maxima ex parte quisque in

Cultus similitudo.

Nemo ciuium expers artificii.

woollen cloths was so important an industry both in Flanders, where he wrote, and in his native country. Masonry may have been placed next, from the great activity in building shown in England during the fifteenth century. See Denton's *England in the Fifteenth Century,* 1888, and Professor Thorold Rogers' Introduction to Gas-coigne's *Loci,* 1881, p. xxiv.

[1] 'I knewe the time,' says one of the interlocutors in *The Common Weal of this Realm of England,* 1549 (ed. 1893, p. 125), 'when men weare con-tented with cappes, hattes, girdelles, and poyntes and all maner of gar-mentes made in the townes next adioyninge ... Nowe the porest yonge man in a countrey can not be con-tented either with a lether girdle, or lether pointes, gloues, knyues, or daggers made nighe home.'

his fathers craft.   For moste commonly they be naturally
therto bente and inclined.   But yf a mans minde stonde
to anny other, he is by adoption put into a famelye of
that occupation which he doth most fantasy.   Whome not
only his father, but also the magistrates do diligently looke
to, that he be putt to a discrete and an honest householder.
Yea and if anny person, when he hath lerned one crafte,
be desierous to lerne also another, he ys lykewyse suffrede
and permytted.   When he hathe learned bothe, he oc-
cupyethe whether he wyll; onles the cytye haue more
neade of the one then of the other.

The chyefe and almoste the onelye offyce of the Syphograuntes ys to see and take hede that no man sytte ydle,
but that euerye one applye hys owne crafte wyth earneste
delygence; and yet for all that not to be weryed from
earlye in the mornynge to late in the euennynge wyth
contynuall woorke, lyke laborynge and toolynge beastes.
For thys ys worse then the myserable and wretced condytyon of bondemen; whyche neuer the lesse is almoste
euery where the lyffe of woorkemen and artyfycers,
sauynge in vtopia.   For they, dyuydinge the daye and the
nyghte into xxiiii. iust houres, appoynte and assygne only

Marginal notes (handwritten): Inherited craft · changes of crafts, & family · The officers' duty · no idleness. · The Day

patriis artibus educatur, nam eo plerique natura feruntur.   Quod si
quem animus alio trahat, in eius opificii, cuius capitur
studio, familiam quampiam adoptione traducitur, cura
non a patre modo eius, sed magistratibus etiam prae-
stita, ut graui atque honesto patrifamilias mancipetur.
Quin si quis unam perdoctus artem aliam praeterea
cupiuerit, eodem modo permittitur.   Vtramque nactus, utram uelit
exerceat, nisi alterutra ciuitas magis egeat.

Margin: Ad quam quisque natura sit appositus, eam discat artem.

Syphograntorum praecipuum ac prope unicum negocium est,
curare ac prospicere ne quisquam desideat ociosus,
sed uti suae quisque arti sedulo incumbat, nec ab
summo mane tamen, ad multum usque noctem perpetuo labore, uelut iumenta, fatigatus.   nam ea plusquam seruilis erumna est; quae tamen ubique fere
opificum uita est, exceptis Vtopiensibus; qui cum in
horas uiginti quatuor aequales diem connumerata nocte diuidant,

Margin: Ociosi pellendi e Republica.

Margin: Moderandus opificum labor.

6 hrs work.

3-2-3

vi. of those houres to woorke ; iii.[a] before none, vpon the whyche they goo streyghte to dyner; and after dyner, when they haue rested ii houres, then they woorke iii.[b]; and vpon that they goo to supper[1]. Aboute viii. of the clocke in the euenynge (cowntynge one of the clocke at the fyrste houre after none) they go to bedde. viii. houres they giue to sleape[2]. All the voide time, that is betwene the houres of woorke, slepe, and meate, that they be

[a] iii. *omitted.*   [b] iii. houres.

sex duntaxat operi deputant; tres ante meridiem, a quibus prandium ineunt; atque a prandio duas pomeridianas horas quum interquie-uerint, tres deinde rursus labori datas coena clau|dunt. Quum primam 81 horam ab meridie numerent, sub octauam cubitum eunt. horas octo somnus uendicat. Quicquid inter operis horas ac somni cibique me-

---

[1] These Utopian hours of labour must have presented a sharp contrast to those actually in use in More's time. By a statute of 11 Hen. VII. (1495-6), cap. 22, it was enacted 'that every artificer and labourer be at his work, between the midst of the month of March and the midst of the month of September, before five of the clock in the morning, and that he have but half an hour for his breakfast, and an hour and a half for his dinner, of such time as he hath season for sleeping, to him appointed by this said statute; and at such time as is here appointed that he shall not sleep, then he to have but one hour for his dinner, and half an hour for his noon-meat; and that he depart not from his work, between the midst of the said months of March and September, till between seven and eight of the clock in the evening . . . and that, from the midst of September to the midst of March, every artificer and labourer be at their work in the springing of the day, and depart not till night of the same day.' See Eden's *State of the Poor*, 1797, i. p. 75, and Cunningham's *Growth of English Industry*, 1890, p. 476. In 1514 an act was passed, almost identical in terms with this of 1495; but a special exemption had to be made in it in respect of London, where a higher rate of wages prevailed. The subject, as we may thus see, had been very recently brought under More's notice.

[2] This would make four o'clock the hour for rising. Cecil, to whom Robynson's translation was dedicated, used to rise at that hour when at St. John's College, Cambridge; a College which had, 'as I have heard grave men of credit report, more candles lighted in it every winter morning before four of the clock, than the four of the clock bell gave strokes.' T. Nash, quoted in Mayor's edition of Ascham's *Scholemaster*, 1863, p. 277. For More's own custom in this respect, see above, p. 4 n.

suffered to bestowe, euerye man as he lyketh beste hym selfe: not to thyntente they[a] shoulde myspende thys tyme in ryote, or sloughfullenes; but, beynge then lycensed from the laboure of theyr owne occupacyons, to bestowe the time wel and thriftely vpon some other good[b] science, as shall please them. For yt ys a solempne custome there, to haue lectures daylye earlye in the morning; wher to be present they onlye be constreined that be namelye chosen and appoynted to learnynge. Howe be yt a greate multy-tude of euerye sorte of people, bothe men and women, goo to heare lectures; some one and some an other, as euerye mans nature is inclyned. Yet, this notwithstonding, yf any man had rathere bestowe thys tyme vpon hys owne occupatyon (as yt chaunceth in manye, whose myndes ryse not in the contemplatyon of annye scyence lyberal), he is not letted nor prohibited, but is also praysed and commended, as profitable to the common wealthe.

After supper they bestowe one houre in playe; in somer in their gardeyncs, in winter in their commen halles, where they dyne and suppe. There they exercise them selfes in musyke, or cls in honeste and holsome communicacion.

[a] that they. [b] good *omitted*.

dium esset, id suo cuiusque arbitrio permittitur; non quo per luxum aut segnitiem abutatur, sed quod ab opificio liberum ex animi sententia in aliud quippiam studii bene collocet. has intercapedines plerique impendunt literis. Solenne est enim publicas cotidie lectiones haberi antelucanis horis, quibus ut intersint ii dumtaxat adiguntur, qui ad literas nominatim selecti sunt. Caeterum ex omni ordine mares simul ac foeminae, multitudo maxima, ad audiendas lectiones, alii alias, prout cuiusque fert natura, confluit. Hoc ipsum tempus tamen, si quis arti suae malit insumere, quod multis usu uenit (quorum animus in nullius contem-platione disciplinae consurgit) haud prohibetur: quin laudatur quoque, ut utilis reipublicae.

Super coenam tum unam horam ludendo producunt, aestate in hortis, hyeme in aulis illis communibus, in quibus comedunt. Ibi aut musicen exercent, aut se sermone

Studia literarum.

Lusus in coenis.

*Gambling
forbidden.*

*chess.
moralized
= cf.
Caxton*

*Allegorical
sense of
play*

Diceplaye, and suche other folish and pernicious games,
they knowe not[1] ; but they vse .ii. games not muche vnlike
the chesse.　The one is the battell of nombers, wherin
one numbre stealethe awaye another.　The other is wherin
vices fyghte wyth vertues[2], as it were in battell array, or
a set fyld.　In the which game is verye properlye shewed
bothe the striffe and discorde that vices haue amonge
themselfes, and agayne theire unitye and concorde againste
vertues ; and also what vices be repugnaunt to what
vertues ; with what powre and strenght they assaile them
openlye ; by what wieles and subteltye they assaute them
secretelye ; with what helpe and aide the vertues resiste,
and ouercome the puissaunce of the vices ; by what craft

recreant.　Aleam atque id genus ineptos ac perniciosos ludos ne

*At nunc alea
principum lusus
est.*

*Lusus utiles
quoque.*

cognoscunt quidem.　caeterum duos habent in usu
ludos, latrunculorum ludo non dissimiles : alterum,
numerorum pugnam, in qua numerus numerum praedatur : alterum, in quo collata acie cum uirtutibus uitia
confligunt.　Quo in ludo perquam scite ostenditur

et uitiorum inter se dissidium, et aduersus | uirtutes concordia ; item 82
quae uitia quibus se uirtutibus opponant, quibus uiribus aperte
oppugnent, quibus machinamentis ab obliquo adoriantur, quo praesidio uirtutes uitiorum uires infringant, quibus artibus eorum conatus

---

[1] More is here almost describing by
anticipation the life of his own household at Chelsea.　' It was one of the
necessities of his dignity at court that
he should have several attendants
when he went out.　When they were
not engaged in this service he would
not allow them to remain idle.　He
divided his garden into portions, to
each of which he assigned one of his
men as its cultivator.　Some learnt to
sing, others to play on the organ ; but
he absolutely forbade games of cards
or dice, even to the young gentlemen
in his house.'—Bridgett's *Life*, p. 139.

[2] ' Playing at Vertues ' is the heading of one game for maidens in *The
French Garden for English Ladies and
Gentlewomen*, 1621, quoted in Brand's
Popular Antiquities The ' battell of
nombers,' at which one ' makes booty
of (*praedatur*) another,' might answer
to more than one still-familiar game.
Playing at ' odd and even ' is mentioned by Plato, *Lysis*, § 206 E, and
commentators on the *Republic*, § 422
(*sub fin.*), tell us that there was ' a
game called " Cities " played with
counters.'　See Davies and Vaughan,
as before, p. 121 n.

they frustate their purposes ; and finally by what sleight
or meanes the one getteth the victory.

But here, lease [1] you be deceaued, one thinge you muste
looke more narrowly vpon.   For seinge they bestowe but
vi. houres in woork [2], perchaunce you maye thinke that
the lacke of some necessarye thinges herof may ensewe.
But this is nothinge so.   For that small time is not only
inough, but also to muche, for the stoore and abundaunce
of all thinges that be requisite, other for the necessitie or
commoditie of liffe.   The whiche thing yow also shall perceaue, if you weye and consider with your selfes how
great a parte of the people in other contreis lyueth ydle.
First, almoost all women, which be the halfe of the hole
numbre ; or els, if the women be annye [a] where occupied,
their most comonlye in their steade the men be ydle.
Besydes thys, how great, and howe ydle a companye ys
theyr of prystes, and relygyous men, as they call them [3] ?

[a] some.

eludant, quibus denique modis alterutra pars uictoriae compos
fiat.

Sed hoc loco, ne quid erretis, quiddam pressius intuendum est.
Etenim quod sex dumtaxat horas in opere sunt, fieri fortasse potest
ut inopiam aliquam putes necessariarum rerum sequi.   Quod tam longe
abest ut accidat, ut id temporis ad omnium rerum copiam, quae quidem ad uitae uel necessitatem requirantur uel commoditatem, non
sufficiat modo sed supersit etiam : id quod uos quoque intelligetis, si
uobiscum reputetis apud alias gentes quam magna
populi pars iners degit.   primum mulieres fere omnes,   *Ociosorum homi-*
totius summae dimidium ; aut, sicubi mulieres nego-   *num genera.*
ciosae sunt, ibi ut plurimum earum uice uiri stertunt.   ad haec, sacerdotum ac religiosorum, quos uocant, quanta quamque ociosa turba.

---

[1] Lest.

[2] This is the estimate of the time
necessary for labour formed by many
modern socialists. ' If six hours' work
per diem,' says Marx, ' would suffice to
keep the labourer and his family, and
he works ten, who gets the benefit
of the other four ? '—See Woolsey's

Communism and Socialism, p. 162.

[3] Compare what Pole is made to
say in the *Dialogue* (p. 156) about
the ' grete nombur and vnprofytabul'
of ' relygyouse personys ; ' and the
passage in Erasmus's *De sarcienda
Ecclesiae concordia* beginning ' Dolen-
dum est tam multos esse monachos.'

L

vs.
idleness
&
waste of
time

Put there to all ryche men, speciallye all landed men, whyche comonly be called gentylmen, and noble men. Take into this numbre also their seruauntes; I meane, all that flocke of stout, bragging, russhe bucklers[1]. Ioyne to them also sturdy and valiaunt beggers[2], clokinge their idle leffe[3] vnder the colour of some disease or sickenes. And truely yow shall find them much fewer then yow thought, by whose labour all these thynges be gotten[a], that men vse and lyue bye[b]. Nowe consyder wyth youre selfe, of thies fewe that do woorke, how few be occupied in necessary woorkes. For where money beareth all ye swing, ther many vayne and superfluous occupations must nedys be vsed, to serue only for ryotous superfluyte and vnhonest pleasure. For the same multytude that now is occupied in woorke, if they were deuided into so few occupations as the necessary vse of nature requyreth, in so great plentye of thinges, as then of necessity wolde

vs.
money
as
evil

[a] are wrought.   [b] that in mens affaires are daylye vsed and frequented.

adiice diuites omnes, maxime praediorum dominos, quos uulgo generosos appellant, ac nobiles : his adnumera ipso-rum famulitium, totam uidelicet illam cetratorum nebulonum colluuiem : robustos denique ac ualentes mendicos adiunge, morbum quempiam praetexentes inertiae : multo certe pauciores esse quam putaras inuenies eos, quorum labore con-stant haec omnia quibus mortales utuntur. Expende nunc tecum ex his ipsis quam | pauci in necessariis opificiis uersantur ; siquidem Ε3 ubi omnia pecuniis metimur, multas artes necesse est exerceri inanes prorsus ac superfluas, luxus tantum ac libidinis ministras. nam haec ipsa multitudo, quae nunc operatur, si partiretur in tam paucas artes, quam paucas com-modus naturae usus postulat, in tanta rerum abundantia, quanta nunc

δορυφόρημα
nobilium.

Prudentissime
dictum.

---

[1] The 'swashbucklers' of Shak-spere; or, to borrow Scott's descrip-tion of a Highland laird, the 'dozen young lads besides, that have no business, but are just boys of the belt, to follow the laird, and do his honour's bidding.' Dibdin tries, but wrongly, to show that the word means men with bucklers 'as flimsy as rushes.' See Nares's *Glossary, s. v.*

[2] See the Introduction, § 2.

[3] That is, *life.*

ensue, doubtles the prices wolde be to lytle for the arti-
fycers to maynteyne theyre lyuynges.   But yf all thyes,
that be nowe bisiede about vnprofitable occupations, with
all the hole flocke of them that lyue ydellye and slouth-
fullye, whyche consume and waste euerye one of them
more of thies thynges that come by other mens laboure,
then ii. of the work men themselfes doo; yf all thyes
(I saye) were sette to profytable occupatyons, yowe easelye
perceaue howe lytle tyme wolde be enoughe, yea and to
muche, to stoore vs wyth all thynges that maye be requysyte other for necessytye, or for commodytye ; yea, or
for pleasure, so that the same pleasure be trewe and
naturall.

[margin: Possible use of pleasure raised?]

And thys in Vtopia the thynge yt selfe maketh manifeste
and playne.   For there in all the citye, wyth the hole
contreye or shyere adioynynge to yt, scaselye 500 persons
of all the hole numbre of men and women, that be nother
to olde nor to weake to woorke, be licensed from [a] labour.
Amonge them be the Siphograuntes, which (though they
be by the lawes exempte and pryuyleged from labour) yet
they exempte not themselfes ; to the intent they [b] maye the

[margin: (neither) 500 not laborers]

> [a] and discharged from.   [b] that they.

esse necesse sit, precia nimirum uiliora forent quam ut artifices inde
uitam tueri suam possent. At si isti omnes quos nunc inertes artes
distringunt, ac tota insuper ocio ac desidia languescens turba, quorum
unus quiuis earum rerum quae aliorum laboribus suppeditantur,
quantum duo earundem operatores consumit, in opera uniuersi atque
eadem utilia collocarentur, facile animaduertis quantulum temporis
ad suppeditanda omnia, quae uel necessitatis ratio uel commoditatis
efflagitet (adde uoluptatis etiam quae quidem uera sit ac naturalis)
abunde satis superque foret.

Atque id ipsum in Vtopia res ipsa perspicuum facit.   Nam illic in
tota urbe cum adiacente uicinia uix homines quin-
genti [a] ex omni uirorum ac mulierum numero, quorum
aetas ac robur operi sufficit, uacatio permittitur. In hiis
syphogranti (quanquam leges eos labore soluerunt)
ipsi tamen sese non eximunt, quo facilius exemplo suo reliquos

[margin: Ne magistratus quidem ab opere cessant.]

> [a] B. *recte* hominibus quingentis. *Al.* homines quingenti quibus.

Exemplary magistrates

rather by their example prouoke other to woorke. The same vacation from labour do they also enioye, to whome the people, persuaded by the commendation of the priestes and secrete election of the Siphograntes, haue geuen a perpetual licence from labour to learnyng. But if anny one of them proue nott accordinge to the expectation and hoope of him conceaued, he is furth with plucked backe to the company of artificers. And contrarye wise, often yt chaunceth that a handicraftes man doth so earnestly bestowe hys vacaunte and spare houres in learninge, and through dilygence so profytte therin, that he is taken frome hys handy occupation, and promoted to the company of the learned.

The learned

change of occupation

Learned officers

Owt of this ordre of the learned be chosen ambassadours, priestes, Tranibores, and finallye the prince him selfe; whome they in their olde tonge call Barzanes[1], and by a newer name, Adamus[2]. The residewe of the people being nother ydle, nother[a] occupied about vnprofitable

A-demus

[a] nor yet.

ad labores inuitent. Eadem immunitate gaudent hi, quos commendatione sacerdotum persuasus populus occultis syphograntorum suffragiis ad perdiscendas disciplinas perpetua uacatione indulget. Quorum si quis conceptam de se spem fefellerit, ad opifices retruditur. contraque non rarenter[3] usu uenit, | ut mechanicus quispiam 84 subcisiuas illas horas tam gnauiter impendat literis, tantum diligentia proficiat, ut opificio suo exemptus in literatorum classem prouehatur.

Ex hoc literatorum ordine legati, sacerdotes, Tranibori, ac ipse denique deligitur princeps, quem illi prisca ipsorum lingua Barzanem, recentiore Ademum, appellant. Reliqua fere multitudo omnis, quum neque ociosa sit, nec inutilibus opificiis occupata, procliuis aestimatio est quam

Soli literati ad magistratus uocantur.

---

[1] It has been before noticed (p. 135), that More describes the Utopian language as being, with the exception of 'divers signs and tokens of the Greek,' 'in all other points not much unlike the Persian tongue.' See below, p 214. The choice of Barzanes for the name of a chief ruler is in accordance with this.

[2] As the river of the Amaurotes was Anydrus, 'without water,' so the king, by his later Greek name, was Adēmus, 'without people.' Why Robynson turned the name into Adamus, is not clear. He or his compositor may perhaps have been thinking of Adam.

[3] *Rarenter* is post-classical for *raro*.

exercises, it may be easely iudged in how fewe howres   *efficiency*
how much good woorke by them maye be doone[a] towardes
those thinges that I haue spoken of. This commodity
they haue also abouc other, that in the most part of
necessary occupations they neade nott so muche worke,
as other nations doo. For firste of all the buildinge or   *English*
repayring of houses asketh euery where so manye mens   *problems.*
continuall labour, bicause that the vnthyfty heyre suffreth
the howses that hys father buylded, in contynewaunce of
tyme to fall in decay. So that which he myghte haue
vpholden wyth lytle coste, hys successoure is constreynede   *Waste*
to buylde yt agayne a newe, to hys great chardge. Yea,   *of*
manye tymes also the howse that stoode one man in   *housing*
muche moneye, anothere ys of so nyce and soo delycate
a mynde that he settethe nothynge by yt. And yt beynge
neglected, and therefore shortclye fallynge into ruyne, he
buyldethe vppe anothere in an othere place wyth no lesse
coste and chardge. But emonge the Vtopyans, where all
thynges be sett in a good ordre, and the common wealthe
in a good staye, yt very seldome chaunceth, that they chuse
a new plotte to buylde an house vpon. And they doo
not only finde spedy and quicke remedies for present

a doone and dispatched.

paucae horae quantum boni operis pariant. ad ea quae commemoraui, hoc praeterea facilitatis accedit, quod in necessariis
plerisque artibus minore opera quam aliae gentes opus habent.
Nam primum aedificiorum aut structura aut refectio
ideo tam multorum assiduam ubique requirit operam,   Quomodo uiten-
quod quae pater aedificauit, haeres parum frugi paula-   tur impensae in
tim dilabi sinit: ita, quod minimo tueri potuit, successor   aedificiis.
eius de integro impendio magno cogitur instaurare. Quin frequenter
etiam quae domus alii ingenti sumptu stetit, hanc alius delicato animo
contemnit: eaque neglecta atque ideo breui collapsa, aliam alibi
impensis non minoribus extruit. At apud Vtopienses, compositis
rebus omnibus et constituta republica, rarissime accidit uti noua
collocandis aedibus area deligatur; et non modo remedium celeriter

See end of chapter on 'freedom of mind'?

The problem of efficiency

useless labor?

fautes, but also preuente them that be like to fall. And by this meanes their houses continewe and laste very longe with litle labour and small reparacions; in so much that that[a] kind of woorkemen sumtimes haue almost nothinge to doo; but that they be commaunded to hewe timbre at home, and to square and trime vp stones, to the intente that if annye woorke chaunce, it may the spedelier rise.

Sir = More?

Now[1], Syre, in theire apparell marke, I praye yow, howe few woorkemen they neade. Fyrste of all, whyles they be at woorke, they be couered homely with leather or skinnes that will last .vii. yeares. When they go furthe a brode, they caste vpon them a cloke, whyche hydeth the other homelye apparell. Thyes clookes thoroughe owte the hole Ilande be all of one coloure, and that is the naturall colour of the wul. They therfor do not only spende muche lesse wullen clothe then is spente in othere contreys, but also the same standeth them in muche lesse coste. But lynen clothe ys made wyth lesse laboure, and

Garments

natural wool clouk.

> [a] this.

praesentibus uitiis adhibetur, sed etiam imminentibus occurritur. Ita fit ut minimo labore diutissime perdurent aedificia, et id genus artifices uix habeant interdum quod agant; nisi | quod materiam dolare 85 domi et lapides interim quadrare atque aptare iubentur, quo (si quod opus incidat) maturius possit exurgere.

Iam in uestibus uide quam paucis operis egeant : primum, dum in opere sunt, corio neglectim aut pellibus amiciuntur,

Quomodo in amictu. quae in septennium durent. quum procedunt in publicum, superinducunt chlamydem uestem, quae rudiores illas uestes contegat. eius per totam insulam unus color est, atque is natiuus. Itaque lanei panni non modo multo minus quam[a] usquam alibi sufficit, uerum is ipse quoque multo minoris impendii est. at lini minor est labor, eoque usus crebrior. sed in lineo solus candor,

> [a] *sic* A. *recte pro* quae.

---

[1] Robynson shows, though a little cumbrously, his knowledge of the force given to a sentence by beginning with *Iam.* Burnet's 'As to their Cloaths, observe how little Work is spent in them,' though simpler, ignores this.

ys therefore hadde more in vse. But in lynen clothe *linen*
onlye whytenese, in wullen onlye clenlynes, ys regardede.
As for the smalnese or fynesse of the threde, that ys no
thynge passed for. And thys ys the cause wherfore in
other places .iiii. or v. clothe gownes of dyuers colours, and *English*
as manye sylke cootes, be not enoughe for one man. Yea, *taste,*
and yf he be of the delycate and nyse sorte, x. be to fewe ; *in*
where as there one garmente wyll serue a man mooste *garments*
commenlye .ii. yeares. For whie shoulde he desyre moo ?
seing if he had them, he should not be the better hapt[1] or *naive*
couered from colde, nother in his apparell any whyt the *question*
cumlyer.

　　Wherefore, seynge they be all exercysed in profytable
occupatyons, and that fewe artyfycers in the same craftes
be suffycyente, thys ys the cause that, plentye of all
thynges beynge emonge them, they doo sumtymes bring *mass*
furthe an innumerable companye of people to amende the *work on*
hyghe wayes, yf annye be broken. ⌋Manye times also, *roads*
when they haue no such woorke to be occupied about, an
open proclamation is made that they shall bestowe fewer *increased*
houres in woorke. For the magistrates do not exercise *leisure*

in laneo sola mundicies conspicitur : nullum tenuioris fili precium
est. Itaque fit ut, quum alibi nusquam uni homini quatuor aut quinque togae laneae diuersis coloribus, ac totidem sericiae tunicae sufficiant, delicatioribus paulo ne decem quidem, ibi una quisque contentus
est[a], plerunque in biennium. Quippe nec causa est ulla cur plures
affectet ; quas consecutus neque aduersus frigus esset munitior, neque
uestitu uideretur uel pilo cultior.

　　Quamobrem quum et omnes utilibus sese artibus exerceant, et
ipsarum etiam opera pauciora sufficiant, fit nimirum ut abundante
rerum omnium copia, interdum in reficiendas (si quae detritae sunt)
uias publicas immensam multitudinem educant ; persaepe etiam quum
nec talis cuiuspiam operis usus occurrat, pauciores horas operandi
86 publice denuntient. neque enim superuacaneo | labore ciues inuitos
exercent magistratus, quandoquidem eius reipublicae institutio hunc

　　　　　　　[a] *om.* A.　*Legend.* sit.

───────────────

　　　　　　[2] Wrapt. See the Glossary.

their citizens againste theire willes in vnneadfull laboures. For whie? in the institution of that weale publique this ende is onlye and chiefely pretended and mynded, that what time maye possibly be spared from the necessary occupations and affayres of the commen wealthe, all that the cytizeins sholde withdrawe from the bodcly seruice to the free liberty of the mind and garnisshing of the same. For herin they suppose the felicity of this liffe to consist.

felicity.

free mind.

unum scopum in primis respicit, ut, quoad per publicas necessitates licet, quamplurimum temporis ab seruitio corporis ad animi libertatem cultumque ciuibus uniuersis asseratur.   In eo enim sitam uitae felicitatem putant.

Felicity:

Pleasure: {147: {166; 187— 202; 202 —212 (True Pleasures).

cf. 281 Celibates: 282 wiser sort:

Pride: 157, 196, 232, 306.

Of their ly=

uing and mutuall conuersation together, in cities :

B Ut now will I declare how the citizens vse themselfes *Personal* one towardes another ; what familiar occupieng and *&* enterteynement there is emong the people; and what *public* fasion they vse in distributinge euery thynge.   First, the *living* city consisteth of families : the families most commonlie be made of kinredes.   For the women, when they be maryed at a lawfull age, they goo into their husbandes houses.   But the male chyldren, with al the hole male ofspring, continewe still in their owne familie, and be gouerned of the eldest and auncientest father, onles he *eldest is* dote for age ; for then the next to hym in age is put[a] in *governor* his rowme.

But to thintent the prescript numbre of the citezens *Population* shoulde nether decrease, nor aboue measure increase, it *control* is ordeined that no famylie, whiche in euerye citie be vi.

[a] placed.

DE COMMERCIIS MVTVIS.

S Ed iam quo pacto sese mutuo ciues utantur, quae populi inter se commercia, quaeque sit distribuendarum rerum forma, uidetur explicandum.   Quum igitur ex familiis constet ciuitas, familias ut plurimum cognationes efficiunt.   Nam foeminae (ubi maturuerint) collocatae maritis in ipsorum domicilia concedunt.   at masculi filii ac deinceps nepotes in familia permanent, et parentum antiquissimo parent, nisi prae senecta mente parum ualuerit : tunc enim aetate proximus ei sufficitur.

Verum ne ciuitas aut fieri infrequentior, aut ultra   Numerus ciuium. modum possit increscere, cauetur ne ulla familia, qua-

6000
familie

thousand in the hole, besydes them of the contrey, shall at
ones haue fewer chyldren of the age of xiiii. yeares or there
aboute [1] then x., or mo then xvi.; for of chyldren vnder
thys age no numbre can be [a] appointed. This measure or
numbre is easely obserued and kept, by puttinge them that
in fuller families be aboue the numbre into families of
smaller increase. But if chaunce be that in the hole citie
the stoore encrease aboue the iust numbre, therewith they
fyll vp the lacke of other cityes. But if so be that the
multitude throughout the hole Ilande passe and excede
the dew numbre, then they chewse out of euery citie
certeyn cytezens, and buylde vp a towne vnder their ownc
lawes in the nexte lande [2] where the inhabitauntes haue

[a] be prescribed or.

rum millia sex quaeque ciuitas, excepto conuentu [3], complectitur, pauciores quam decem, pluresue quam sexdecim puberes habeat. Impu-
berum enim nullus praefiniri numerus potest. Hic modus facile
seruatur, transcriptis hiis in rariores familias, qui in plenioribus
excrescunt. At si quando in totum plus iusto abundauerit, aliarum
urbium suarum infrequentiam sarciunt. Quod [a] si forte per totam |
insulam plus aequo moles intumuerit, tum ex qualibet urbe descriptis 87
ciuibus in continente proximo, ubicunque indigenis agri multum
superest et cultu uacat, coloniam suis ipsorum legibus propagant,

[a] *om.* A.

---

[1] This is a diffuse explanation of
puberes, by which More no doubt
simply meant 'adults,' as he meant
'children' by *impuberes*.

[2] Lat. *in continente proximo*, 'on the
nearest part of the mainland,' Utopia
being an island. The possibility of
such an outlet for surplus population
was necessary for More's purpose, and
the assumption made must not be too
severely scrutinized. In fact, with
the sparse population of England in
his day (not exceeding $2\frac{1}{2}$ millions in
England and Wales together) there

must have been no lack of 'waste
lands' within easy reach of many of
its cities. See Professor J. E. Thorold
Rogers' *Industrial and Commercial
History of England*, 1892, p. 48.

[3] This was the word used by More
towards the end of the first chapter,
to express the district assigned to each
city. It is found in Pliny in the sense
of a judge's district. Then, like the
low Latin 'districtus,' it came to signify the diocese of a bishop; or, as
here, an adjacent territory in general.
See Maigne d'Arnis *s. v.*

[handwritten margin notes: "Taking unused land by agreement or force:", "aggressive war.", "law of Nature; sanctions war"]

muche waste and vnoccupied grounde, receauinge also of
the inhabitauntes[a] to them, if they wil ioyne and dwel
with them.   They, thus ioyning and dwelling together,
do easelye agre in one fassion of liuing, and that to the
great wealth of both the peoples.   For they so brynge
the matter about by their lawes, that the grounde which
before was nether good nor profitable for the one nor for
the other, is nowe sufficiente and frutefull enough for them
both.   But if the inhabitauntes of that lande wyll not
dwell with them, to be ordered by their lawes, then they
dryue them out of those boundes, which they haue limited[1]
and apointed out for themselues.   And if they resiste and
rebell, then they make warre agaynst them.   For they
counte this the moste iust cause of warre[2], when any
people holdeth a piece of grounde voyde and vacaunt to
no good nor profitable vse, kepyng other from the vse and
possession of it, whiche notwithstandyng by the lawe of
nature ought thereof to be nowryshed and relieued.   If
any chaunce do so muche dimynishe the numbre of anye

[a] the same countrey people.

ascitis una terrae indigenis, si conuiuere secum uelint. Cum uolentibus coniuncti in idem uitae institutum eosdemque mores facile coales-
cunt; idque utriusque populi bono. efficiunt enim suis institutis ut
ea terra utrisque abunda[3] sit, quae alteris aut[a] parca ac maligna uidebatur. Renuentes ipsorum legibus uiuere propellunt his finibus quos
sibi ipsi describunt. Aduersus repugnantes bello confligunt. nam
eam iustissimam belli causam ducunt, quum populus quispiam eius
soli, quo ipse non utitur, sed uelut inane ac uacuum possidet, aliis
tamen qui ex naturae praescripto inde nutriri debeant, usum ac pos-
sessionem interdicat. Si quando ullas ex suis urbibus aliquis casus

[a] ante, A. *recte.*

---

[1] Rather, 'which they now mark
out for themselves';—not that they
had done so before.

[2] Mr. St. John, in his note on the
passage, justifies the doctrine here

laid down by an appeal to Grotius,
De Jure, Lib. II. cap. 2 § iv. [qu.
§ xvii?]

[3] The word is unclassical as an
adjective.

Immigrants from colonies:

Plagues: 1500 1508 1517

Family life:

of their cyties, that it cannot be fylled vp agayne wythout the diminishynge of the iust numbre of the other cyties (whiche they say chaunced but twyse syns the begynnynge of the lande, through a greate pestilente plage[1]), then they make[a] vp the numbre with cytezens fetched out of their owne forreyne townes ; for they hadde rather suffer theyr forreyn townes to decaye and peryshe, then annye cytie of their owne Ilande to be dimynyshed.

But nowe agayne to the conuersation of the cytezens amonge themselfes. The eldeste (as I sayde) rueleth the familie. The wyfes bee ministers to theyr husbandes, the chyldren to theyr parentes, and, to bee shorte, the yonger to theyr elders. Euerye cytie is diuided into foure[2] equall partes[b]. In the myddes of euery quarter there is a market place of all maner of thynges. Thether the workes of euery familie be brought in to certeyne houses. And

[a] fulfyll and make.   [b] partes or quarters.

eousque imminuerit, ut ex aliis insulae partibus, seruato suo cuiusque urbis modo, resarcıri non possint (quod bis dumtaxat ab omni aeuo, pestis grassante saeuitia, fertur contigisse), remigrantibus e colonia ciuibus replentur. Perire enim colonias potius patiuntur quam ullam ex insularis urbibus imminui.

Sed ad conuictum ciuium reuertor. Antiquissimus (ut dixi) praeest familiae. Ministri sunt uxores maritis, et liberi paren-
Sic excludi potest ociosa turba ministrorum. tibus, atque in summa minores natu maioribus. Ciuitas omnis in quatuor aequales partes diuiditur. In medio cuiusque | partis forum est omnium rerum. Eo in 88 certas domos opera cuiusque familiae conuehuntur, atque in horrea

---

[1] The subject might be fresh in More's thoughts from the visitation in 1508, when, as a contemporary writer relates : ' passim undique occidunt vicatim in urbe hac non pauci.' Prayers were publicly offered in St. Paul's, in August of that year, 'ob hanc sudoris plagam.' In 1517 it broke out again still more dreadfully. Bishop Longland, preaching soon after, speaks of the 'terribilem sudandi novitatem,' through which all was 'longe lateque depopulata.'—See the *Sermones Ioannis Longlandi*, 1518, ff. 15, 64; Gairdner's *Historia . . . a Bernardo Andrea Tholosate conscripta*, 1858, pp. 126, 127; Godwin's *Annales*, 1630. p. 27.

[2] These are the four wards mentioned above, p. 136.

euery kynde of thynge is layde vp seuerall in barnes or store houses. From hence the father of euery famelie or euery housholder fetcheth whatsoeuer he and hys haue neade of, and carieth it awaye with hym without money, without exchaunge, without annye gage or [a] pledge. For whye should anye thynge be denyed vnto hym; seyng there is abundaunce of all thynges, and that it is not to be feared lest anye man wyll aske more then he neadeth? For whie should it be thoughte that man would aske more then enough, which is sewer neuer to lacke? Certeynly, in all kyndes of lyuynge creatures, other fere[1] of lacke doth cause couetousnes and rauyne, or in man only pryde; whiche counteth it a gloryouse thynge to passe and excell other in the superfluous and vayne ostentacion of thynges. The whyche kynde of vice amonge the Vtopians can haue no place.

Next to the market places that I spake of stonde meate markettes[2], whether be brought not onlye all sortes of

[a] gage, pawne, or.

(marginal notes: common store house. / Causes of greed: / fear / or / Pride)*

singulae seorsum species distributae sunt. Ab hiis quilibet paterfamilias, quibus ipse suique opus habent, petit, ac sine pecunia, sine omni prorsus hostimento[3], quicquid petierit, aufert. Quare enim negetur quicquam? quum et omnium rerum abunde satis sit, nec timor ullus subsit, ne quisquam plus quam sit opus flagitare uelit? Nam cur superuacua petiturus putetur is, qui certum habeat nihil sibi unquam defuturum? Nempe auidum ac rapacem aut timor carendi facit, in omni animantum genere, aut in *Rapacitas unde.* homine sola reddit superbia, quae gloriae sibi ducit superflua rerum ostentatione caeteros antecellere; quod uitii genus in Vtopiensium institutis nullum omnino locum habet.

Adiuncta sunt foris (quae commemoraui) fora cibaria, in quae non

---

[1] As Mr. St. John points out (quoting Hobbes, *De Cive*, i. c. i.), while fear might be a motive for the formation of human societies, it is not the apprehension, but the actual consciousness, of want that rouses the savage instincts of animals.

[2] ' Provision markets,' as we should now call them; ' meat' being used in its old sense.

[3] Found in Plautus, *Asin.* i. 3. 20, in the sense of requital, ' Par pari datum hostimentum est; opera pro pecunia.'

herbes, and the fruites of trees with breade, but also fishe, and all maner of iiii. footed beastes, and wilde foule that be mans meate. But first the fylthynes and ordure therof is *sewage.* clene washed awaye in the runnynge ryuer, without the cytie[1], in places appoynted, mete for the same purpose. From thence the beastes brought[a] in kylled, and cleane wasshed by the handes of their bondemen. For they *Bondmen do slaughtering* permytte not their frie citezens to accustome there selfes to the killing of beastes; through the vse whereof they thinke that[b] clemencie, the genteleste affection of our nature, doth[c] by litle and litle decaye[d] and peryshe. Nother they suffer anye thynge that is fylthye, lothesome, or vnclenlye, to be brought into the cytie; least the ayre, by the stenche therof infected and corrupte, shoulde cause pestilente diseases[2].

   [a] be brought.   [b] that *omitted*.   [c] doth *omitted*.   [d] to decaye.

olera modo[a], arborumque fructus et panes comportantur, sed pisces praeterea, quadrupedumque et auium quicquid esculentum est, extra

Tabes ac sordes pestem inuehit ciuitatibus. urbem locis appositis, ubi fluento tabum ac sordes eluantur. Hinc deportant pecudes occisas depuratasque manibus famulorum; nam neque suos ciues

Ex pecudum laniena didicimus et homines iugulare. patiuntur assuescere laniatu animalium, cuius usu clementiam, humanissimum naturae nostrae affectum, paulatim deperire putant; neque sordidum quicquam atque immundum, cuius putredine corruptus aer morbum posset inuehere, perferri in urbem sinunt.

   [a] *Post* olera modo A. *exhibet*: fructusque et panes comportantur, sed pisces praeterea carnesque extra urbem locis appositis, ubi fluento tabum ac sordes eluantur, pecudes occisas. B. *rectius* pecudes occisae depurataeque.

---

[1] See the note before, p. 128. In this respect More had not risen, nor in fact have we, above the ideas of his age, which allowed rivers to be made receptacles for garbage.

[2] We have of late years made some progress in this direction. But we leave in full swing another abuse, as regards the pollution of the atmosphere, which could hardly have occurred to the mind of More. The mill chimneys, in many manufacturing towns, still discharge their volumes of smoke into the air, in defiance of all restraint. That so many tons of fuel should be daily wasted, appears to be a matter of no more concern than the blighting of the herbage for miles around, or the injury done to the health of thousands.

Moreouer euerye strete hath certeyne great large halles sett in equal distaunce one from an other, euerye one knowne by a seuerall name. In thies halles dwell the Syphograuntes[1]. And to eucry one of the same halles be apoynted xxx. families, of[a] ether side xv. The stewardes of euery halle at a certayn houre come in to the meate markettes, where they receyue meate accordinge to the numbre of their halles[2].

30 — family halls

But first and chieflie of all, respect is had to the sycke that be cured[3] in the hospitalles. For in the circuite of the citie, a litle without the walles, they haue .iiii. hospitalles; oo bygge, so wyde, so ample, and so lardge[4], that they may scme .iiii. litle townes; which were deuised of that bygnes, partly to thintent the sycke, be they neuer so many in numbre, shuld not lye to thronge or strayte, and thcrfore uneasely and incomodiously; and partly that they which were taken and holden with contagious diseases, suche as be wonte by infection to crepe from one to an other, myght be laid a part farre from the company

Care of the sick: hospitals

quarantine

^a on.

Habet praetcrea quilibet uicus aulas quasdam capaces, aequali ab
89 sese inuicem | interuallo distantes, nomine quanque suo cognitas. Has colunt Syphogranti; quarum unicuique triginta familiae, uidelicet ab utroque latere quindecim, sunt adscriptae, cibum ibi sumpturae. Obsonatores cuiusque aulae certa hora conueniunt in forum, ac relato suorum numero cibum petunt.

Sed prima ratio aegrotorum habetur; qui in publicis hospitiis curantur. Nam quatuor habent in ambitu ciuitatis hospitia, paulo extra muros, tam capacia ut totidem opplduhs aequari possint, tum ut neque aegrotorum numerus quamlibet magnus auguste collocaretur, et per hoc incommode, tum quo hii qui tali morbo tenerentur, cuius contagio solet ab alio ad alium serpere,

Cura aegrotorum.

---

[1] See above, p. 135.
[2] That is, to the number of persons in their respective halls.
[3] In the old sense of 'cured,' that

is, being attended to, or taken care of.
[4] Note the four equivalents for *capacia*.

Hospitals

cunning physicians (Linacre)

good food for Prince Bishop See last chapter}

of the residue [1]. Thies hospitalles be so well apointed, and with al thynges necessary to health so furnished; and more ouer so diligent attendaunce through the continual presence of cunnyng phisitians is geuen, that though no man be sent thither against his will, yet notwithstandinge there is no sicke persone in all the citie, that had not rather lye there then at home in his owne house [2]. When the stewarde of the sicke hath receiued suche meates as the phisitians haue prescribed, then the beste is equally deuided among the halles, according to the company of euery one, sauing that there is had a respect to the prince, the byshop [3], the tranibours, and to ambassadours, and all straungers, if there be any, whiche be verye fewe and

longius ab [a] aliorum coetu semoueri possint. Haec hospitia ita sunt instructa, atque omnibus rebus quae ad salutem conferant referta, tum tam tenera ac sedula cura adhibetur, tam assidua medicorum peritissimorum praesentia, ut quum illuc nemo mittatur inuitus, nemo tamen fere in tota urbe sit, qui aduersa ualetudine laborans non ibi decumbere quam domi suae praeferat. Quum aegrotorum obsonator cibos ex medicorum praescripto receperit, deinceps optima quaeque inter aulas aequabiliter pro suo cuiusque numero distribuuntur, nisi quod principis, pontificis, et Tranibororum [b] respectus habetur, ac legatorum etiam, et exterorum omnium (si qui sunt, qui pauci ac raro

      [a] *om.* A.   [b] traniborum, A.

---

[1] More's enlightened discernment in all this will be readily acknowledged. But the fact that so much provision for the sick should be contemplated by him in his happy island, shows how heavily Death and Disease had laid their hands on society in his age. Comp. Wright's *History of Caricature and Grotesque in Art*, 1865, p. 217.

[2] In reading this, we should remember what scanty provision for the sick there was in London when More wrote. St. Bartholomew's, indeed, existed; but St. Thomas's, founded as

an almonry, was not opened for its present purpose till 1552. Guy's and St. George's are both of last century. The foundation of the Royal College of Physicians, with its attendant improvements in medical science, was in 1518, two years after the appearance of *Utopia*. Possibly Linacre was stimulated in his good work by the picture here drawn.

[3] He is mentioned in the last chapter as 'the chiefe heade of them all'—that is, of the priests; but comparatively little is said about him.

seldome.   But they also, when they be there, haue certeyne[a] houses apointed and prepared for them.

To thies halles at the set houres of dinner and supper
cummith all the hole Siphograuntie or warde, warned by
the noyse of a brasen trumpet; except such as be sicke in
the hospitalles or els in their owne houses.   Howe be it,
no man is prohibited or forbid, after the halles be serued,
to fetch home meate out of the market to his own house.
For they knowe that no man wyl doo it without a cause
resonable.   For thoughe no man be prohibited to dyne
at home, yet no man doth it willynglye, because it is
counted a pointe of small honestie.   And also it were
a follye to take the payne to dresse a badde dyner at
home, when they maye be welcome to good and fyne fare
so nyghe hande at the hall.   In this hal all vyle seruice,
all slauerie and drudgerye, with all laboursome toyle and[b]
busines, is done by bondemen.   But the women of euery
famelie by course haue the office and charge of cokerye,
for sethinge and dressynge the meate, and orderyng al
thinges therto belonging.   They syt at iii. tables or moo,

[a] certeyne seuerall.   [b] and base.

---

sunt) : sed hiis quoque, cum adsunt, domicilia certa atque instructa
parantur.

90   Ad has aulas prandii coenaeque statis horis tota | syphograntia
conuenit, aeneae tubae clangore commonefacta, nisi
qui aut in hospitiis aut domi decumbunt. quanquam
nemo prohibetur, postquam aulis est satisfactum, e
foro domum cibum petere.   Sciunt enim neminem id
temere facere.   nam etsi domi prandere nulli uetitum
sit, nemo tamen hoc libenter facit, cum neque honestum
habeatur, et stultum sit deterioris parandi prandii
sumere laborem, cum lautum atque opiparum praesto
apud aulam tam propinquam sit.   In hac aula mini-
steria omnia, in quibus paulo plus sordis aut laboris
est, obeunt serui.   Caeterum coquendi parandique
cibi officium, et totius denique instruendi conuiuii
solae mulieres exercent, cuiusque uidelicet familiae per uices. Tribus

Conuiuia com-
munia, promis-
cuaque.

Vt ubique
libertatis habetur
ratio, ne quid fiat
a coactis.

Foeminae
ministrae in
conuiuiis.

M

Dining

accordyng to the numbre of their company. The men syt vpon the benche next the wall, and the women agaynst them on the other syde of the table ; that, if anye sodeyne euell should chaunce to them, as many tymes happeneth to women with chylde, they maye ryse wythout trouble or disturbaunce of anye body, and go thence into the nurcerie.

women on outside for exit

The nourceis sitte seuerall alone with their yonge suckelinges in a certayne parloure apointed and deputed to the same purpose, neuer without fire and cleane water, nor yet without cradels ; that when they wyll they maye laye downe the yong infauntes, and at their pleasure take them out of their swathynge clothes and holde them to the fyere, and refreshe them with playe. Euery mother is nource to her owne chylde [1], onles other death or syckenes be the let. When that chaunceth, the wyues of the Siphograuntes quyckelye prouyde a nource. And that is not harde to be done. For they that can doo it do [a] proffer themselfes to no seruice so gladlye as to that. Because

Nurses—mothers

swaddling

[a] do *omitted.*

pluribusue mensis pro numero conuiuarum discumbitur. Viri ad parietem, foeminae exterius collocantur ; ut si quid his subiti oboriatur mali, quod uterum gerentibus interdum solet accidere, imperturbatis ordinibus exurgant, atque inde ad nutrices abeant. Sedent illae quidem seorsum cum lactentibus [a] in coenaculo quodam ad id destinato, nunquam sine foco atque aqua munda, nec absque cunis interim, ut et reclinare liceat infantulos, et ad ignem cum uelint exemptos fasciis liberare ac ludo reficere. suae quaeque soboli nutrix est, nisi aut mors aut morbus impediat. id cum accidit, uxores Syphograntorum propere nutricem quaerunt, nec id difficile est. Nam quae id praestare possunt, nul|li officio sese offerunt 91

[a] lactantibus, A.

---

[1] On the neglect of this first of parental duties, Erasmus has some bitter remarks in his dialogue *Puerpera.* ' In tales feminas,' he says, ' mihi competere Graecorum videtur etymologia, qui μήτηρ dici putant a μὴ τηρεῖν, hoc est *a non servando.* Nam prorsus conducticiam nutricem infantulo adhuc a matre tepenti adsciscere, genus est expositionis.'

Prause of nurses

that there thys kynde of pitie is muche praysed; and the
chylde that is nouryshed euer after taketh hys nource for
his owne naturall mother. Also amonge the nourceis syt
all the chyldren that be vnder the age of v. yeares. All
the other children of both kyndes, aswell boyes as gyrles,
that be vnder the age of marryage, doo other serue at the
tables [1], or els if they be to yonge therto, yet they stande
by with meruelous silence [2]. That whiche is giuen to them
from the table they eate, and (other seuerall dynner tyme
they haue none.) The Siphograunt and his wife sitteth in
the middes of the highe table, forasmuche as that is
counted the honerablest place, and because from thence al
the hole companye is in their syght. For that table
standeth ouer wharte [3] the ouer ende of the halle. To

nurse = mother.

children over 5 serve or wait

A high table

libentius, quoniam et omnes eam misericordiam laude prosequuntur,
et qui educatur nutricem parentis agnoscit loco. In   Laude et officio
antro nutricum considunt [a] pueri omnes, qui primum   ciues optime
lustrum non [b] explenere. caeteri impuberes, quo in   inuitantur ad
numero ducunt quicunque sexus alterius utrius intra   recte agendum.
nubiles annos sunt, aut ministrant discumbentibus, aut   Educatio sobolis,
qui per aetatem nondum ualent, abstant tamen, atque id summo cum
silentio. utrique quod a sedentibus porrigitur, eo uescuntur, nec aliud
discretum prandendi tempus habent. In medio primae mensae, qui
summus locus est, et cui (nam ea mensa suprema in parte coenaculi
transuersa est) totus conuentus conspicitur, Syphograntus cum uxore

a consident, A.   b om. A.

---

[1] In a little tract, *De disciplina et
institutione Puerorum*, of which the
fourth edition was published in Paris
in 1531, the well-taught boy has a
chapter of instructions *De gestibus in
ministerio mensae*. He is first taught
how and in what order to 'lay the
table.' Then, when all is ready, the
direction is given him : 'Erectus et
compositis pedibus sta, sollicite ani-
maduertens ne desit quid. Et cum
infundendum, siue quid porrigendum,

apponendum, aut tollendum, ciuiliter
id feceris.' As to the silence mentioned just after in the text, the rule
is : 'Astans non turbabis, uel inter-
turbabis aliorum sermonem; sed inter-
rogatus breuiter respondeto' (p. 29).

[2] In Holbein's drawing of the family
of Sir Thomas More, only two out of
the ten figures are seated—Sir Thomas
and his aged father. The rest are all
either standing or kneeling.

[3] That is, overthwart, or across.

The high table

them be ioyned ii. of the anctientest and eldest. For at euery table they syt iiii. at a meesse [1]. But if there be a church standing in that Siphograuntie, or warde, then

priest

the priest and his wyfe sitteth with the Siphograunte, as chiefe in the company. On both sydes of them sytte yonge men, and nexte vnto them agayne olde men. An thus throughe out all the house [2] equall of age be sette together,

young with old

and yet be myxte with [a] vnequall ages. Thys they saye was ordeyned, to the intent that the sage grauitie and reuerence of the elders should kepe the yongers from wanton licence of wordes and behauiour; for as muche as

control of young

nothyng can be so secretly spoken or done at the table, but either they that syt on the one syde or on the other must nedes perceiue it. The disshes be not set downe in ordre from the first place, but all the old men (whoes places be marked with som speciall token to be knowen) be first serued of there meate, and then the residue equally. The old men deuide their dainties [3], as they think best, to

    [a] and matched with.

considet. His adiunguntur duo ex natu maximis. Sedent enim per omnes mensas quaterni. At si templum in ea Syphograntia situm est,

Sacerdos supra principem. At nunc etiam et Episcopi iis mancipiorum uice sunt.

sacerdos ciusque uxor cum Syphogranto sedent ut praesideant. Ab utraque parte collocantur iuniores; post senes rursus; atque hoc pacto per totam domum : et aequales inter se iunguntur, et dissimilibus tamen

Iuniores maioribus admixti.

immiscentur; quod ideo ferunt institutum, ut senum grauitas ac reuerentia (quum nihil ita in mensa fieri diciue potest, ut eos ab omni parte uicinos effugiat)

Senum habita ratio.

iuniores ab improba uerborum gestuumque licentia cohibeat. Ciborum fercula non a primo loco deinceps apponuntur, sed senioribus primum omnibus (quorum insignes | loci 92 sunt) optimus quisque cibus infertur ; deinde reliquis aequaliter ministratur. At senes lautitias suas (quarum non tanta erat copia ut

---

[1] See the Introduction, pp. xviii, xlv.

[2] That is, the hall. We still speak of 'a full house' at a theatre, 'houses of parliament,' &c. In some parts of England, the one large living-room in a farmhouse, answering to the hall in a mansion, is called the 'house-place' or 'house.'

[3] The clause within parentheses in the Latin is left out by the translator.

the yonger that sit of both sides them [a]. Thus the elders be not defrauded of their dewe honoure, and neuerthelesse equall commoditie commeth to euery one.

They begin euerye dynner and supper of reading sumthing that perteineth to good maners and vertue [1]. But it is short, becawse no man shalbe greued therwith. Here of thelders take occasion of honest communication, but nother sad nor vnpleasaunt [2]. Howbeit, they do not spend all the hole dyner time themselfes with long and tedious talkes ; but they gladly here also the yong men ; yea and do [b] purposly prouoke them to talke, to thentent that they maye haue a profe of euery mans wit and towardnes or disposition to vertue, which commonly in ye liberte of

[a] yonger on eche syde of them.   [b] do *omitted.*

posset totam per domum affatim distribui) pro suo arbitratu circumsedentibus impartiuntur. Sic et maioribus natu suus seruatur honos, et commodi tantundem tamen ad omneis peruenit.

Omne prandium coenamque ab aliqua lectione auspicantur, quae ad mores faciat ; sed breui tamen, ne fastidio sit. Ab hac seniores honestos sermones, sed neque tristes ac [a] intacetos, ingerunt. At nec longis logis [3] totum occupant prandium. quin audiunt libenter iuuenes quoque ; atque [b] adeo de industria prouocant, quo et indolis cuiusque et ingenii per conuiuii libertatem prodentis sese

Id hodie uix monachi obseruant.

Sermones in conuiuiis.

[a] nec, A.   [b] *om.* A.

Burnet supplies it : ' if there is not such an Abundance of them that the whole Company may be served alike.'

[1] A common custom at the time, though the marginal note seems to point to its being on the decline. When Ralph Collingwood, Dean of Lichfield, who died in 1518, was making further provision for the College of St. Thomas in Stratford-on-Avon, he ordained that his choristers ' at dinner and supper time should constantly be in the College, to wait at the Table, and to read the Bible, or

some other authentic Book.'—Lansdowne MS. 978, fol. 210. More practised the same custom at his own table. See Bridgett's *Life,* p. 140.

[2] Compare what Erasmus says of Colet, when similarly engaged : ' He would so season the discourse that, though both serious and religious, it had nothing tedious or affected about it.' *Letter to Justus Jonas* (ed. 1883), p. 26.

[3] Comp. Plautus, *Men.* v. 2. 29, ' Loquere, uter meruistis culpam, paucis ; non longos logos.'

{Pleasures selected & encouraged.

Suppers

feasting doth shew and vtter it selfe. Theire dyners be verye short; but there suppers be sumwhat longer; because that after dynner followeth laboure; after supper sleape and naturall reste; whiche they thynke to be of no [a] more strengthe and efficacy to holsome and healthfull digestion. No supper is passed without musicke[1]; nor

{music conceits junkets

their bankettes lacke no conceytes nor ionckettes. They burne swete gummes and speces for [b] perfumes and pleasaunt smelles, and sprincle about swete oyntmentes and waters; yea they leaue nothyng vndone that maketh for the cheryng of the company. For they be muche enclyned

pleasure {

to this opinion: to thinke no kynde of pleasure forbidden, wherof cummeth no harme.

Thus therfore and after this sorte they lyue togethers in the citie; but in the contrey they that dwell alone, farre from anye neyghbours, do dyne and suppe at home in their own houses. For no famelie there lacketh anye

Country life different

kynde of victualles, as from whome cummeth all that the cytezens eate and lyue bye.

     [a] no *omitted.*   [b] or.

---

capiant experimentum. Prandia brcuiuscula sunt, coenae largiores;

Id hodie medici damnant [2].

quod labor illa, has somnus et nocturna quies excipit; quam illi ad salubrem concoctionem magis efficacem putant. Nulla coena sine musica transigitur, nec ullis

Musica in conuiuio.

caret secunda mensa bellariis. odores incendunt et unguenta spargunt [a], nihilque non faciunt quod exhilarare conuiuas possit. sunt enim hanc in partem

Voluptas innoxia non aspernanda.

aliquanto procliuiores, ut nullum uoluptatis genus (ex quo nihil sequatur incommodi) censeant interdictum.

Hoc pacto igitur in urbe conuiuunt; at ruri, qui longius ab sese dissiti sunt, omnes domi quisque suae comedunt. nulli enim familiae quicquam ad uictum deest, quippe a quibus id totum uenit quo uescantur urbici.

     [a] spergunt, A.

---

[1] On More's fondness for music, see the Introduction, p. xxiv, and the note below, p. 295. A viol is seen hanging up

in Holbein's drawing of his household.
[2] See Ray: *English Proverbs*, 1768, p. 27.

❡ Of their

iourneyenge or trauaylynge a brode,
with dyuers other matters cun-
nyngly reasoned and witti-
lie discussed [1].

But if any be desierous to vysite other their fryndes
that dwel[a] in an other Cytie, or to see the place it
selfe, they easelye obteyne lycence of their Siphograuntes
and Tranibores, oneles there bee some profitable let [2].
No man goeth out alone; but a companye is sente furth to
gether with their princes letters, whiche do testifie that
they haue licence to go that iorney, and prescribeth also
the day of their retourne [3]. They haue a wageyn geuen
them, with a common bondman, whiche driueth the oxen

visits

no man
alone

bondman.

^a dwelling.

93　　　　DE PEREGRINATIONE VTOPIENSIVM.

AT si quos aut amicorum alia in urbe commorantium, aut ipsius
etiam uidendi loci desyderium coeperit, a Syphograntis ac
Traniboris suis ueniam facile impetrant, nisi siquis usus impediat. Mittitur ergo simul numerus aliquis cum epistola principis,
quae et datam peregrinandi copiam testatur, et reditus diem praescribit. Vehiculum datur cum seruo publico, qui agat boues et curet.

---

[1] Robynson properly expands the
title of this chapter, which treats of
many subjects besides the *Peregrinatio*
of the Utopians.

[2] That is, as Burnet words it, 'when
there is no particular occasion for him
[them] at Home.'

[3] This may have been suggested by
what Plutarch tells us of an ordinance
of Lycurgus for the Spartans: 'For
the same reason he would not permit
all that desired it to go abroad and see
other countries, lest they should contract foreign manners, [or] gain traces
of a life of little discipline, and of a
different form of government.'—*Lives*,
tr. by the Langhornes, ed. 1805, i.
p. 155.

and taketh charge of them. But onles they haue women in their company, they sende home the wageyn againe, as an impediment and a let. And though they carrye nothyng furth wit them, yet in all their iorney they lacke nothing. For whersoeuer they come they be at home. If they tary in a place longer then one day, than there euery one of them falleth to his own occupation, and be very gentilly enterteined of the workmen and companies of the same craftes. If any man of his owne head and without leaue walke out of his precinct and boundes, taken without the princes lettres, he is brought again for a fugitive or a runaway with great shame and rebuke, and is shapely [a] punished. If he be taken in that faulte agayne, he is punished with bondage.

wandering is bondage

If anye be desierous to walke a brode into the fieldes, or into the contrey that belongeth to the same citie that he dwelleth in, obteynyng the good will of his father, and the consent of his wife [1], he is not prohibited. But into what part of the contrey soeuer he cummeth, he hath no meat geuin him untill he haue wrought out his forenones taske, or els dispatched so muche worke as there is wonte to be

[a] sharpely.

caeterum nisi mulieres in coetu habeant, uehiculum uelut onus et impedimentum remittitur. Toto itinere cum nihil secum efferant, nihil defit tamen; ubique enim domi sunt. Si quo in loco diutius uno die commorentur, suam ibi quisque artem exercet, atque ab artis eiusdem opificibus humanissime tractantur. Si semet autore quisquam extra suos fines uagetur, deprehensus sine principis diplomate, contumeliose habitus, pro fugitiuo reducitur, castigatus acriter. idem ausus denuo, seruitute plectitur.

Quod si quem libido incessat per suae ciuitatis agros palandi, uenia patris et consentiente coniuge non prohibetur. Sed in quodcunque rus peruenerit, nullus ante cibus datur, quam ante meridianum operis pensum (aut quantam ante coenam ibi laborari solet)

---

[1] 'The complaisance of the Utopians towards their wives is truly exemplary. I fear the Europeans do not in every respect imitate their example!'— DIBDIN.

wrought befor supper. Obseruing this lawe and condition, he may go whether he well within the boundes of
his owne citie. For he shalbe no les profitable to the
citie, then if he werc within it.

Now yow see howe litle libertie they haue to loyter;
how they can haue no cloke or pretence to ydelnes.
There be nether wyn tauernes, nor ale houses, nor stewes,
nor any occasion of uice or wickednes, no lurking corners,
no places of wicked councelles or vnlawfull assembles;
but they be in the present sight, and vnder the iyes of
euery man; so that of necessitie they must other applie
their accustomed labours, or else recreate themselues with
honest and laudable pastymes.

This fassion being [a] vsed among the people, they must
of necessitie haue [b] store and plentie of all thinges. And
seing they be al therof parteners equally, therfore cane
no man there be poore or nedye. In the councel of
Amaurot (whether, as I sayde[1], euery citie sendeth .iii.

[a] and trade of life being.
[b] it cannot be chosen but that they must haue.

absoluerit. Hac lege quouis intra suae urbis fines ire licet. Erit
enim non minus utilis urbi quam si in urbe esset.

    Iam uidetis quam nulla sit usquam ociandi licentia, nullus inertiae
praetextus, nulla taberna uinaria, nulla ceruisiaria,
94 nusquam | lupanar, nulla corruptelae occasio, nullae   O sanctam rem-
latebrae, conciliabulum [2] nullum, sed omnium prae-   publicam, et uel
                                                              Christianis
sentes oculi necessitatem aut consueti laboris aut ocii   imitandam.
non inhonesti faciunt.

    Quem populi morem necesse est omnium rerum copiam sequi.
atque ea quum aequabiliter ad omnes perueniat, fit
                                                            Aequabilitas
nimirum ut inops esse nemo aut mendicus possit. In   facit ut omnibus
senatu Amaurotico [3] (quem uti dixi terni quotannis   sufficiat.

---

[1] See above, p. 119.
[2] So used in Plautus, *Bacchid*. I.
i. 47: 'ut solet in istis fieri concilia-
bulis.'
[3] In the first edition, instead of
Amaurotico, the word is here *Menti-*

rano, suggesting the derivation from
mentiri 'to lie.' As More's other
imaginary names are mostly from the
Greek, and as *Mentirano* might sound
rather too blunt, we can see reasons
why he should have made the altera-

men a pece yearly), assone as it is perfectly knowen of what thynges there is in euery place plentie, and agayne what thynges be skant in anye place ; incontinent the lacke of the one is performed [1] and fylled vp with the aboundaunce of the other. And this they doo frelye without any benifite, takyng nothing agayn of them to whom the thinges is geuen; but those cyties that haue geuen of their store to anye other cytie that lacketh, requyrynge nothynge agayne of the same cytie, do take suche thinges as they lacke of an other cytie, to whome [a] they gaue nothynge. So the hole Ilande is as it were one famelie or housholde.

one family.

But when they haue made sufficiente prouision of stoore for them selfes (whiche they thinke not doone untyll they haue prouyded for two yeares followynge, bicause of the vncertentie of the nexte yeares proffe [2]), then of those thynges wherof they haue abundaunce they carry furthe into other contreis greate plenty; as grayne, honnye, wulle, flaxe, woode, madder, purple die [b]

2 yr. supply

     [a] to the which.   [b] died.

omni ex urbe frequentant) ubi primum constiterit quae res quoque loco abundet, rursum cuius alicubi malignior prouentus fuerit, alterius inopiam alterius protinus ubertas explet; atque id gratuito faciunt. nihil uicissim ab his recipientes quibus donant. Sed quae de suis rebus unicuipiam urbi dederint, nihil ab ea repetentes, ab alia cui nihil impenderunt, quibus egent accipiunt. Ita tota insula uelut una familia est.

Respublica nihil aliud quam magna quaedam familia est.   At postquam satis prouisum ipsis est (quod non antea factum censent quam in biennium propter anni sequentis euentum prospexerint) tum ex his quae supersunt magnam uim frumenti, mellis, lanae, ligni, cocci et

---

tion. But why, when he had the council of Amaurote (already so named) in his mind, he should ever have coined this other word, is a little curious. Was the familiar sound of ' in Parlia*mento* ' in his thoughts, and did he wish to convey that the council

at St. Stephen's was not so much the ' national palaver,' as Carlyle called it, as something worse ?

   [1] That is, completed. See the Glossary.

   [2] From being used to render the Latin *euentum*, this appears intended

felles [1], waxe, tallowe, lether, and liuyng beastes. And the
seuenth part of all thies thynges they gyue franckely
and frelye to the poore of that contrey. The resydewe
they sell at a reasonable and meane price. By this trade
of traffique or marchandise, they bring into their own
contrey not only great plentie of golde and siluer, but
also all suche thynges as they lacke at home, whych is
almoste nothynge but Iron [2]. And by reason they haue
longe vsed thys trade, nowe they haue more abundaunce
of thies thynges then any man wyll beleue. Nowe,
therfore, they care not whether they sell for reddye
moneye, or els vpon truste to be paide at a daye, and
to haue the most part in debtes. But in so doyng [3] they
neuer followe the credence of pryuat men, but the
assureaunce or warrauntise of the hole citye, by instrumentes and writinges made in that behalfe accordinglye.

(margin notes: ⅟7 given away. trade. Iron. foreign credit.)

conchyliorum, uellerum, cerae, seui, corii, ad haec animalium quoque
in alias regiones exportant. quarum rerum omnium
septimam partem inopibus eius regiones dono dant: Negotiatio
reliquam precio modico uenditant. quo ex commercio   Vtopiensium.
non eas modo merces quibus domi egent (nam id fere nihil est
practer ferrum) sed argenti atque auri praeterea magnam uim in
95 patriam reportant. Cuius rei diutina consuetudine su|pra quam
credi possit, ubique iam carum rerum copia abundant. Itaque nunc
parum pensi habent, praesente ne pecunia an in diem uendant, multoque maximam partem habeant in nominibus; in quibus tamen
faciendis non priuatorum unquam sed confectis ex more instrumentis

---

to mean 'what the next year might
prove to be.' But see the Glossary.
  [1] Robynson's first reading is here
more correct than his second. It
should be 'purple die, felles,' &c. ; the
items being separate. Burnet leaves
the words out.
  [2] There is nothing to show that
More is here thinking of the imports
and exports of his own country. But,
as a matter of fact, steel and iron

were then among its imports. In *The
Common Weal of the Realm of England*,
before quoted, among the articles which
the king must import from abroad, are
'yron, steile, handgonns, gonpowder,'
and many other things. p. 34.
  [3] Robynson has not understood the
idiom *nomina facere*, 'to lend.' Comp.
Seneca, *De Vita beata*, c. 24: 'Nunquam magis nomina facio quam cum
dono.'

When the daye of paymente is come and expyred, the cytye[1] gathereth vp the debte of the priuate dettours, and putteth it into the common boxe, and so long hath the vse and proffytte of it, vntyll the vtopians their creditours demaunde it. The mooste parte of it they neuer aske. For that thynge whyche is to them no proffyte, to take it from other to whom it is proffytable, they thinke it no righte nor conscience. But yf the case so stande, that they must lende parte of that money to an other people, then they requyre theyre debte; or when they haue warre. For the whyche purpose onelye they keap at home al the treasure which they haue, to be holpen and socoured by yt other in extreame ieopardyes, or in suddeyne daungers; but especyallye and chieflye to hiere therwyth, and that for vnreasonable greate wayges, straunge soldyours. For they hadde rather put straungers in ieopardye then theyre owne contreye men ; knowinge that for moneye enoughe theire enemyes themselfes manye tymes may be bowghte and[a] solde, or els throughe treason be sette togethers

[a] or.

publicam urbis fidem sequuntur. Ciuitas, ubi solutionis dies aduenerit, a priuatis debitoribus exigit creditum, atque in aerarium redigit, eiusque pecuniae quoad ab Vtopiensibus repetatur, usura fruitur. Illi maximam partem nunquam repetunt. Nam quae res apud se nullum habet usum, eam ab his auferre, quibus usui est, haud aequum censent. Caeterum si res ita poscat ut eius aliquam partem alii populo mutuam daturi sint[2], tum demum poscunt, aut quum bellum gerendum est; quam in rem unam totum illum thesaurum quem habent domi seruant, uti aut extremis in periculis, aut in subitis, praesidio sit; potissimum quo milites externos (quos libentius quam suos obiiciunt discrimini) immodico stipendio conducant, gnari multitudine pecuniae hostes ipsos plerunque mercabiles, et uel proditione uel infestis etiam

Vt nusquam non meminerunt suae communitatis.

Qua ratione possit esse utiles pecunia.

Satius est bellum pecunia aut arte declinare, quam multa sanguinis humani iactura gerere.

---

[1] That is, the foreign city, to which merchandise has been exported.

[2] Instead of *daturi sint*, it should rather have been *dent*.

by the eares emonge themselfes. For thys cause they
kype an inestymable treasure ; but yet not as a treasure ;
but so they haue yt and vse yt as in good faythe I am
ashamede to shewe, fearynge that my woordes shal not
be beleued [1]. And thys I haue more cause to feare, for
that I knowe howe dyffucultlye and hardelye I meselfe
wolde haue beleued an othere man tellynge the same,
yf I hadde not presentlye seene yt wyth myne owne
iyes. For yt muste nedes be, that howe farre a thing
is dissonaunt and disagreinge from the guyse and trade [2]
of the hearers, so farre shall yt be owte of theyr beleffe
Howe be yt, a wyse and indyfferente estymer of thynges
wyll not greatly marueil perchaunce, seing al theyre other
lawes and customes doo so muche dyfferre from owres,
yf the vse also of golde and syluer amonge them be
applyed [3] rather to theyr owne fassyons then to owers.
I meane, in that they occupye [4] not moncye themselfes,
but kepe yt for that chaunce ; whyche as yt maye happen,
so yt maye be that yt shall neuer come to passe.

Raphael

signis inter se committi. Hanc ob causam inaestimabilem thesaurum
seruant ; at non ut thesaurum tamen, sed ita habent, quomodo me
narrare profecto deterret pudor, metuentem ne fidem
oratio non sit habitura ; quod eo iustius uereor, quo   _O artificem._
magis mihi sum conscius, nisi uidissem praesens, quam aegre potuissem
96 ipse perduci ut alte|ri idem recensenti crederem. Necesse est enim
fere, quam quicquam est ab eorum qui audiunt moribus alienum, tam
idem procul illis abesse a fide. quanquam prudens rerum aestimator
minus fortasse mirabitur, quum reliqua eorum instituta tam longe ab
nostris differant, si argenti quoque atque auri usus ad ipsorum potius
quam ad nostri moris rationem accommodetur : nempe quum pecunia
non utantur Ipsi, sed in eum seruent euentum, qui ut potest usu
uenire, ita fieri potest ut nunquam incidat.

---

[1] The art shown in this prelude
is pointed out in the marginal note.
What More is thus prefacing is the
conduct of the Utopians in despising
gold and silver in comparison with
iron, but keeping a great store of those
metals, to buy the services of such as
held them precious.

[2] We should now say 'from the
manners and customs ;' Lat. _moribus._
See the Glossary.

[3] That is, adapted.

[4] Compare the 'new ropes never
occupied' (used) of Judges xvi. 11.

*Gold
vs.
Iron*

    In the meane tyme golde and syluer, whereof moneye ys made, they doo soo vse, as none of them dothe more estyme yt, then the verye nature of the thynge deseruethe. And then who dothe not playnlye see howe farre yt ys vnder Iron ? as wythoute the whyche men canne no better lyue then withowte fyere and water ; whereas to golde and syluer nature hathe geuen no vse that we may not wel lacke, yf that the folly of men hadde not sette it in hygher estymacyon for the rarenes sake. But, of the contrary parte, nature, as a moste tender and louynge mother, hath placed the beste and moste necessarye thynges open a brode ; as the ayere, the water, and the earth it selfe ; and hath remoued and hydde farthest from vs vayne and vnprofytable thynges [1]. Therfore yf thies metalles among them shoulde be fast locked vp in some tower, it myghte be suspected that the prynce and the cowncell (as the people is euer foolyshelye ymagininge) intended by some subtyltye to deceaue the commons, and to take some proffette of it to themselfes. Furthermore,

Interim aurum argentumque (unde ea fit) sic apud se habent, ut ab
                        nullo pluris aestimetur quam rerum ipsarum natura
Aurum ferro   meretur. qua quis non uidet quam longe infra ferrum
uilius, quantum
ad usum attinet.   sunt ? ut sine quo non hercle magis quam absque
                        igni atque aqua uiuere mortales queant, quum [a] interim
auro argentoque nullum usum, quo non facile careamus, natura tribu-
erit, nisi hominum stultitia precium raritati fecisset. quin contra,
uelut parens indulgentissima optima quaeque in propatulo posuerit,
ut aerem, aquam ac tellurem ipsam ; longissime uero uana ac nihil
profutura semouerit. Ergo haec metalla si apud eos in turrim aliquam
abstruderentur, princeps ac senatus in suspicionem uenire posset (ut
est uulgi stulta solertia) ne, deluso per technam populo, ipsi aliquo
inde commodo fruerentur. porro si phyalas inde aliaque id genus

        [a] quum interim . . . fecisset *desunt in* A.

---

[1] Cicero has a similar thought, *De Nat. Deorum*, ii. c. 60 : ' Nos e terrae cavernis ferrum elicimus, rem ad colendos agros necessariam ; nos aeris, argenti, auri venas, *penitus abditas*, invenimus, et ad usum aptas et ad ornatum decoras.'

if they should make therof plat[1] and such other finely
and cunningly wrought stuffe ; yf at anye tyme they
shoulde haue occasyon to breake it, and melte it agayne,
and[a] therwyth to paye their souldiours wages[2] ; they see   *soldiers*
and perceiue very well that men wolde be lothe to parte
from those thynges that they ons begonne to haue pleasure
and delyte in.

To remedye all thys, they haue fownde owt a meanes,
which, as it is agreable to al their other lawes and customes,
so it is from ours, where golde is so muche set by and so
delygently kepte, very farre discrepant and repugnaunt ;
and therfore vncredible, but only to them that be wise[3].
For where as they cate and drincke in earthen and glasse
vesselles, which in dede be curiously and properlie made,
and yet be of very small value ; of gold and siluer they
make commonlye chamber pottes, and other like[b] vesselles   *chamber*
that serue for moste vile vses, not only in their common   *pots.*
halles, but in euery mans priuate house. Furthermore of

<hr>

[a] and *omitted*.   [b] like *omitted*.

<hr>

opera fabre excusa conficerent, siquando incidisset occasio, ut con-
flanda sint rursus, atque in militum croganda stipendium, uident
97 nimirum fore ut | aegre patiantur auelli quae semel in delitiis habere
coepissent.

His rebus uti occurrant, excogitauere quandam rationem, ut reliquis
ipsorum institutis consentaneam, ita ab nostris (apud quos aurum
tanti fit, ac tam diligenter conditur) longissime abhorrentem, eoque
nisi peritis non credibilem. Nam quum in fictilibus
e terra uitroque, elegantissimis quidem illis sed uilibus   O magnificam
tamen, edant bibantque, ex auro atque argento, non in   auri contu-
communibus aulis modo, sed in priuatis etiam domibus,   meliam.
matellas passim ac sordidissima quaeque uasa conficiunt. Ad haec

<hr>

[1] That is, plate. Burnet has : 'if
they should work it into Vessels, or
any Sort of Plate.'

   sent their plate to Nottingham, to be
converted into money for the king's
use.

[2] As was afterwards done by Charles
I, in 1642, when the two Universities

[3] Rather, 'to those who know it
by experience'—*peritis*.

chains.

the same mettalles they make greate cheynes with ᵃ fetters and giues, wherin they tye their bondmen. Finally, who so euer for any offence be infamed, by their eares hange ringes of golde; vpon their fingers they were ringes of golde, and about their neckes cheynes of gold; and in conclusion their heades be tiede about with golde ¹. Thus, by all meanes that may be ᵇ, they procure to haue gold and siluer emong them in reproche and infamy. And therfore ᶜ thies metalles, which other nations do as gre-uously and sorroufully forgo, as in a maner from their owne liues: if they should all togethers at ones ² be taken from the vtopians, no man there wold thinke that he had lost the worth of one farthing.

pearls
diamonds
carbuncles.

They gather also peerles by the sea side, and Diamondes and Carbuncles vpon certein rockes; and yet they seke not for them; but by chaunce finding them they cutt and

ᵃ with *omitted.*   ᵇ all means possible.   ᶜ therefore *omitted.*

catenas et crassas compedes, quibus cohercent seruos, iisdem ex metallis operantur. Postremo quoscunque aliquod cri-
Aurum gestamen infamium. men infames facit, ab horum auribus anuli dependent aurei, digitos aurum cingit, aurea torques ambit collum, et caput denique auro uincitur. Ita omnibus curant modis, ut apud se aurum argentumque in ignomina sint, atque hoc pacto fit ut haec metalla, quae caeterae gentes non minus fere dolenter ac uiscera sua distrahi patiuntur, apud Vtopienses, si semel omnia res postularet efferri, nemo sibi iacturam unius fecisse assis uideretur.

Margaritas praeterea legunt in littoribus; quin in rupibus quibus-dam adamantes ac pyropos quoque: neque tamen quaerunt, sed

---

¹ 'It is amusing,' as Father Bridgett says in his *Life* (p. 184), 'that the writer of all this should have been made a knight, or, as he was then called, *Eques auratus*, "a gilded knight," because this dignity both entitled him and required of him to wear golden in-signia, and to deck with gold the trappings of his horse; and that he should generally be represented as wearing round his neck one of those massive gold chains, which he made the badge of notorious malefactors among his Utopians.'

² Robynson appears to have taken the Latin *semel* for *simul*.

polish them. And therwith they decke their yonge in-
fanntes. Which, like as in the first yeares of their child-
hod they make much and be fond and proud of such
ornamentes, so when they be a litle more growen in
yeares and discretion, perceiuing that none but children
do were such toies and trifeles, they lay them awaye
euen of theyre owne shamefastenes, wythowte annye
biddyng of there parentes : euen as oure chyldren, when
they waxe bygge, doo caste awaye nuttes, brouches, and
puppettes [1]. Therfore thyes lawes and customes, whych
be so farre dyfferente from all othere natyons, howe diuers
fanseys also and myndes they doo cause, dydde I neuer
so playnlye perceaue, as in the Ambassadoures of the
Anemolians [2].

Thyes Ambassadoures came to Amaurote whyles I was
there. And bycause they came to entreat of greate and
weighty matters, those .iii. citizeins a pece out of euery
city [3] were commen thether before them. But al the

oblatos casu perpoliunt. His ornant infantulos, qui, ut primis pueri-
tiae annis talibus ornamentis gloriantur ac superbiunt,
sic, ubi plusculum accrcuit aetatis, cum ieusmodi nugis
98 non nisi pueros | uti, nullo parentum animaduertunt
monitu sed suomet ipsorum pudore deponunt ; non aliter ac nostri
pueri, quum grandescunt, nuces, bullas et pupas abiiciunt. Itaque haec
tam diuersa ab reliquis gentibus instituta quam diuersas itidem
animorum affectiones pariant, numquam aeque mihi atque in Anemo-
liorum legatis inclaruit.

Gemmae puero rum delitiae.

Venerunt hi Amaurotum (dum ego aderam) et,
quoniam magnis de rebus tractatum ueniebant, aduentum eorum terni illi ciues ex qualibet urbe praeuenerant.

Elegantissima fabula.

---

[1] 'Throwing away nuts,' for 'putting away childish things,' is rather a
Latin proverb than an English one.
The emperor Augustus, we are told,
would play at nuts with little children
(Sueton. *in vita*, c. 83). All three expressions may be illustrated from Persius:—
'. . . . . nucibus facimus quaecunque
      relictis' (*Sat.* i. 10).

' Bullaque succinctis Laribus donata
      pependit' (*ib.* v. 31).
' Nempe hoc quod Veneri donatae a
      uirgine pupae' (*ib.* ii. 70).
[2] An appropriate name, from ἄνεμός,
' the wind.' Compare Cicero's use of
ventosus, where he calls Lepidus ' homo
ventosissimus' (*Epp. ad Fam.* xi. 9).
[3] See above, p. 119.

Ambassadours of the next contreis, which had bene there before, and knewe the fassions and maners of the Vtopians, amonge whome they perceaued no honoure geuen to sumptuous and costelye [a] apparrell, silkes to be contemned, golde also to be enfamed and reprochefull, were wont to come thether in very homely and simple apparrell [b]. But the Anemolianes, bicause they dwell farre thence, and had verye litle acquaintaunce with them, hearinge that they were al apparelled a like, and that verye rudelye and homelye, thynkynge them not to haue the thynges whyche they dydde not weare, beynge therefore more proud then wise, determined in the gorgiousnes of their apparel to represent very goddes, and wyth the bright shynynge and glisteringe of their gaye clothinge to dasell the eyes of the silie poore vtopains. So ther came in iii. Ambassadours with C. seruauntes all apparelled in chaungeable colours; the moost of them in silkes; the Ambassadours themselfes (for at home in their owne countrey they were noble men) in cloth of gold, with great cheines of gold, with

[a] and costelye *omitted*.   [b] araie.

sed omnes finitimarum gentium legati, qui eo ante appulerant, quibus Vtopiensium perspecti mores erant, apud quos sumptuoso uestitui nihil honoris haberi intelligebant, sericum contemptui esse, aurum etiam infame sciebant, cultu quam poterant modestissimo uenire consueuerant. At Anemolii, quod longius aberant, ac minus cum illis commercii habuerant, quum accepissent eodem omnes eoque rudi corporis cultu esse, persuasi[1] non habere eos quo non utebantur, ipsi etiam superbi magis quam sapientes decreuerunt apparatus elegantia deos quosdam repraesentare, et miserorum oculos Vtopiensium ornatus sui splendore praestringere. Itaque ingressi sunt legati tres, cum comitibus centum, omnes uestitu uersicolori, plerique serico, legati ipsi (nam domi nobiles erant) amictu aureo, magnis torquibus, et

---

[1] This personal construction of *persuasus*, as if the verb governed an accusative in the active, is found in Ovid and Phædrus. Valla, while discussing the nice distinctions of *suadere* and *persuadere*, seems to allow it : ' Qui persuasus est, plane acquiescit.' *Elegant.* (1529), leaf 149 vers.

gold hanging at their eares, with gold ringes vpon their
fingers, with brouches and aglettes of gold vpon their
cappes, which glistered ful of peerles and pretious stones;
to be short, trimmed and aduorned with al those thinges,
which emong the vtopians were other the punnishement
of bondmen, or the reproche of infamed persones, or elles
trifels for yonge children to playe with all. Therfore it
wolde haue done a man good at his harte to haue sene
howe proudelye they displeyed theire pecockes fethers;
howe muche they made of their paynted sheathes; and
howe loftely they sett forth and aduaunced them selfes [1],
when they compared their gallaunte apparrell with the
poore rayment of the vtopians. For al the people were
swarmed furth into the stretes. And on the other side
it was no lesse pleasure to consider howe muche they
were deceaued, and how farre they missed of their
purpose; being contrary wayes taken then they thought
they shoulde haue bene. For to the iyes of all the
vtopians, excepte very fewe, whiche had bene in other
contreys for some resonable cause, al that gorgeousnes
of apparrel semed shamefull and reprochefull; in so

inauribus aureis, ad haec anulis aureis in manibus, monilibus insuper
99 appensis in pileo, quae margaritis ac gemmis affulgebant : omni|bus
postremo rebus ornati, quae apud Vtopienses aut seruorum supplicia,
aut infamium dedecora, aut puerorum nugamenta fuere. Itaque
operae precium erat uidere quo pacto cristas erexerint, ubi suum
ornatum cum Vtopiensium uestitu (nam in plateis sese populus effu-
derat) contulere. contraque non minus erat uoluptatis consyderare
quam longe sua eos spes expectatioque fefellerat, quamque longe ab
ea existimatione aberant, quam se consecuturos putauerant. Nempe
Vtopiensium oculis omnium, exceptis perquam [a] paucis, qui alias
gentes aliqua idonea de causa inuiserant, totus ille splendor apparatus
pudendus uidebatur, et infimum quenque pro dominis reuerenter

[a] praeterquam, A.

---

[1] It will be noticed how Robynson   in the Latin, 'quo pacto cristas erexe-
has here amplified the single phrase   rint.'

N 2

much that they most reuerently saluted the vylest and
most abiect of them for lordes; passing ouer the Ambassadours themselfes without any honour; iudging
them, be their wearing of golden cheynes, to be bondemen. Yea, you shuld haue sene children also that had
caste away their peerles and pretious stones, when they
sawe the like sticking vpon the Ambassadours cappes,
digge and pushe their mothers vnder the sides, sayinge
thus to them: 'Loke, mother, how great a lubbor doth yet
were peerles and pretious stoones, as though he were
a litel child still[1].' But the mother, yea, and that also
in good earnest: 'peace, sone,' saith she; 'I thynk he
be some of the Ambassadours fooles.' Some fownde
fawte at theire golden cheynes, as to no vse nor purpose; beynge so small and weake, that a bondeman
myghte easelye breake them; and agayne so wyde and
large, that, when it pleased him, he myght cast them of,
and runne awaye at lybertye whether he wolde.

But when the Ambassadoures hadde bene there a daye
or .ii., and sawe so greate abundaunce of gold so lyghtelye
estymed, yea, in no lesse reproche then yt was wyth them

salutantes, legatos ipsos, ex aurearum usu catenarum pro seruis habitos, sine ullo prorsus honore praetermiserunt. Quin pueros quoque
uidisses, qui gemmas ac margaritas abiecerant, ubi in legatorum pileis
               affixas conspexerunt, compellare matrem ac latus
ὦ τεχνίτην.[a]   fodere: En, mater, quam magnus nebulo margaritis
adhuc et gemmulis utitur, ac si esset puerulus! At parens serio
etiam illa, Tace, inquit, fili; est, opinor, quispiam e morionibus legatorum. Alii catenas illas aureas reprehendere, utpote nullius usus,
quippe tam graciles ut eas facile seruus infringere, tam laxas rursus
uti quum fuerit libitum possit excutere, et solutus ac liber quouis
aufugere.
     Verum legati postquam ibi unum atque alterum diem uersati tan-
tam auri uim in tanta uilitate conspexerunt, nec in | minore contumelia 100

    [a] ο τεχνίτην, A. *Idem quoque* B., *sed nulla accentus nota.*

---

[1] The marginal annotator, whether   deservedly called attention to the
it be Erasmus or Peter Giles, has   artistic effect of this touch.

in honour ; and, besydes that, more golde in the cheynes
and gyues of one fugytyue bondeman, then all the costelye
ornamentes of them .iii. was worth ; they beganne to abate
theyre currage, and for verye shame layde awaye all that
gorgyouse arraye wherof theye were so prowde ; and
specyallye when they hadde talkede famylyerlye wyth
the Vtopyans, and hadde learnede all theyre fassyons
and opynyons.   For they marueyle that annye men be
soo folyshe as to haue delyte and pleasure in the ᵃ glys-
terynge of a lytyll tryfelynge stone, whyche maye beholde
annye of the starres, or elles the soone yt selfe ; or that
annye man ys so madde as to counte him selfe the nobler
for the smaller or fyner threde of wolle, whyche selfe
same woll (be it nowe in neuere so fyne a sponne threde)
dyde ones a shepe weare ᵇ ; and yet was she all that time
no other thing than a shepe ¹.

  They marueyle also that golde, whyche of the owne
nature is a thynge so vnprofytable, is nowe emonge all

          ᵃ the doubteful.   ᵇ a shepe dyde ones.

quam apud se honore habitam uidissent ; ad haec in unius fugitiui
serui catenas compedesque plus auri atque argenti congestum quam
totus ipsorum trium apparatus constiterat, subsidentibus pennis
omnem illum cultum, quo sese tam arroganter extulerant, pudefacti
seposuerunt : maxime uero postquam familiarius cum Vtopiensibus
collocuti mores eorum atque opiniones didicere.
Mirantur ille siquidem quenquam esse mortalium   Dubius dixit,
quem exiguae gemmulae aut lapilli dubius oblectet ful-   ob gemmas
                                                         factitias, aut
gor, cui quidem stellam aliquam atque ipsum denique   certe dubium dixit
solem liceat ᵃ intueri ; aut quenquam tam insanum   exiguum ac
esse, ut nobilior ipse sibi ob tenuioris lanae filum   malignum.
uideatur ; siquidem hanc ipsam (quantumuis tenui filo
sit) ouis olim gestauit, nec aliud tamen interim quam ouis fuit.
  Mirantur item aurum suapte natura tam inutile nunc ubique gen-

              ᵃ *om.* A.

---

  ¹ An anticipation of the familiar lines of Dr. Watts :
          ' When the poor sheep and silkworm wore
          That very clothing long before.'

evils of money:

people in soo hyghe estymatyon, that man hym selfe, by whom, yea and for the vse of whome, yt ys so muche sett by, ys in muche lesse estymatyon then the golde yt selfe. In so muche that a lumpyshe blockehedded churle [1], and whyche hathe no more wytte then an asse, yea, and as full of noughtenes and folyshenes [a], shall haue neuertheles many wyse and good men in subiectyon and bondage, onlye for thys, bycause he hathe a greate heape of golde. Whyche yf yt should be taken from hyme by annye fortune, or by some subtyll wyle [b] of the lawe,

English respect of money

(which no lesse then fortune doth raise vp the lowe, and plucke downe the high) and be geuen to the most vile slaue and abiect dreuell of all his housholde, then shortely after he shall goo into the seruice of his seruaunt, as an augmentation or an [c] ouerplus besyd his money. But they much more marueill at and detest the madenes of them, whyche to those riche men, in whose debte and daunger [2] they be not, do giue almoste diuine honowres,

[a] noughtenes as of follye.   [b] wyle and cautele.   [c] nor [3].

tium aestimari tanti, ut homo ipse per quem atque adeo in cuius usum id precii obtinuit, minoris multo quam aurum ipsum aestimetur; usque adeo ut plumbeus quispiam, et cui non plus ingenii sit quam stipiti, nec minus etiam improbus quam stultus, *Quam uere et quam apte.* multos tamen et sapientes et bonos uiros in seruitute habeat, ob id duntaxat, quod ei magnus contigit aureorum numismatum cumulus; quem si qua fortuna aut aliqua legum stropha (quae nihil minus ac fortuna ipsa summis ima permiscet) ab hero illo ad abiectissimum totius familiae suae nebulonem transtulerit, fit nimirum paulo post ut in famuli sui famu||licium concedat, 101 uelut appendix additamentumque numismatum. Caeterum multo magis eorum mirantur ac detestantur insaniam, qui diuitibus illis quibus neque debent quicquam, neque sunt obnoxii, nullo alio respectu,

---

[1] Burnet, more literally, but not idiomatically, 'a Man of Lead.'

[2] Compare the *Merchant of Venice,* iv. 1, 'You stand within his danger, do you not?'

that is, under obligation to him.

[3] The reading of the second edition, 'nor' for 'or an,' may have been caused by joining the n of the preceding word to 'or.'

for non other consideration, but bicause they be riche;
and yet knowing them to be suche nigeshe penny fathers[1],
that they be sure, as long as they liue, not the worthe
of one farthinge of that hcape of gold shall come to
them.

Thies and such like opinions haue they conceaued, *learning*
partely by education, beinge brought vp in that common
wealth, whose lawes and customes be farre different
from thies kindes of folly, and partely by good littera-
ture and learning.   For though ther be not many in
euery citye, whiche be exempte and discharged of all
other laboures, and appointed only to learninge; that
is to saye, suche in whome euen from theire very childhode they haue perceaued a singuler towardnes, a fyne
witte, and a minde apte to good learning; yet all in their
childhode be instructe in learninge.   And the better parte
of the people, bothe men and women, throughe owte all
theire hole lyffe, doo bestowe in learninge those spare
howres, which we sayde they haue vacante from bodelye *Their*
laboures[2].   They be taughte learninge in theire owne *lanpuage*

quam quod diuites sunt, honores tantum non diuinos impendunt,
idque cum eos tam sordidos atque auaros cognoscunt,   *Quanto plus*
ut habeant certo certius ex tanto nummorum cumulo,   *sapiunt Vtopiani*
uiuentibus illis, ne unum quidem nummulum unquam   *quam Christia-*
ad se uenturum.   *norum uulgus.*

Has atque huiusmodi opiniones partim ex educatione conceperunt,
in ea educti Republica, cuius instituta longissime ab his stultitiae
generibus absunt; partim ex doctrina et literis. Nam et si haud
multi cuiusque urbis sunt, qui caeteris exonerati laboribus soli disciplinae deputantur, hii uidelicet in quibus a pueritia egregiam indolem,
eximium ingenium, atque animum ad bonas artes propensum, depre-
hendere, tamen omnes pueri literis imbuuntur; et populi bona pars,
uiri faeminaeque, per totam uitam, horas illas quas ab operibus
liberas diximus, in literis collocant. Disciplinas ipsorum lingua

---

[1] Niggardly misers. See the Glossary.   from bodily labours' lies the original
[2] See above, p. 143. In this 'vacancy   idea of ' school.'

Language:

natyue tonge. For yt is bothe copious in woordes, and also pleasaunte to the eare, and for the vtteraunce of a mans minde verye perfecte and sure[1]. The mooste parte of all that syde of the wordle[2] vseth the same langage; sauinge that amonge the Vtopians yt is fyneste and puryste; and accordynge to the dyuersytye of the contreys yt ys dyuerslye alterede.

Of all thyes Philosophers, whose names be here famous in thys parte of the wordle to vs knowen, before owre cummynge thether, nott as muche as the fame of annye of them was comen amonge them; and yett in Musycke, Logycke, Arythmetyke, and Geometrye, they haue fownde owte in a manner all that oure auncyente Philosophers haue tawghte. But as they in all thynges be almoste equall to our olde auncyente clerkes, so our newe Logiciens

perdiscunt. est enim neque uerborum inops, nec insuauis auditu,
Studia et nec ulla fidelior animi interpres est. eadem fere (nisi
disciplinae quod ubique corruptior, alibi aliter) magnam eius orbis
Vtopiensium. plagam peruagatur.
Ex omnibus his philosophis, quorum nomina sunt in hoc noto
nobis orbe celebria, ante nostrum aduentum ne fama
Musica, quidem cuiusquam eo peruenerat, et tamen in musica
Dialectica, dialecticaque, ac numerandi et me|tiendi scientia 102
Arithmetica. eadem fere quae nostri illi ueteres inuenere. Caeterum ut antiquos omnibus prope rebus exaequant, ita nuperorum

---

[1] Was More thinking of the yet undeveloped capacity of his own mother tongue, when he wrote this? It should not, at any rate, be forgotten what great services he rendered to his native English speech. He was, as Sir James Mackintosh said, ' the first person in our history distinguished by the faculty of public speaking;' and he was also distinguished ' as our earliest prose writer, and as the first Englishman who wrote the history of his country in the present language.'—*Life of More,*
1831, p. 19. The English tongue in More's day, ' rough, confused, unmetrical, the tongue of business and the vulgar, was, in the lips of the educated, a condescension to vulgar ignorance and infirmity.'—See *English Studies,* by the late Professor Brewer, 1881, p. 226. More's friends, Colet and Lily, at the time when he wrote, were also ' teaching learning in their own native tongue.'

[2] The same transposition of letters is left in the second edition.

anti-

in subtyll inuentyons haue farre passed and gone beyonde scholastic
them[1]. For they haue not deuysed one of all those rules
of restryctyons, amplyfycatyons, and supposytyons, very
wittelye inuented in the small Logycalles[2], whyche heare
oure chyldren in euerye place do learne. Furthermore
they were neuer yet able to fynde out the seconde intentyons[3]; in so muche that none of them all coulde euer see

inuentis dialecticorum longe sunt impares. Nam ne ullam quidem
regulam inuenerunt earum, quas de restrictionibus,
amplificationibus, ac suppositionibus acutissime excogi-   Apparet hoc loco
tatis in paruis logicalibus passim hic ediscunt pueri.   subesse nasum.
Porro secundas intentiones tam longe abest ut inuestigare suffecerint,

second
intention.

---

[1] The marginal note gives a hint of the irony that is coming.

[2] The name of 'Parva Logicalia' (so called, More says laughingly in his letter to Dorp, because they have *little logic* in them) was given to the last treatise in the *Summulae* of Petrus Hispanus (Spanheym), afterwards Pope John XXI. He died in 1277. According to Mansel, his *Summulae Logicales* may be regarded as 'the earliest scholastic treatise on Logic which professes to be anything more than an abridgement of, or commentary on, portions of the Organon.' The last treatise of the work, according to the same writer, 'contains sundry additions to the text of Aristotle, in the form of dissertations on *suppositio, ampliatio, restrictio, exponible proposi-tions*, and other subtleties, more ingenious than useful, and belonging rather to Grammar than to Logic.' There are frequent allusions to the *Parva Logicalia* in the *Epistolae Obscurorum Virorum* (ed. 1557, leaf A 9 of the *Concil. Theolog.*, &c.), and the subject is not forgotten in the *Encomium Moriae* (ed. 1668, p. 182). It is amusing to find Listrius, who joined in the laugh with Erasmus at these 'plusquam scholasticas nugas,' pre-

paring an edition of the *Summulae*, which appeared in 1520. See Gesner's *Bibliotheca*, 1545, leaf 274 vers., and Mansel's *Artis Logicae Rudimenta*, 1852, p. xxxiii.

[3] Of this really important conception in logic, which formed a chief subject of dispute between the Thomists and Scotists, Mr. Mullinger gives a clear account in his *University of Cambridge*, i. p. 181: 'The intellect, as it directs itself (*intendens se*) towards external objects, discerns, for example, Socrates in his pure individuality, and the impression thus received is to be distinguished as the *intentio prima*. But when the existence of Socrates has thus been apprehended, the reflective faculty comes into play; Socrates, by a secondary process, is recognized as a philosopher or as an animal; he is assigned to genus and species. The conception thus formed constitutes the *intentio secunda*. But the *intentio secunda* exists only in relation to the human intellect, and hence cannot be ranked among real existences; while the objects of the external world, and Universals which have their existence in the Divine mind, would exist even if man were not.'

abstract

man hymselfe in commen, as they call hym[1]; thoughe he
be (as yow knowe) bygger then euer was annye gyaunte,
yea, and poynted to of vs euen wyth our fynger. But

serious astronomy

they be in the course of the starres, and the mouynges
of the heauenlye spheres, verye expert and cunnynge[2].
They haue also wyttelye excogytated and diuised instrumentes of diuers fassyons, wherin is exactly comprehended
and conteyned the mouynges and sytuatyons of the sonne,
the moone, and of all the other starres which appere in

no astrology

theyre horyzon. But as for the amityes and dissentyons
of the planettes, and all that deceytefull diuynatyon by the
starres[3], they neuer asmuch as dreamed therof. Raynes,
windes, and other courses of tempestes they knowe before

ut nec hominem ipsum in communi, quem uocant, quanquam (ut
scitis) plane colosseum et quouis gigante maiorem, tum a nobis praeterea digito demonstratum, nemo tamen eorum uidere potuerit. At

Astrologia.   sunt in astrorum cursu, et caelestium orbium motu,
   peritissimi. Quin instrumenta quoque diuersis figuris
solerter excogitarunt, quibus solis ac lunae, et caeterorum item astrorum, quae in ipsorum horizonte uisuntur, motiones ac situs exactis-

At hii regnant   sime comprehensos habent. Caeterum amicitias,
inter Christianos atque errantium dissidia syderum, ac totam denique
hodie.   illam ex astris diuinandi imposturam, ne somniant quidem. Imbres, uentos, ac caeteras tempestatum uicissitudines signis

---

[1] That is, man in the abstract. For
the subject of Universals, in dispute
between the Realists and Nominalists,
see Hampden's *Scholastic Philosophy*,
1833, p. 71, and the passages from
Prantl, quoted by Mullinger, as above,
pp. 182, 183.

[2] This was in accordance with
More's own tastes. 'If an astronomer
came in his way,' says Seebohm,
quoting Stapleton, 'he would get him
to stay awhile in his house, to teach
them all about the stars and planets.'
Oxford Ref., 1869, p. 500.

[3] 'No class of men,' writes the
author of *Philomorus*, 'came more

frequently under the lash than the
pretenders to astrology. Many years
ago More had exposed their notorious failure in his elegy upon the
death of Elizabeth of York, who died
in the very year in which they had
predicted for her all manner of prosperity :—

'Yet was I lately promised otherwise,
This year to live in welthe and
  delice.'
See the *Philomorus*, ed. 1878, pp.
233 sqq., where translations are given
of some of More's epigrams *in astro-
logos.*

[handwritten top margin: Disputes of the good, virtue & pleasure: NB: Hythloday assumes a similarity of argument & interest among Utopians and Europeans; (weather:)]

by certein tokens, which they haue learned by long vse
and obseruation [1]. But of the causes of all thies thinges,
of the ebbinge, flowinge, and saltenes of the sea, and
fynallye of the orygynall begynnyng and nature of heauen
and of the wordle, they holde partelye the same opynyons
that our olde philosophers holde; and partelye, as our
philosophers varye emonge themselfes, so they also, whiles
they bringe new reasons of thynges, doo disagree from all
them, and yet emonge themselfes in all poyntes they doo
not accorde.

[handwritten right margin: origins argued variously: cf. religion Ch IX]

In that part of philosophie which intreateth of manners
and vertue [2], theire reasons and opynyons agree wyth
ours. They dyspute of the good qualytyes of the sowle,
of the body, and of fortune; and whether the name of
goodnes [3] maye be applied to all thies, or onlie to the
endowmentes and giftes of the sowle. They reason of
vertue and pleasure. But the chiefe and principall question
is in what thynge, be yt one or moo, the felycytye of man
consisteth. But in thys poynte theye seme almooste to

[handwritten right margin: Soul. logic & debate felicity]

[handwritten: Rapael critical here: cf. p. 166]

quibusdam longo perspectis usu praesentiunt. Sed de causis earum
rerum omnium, et de fluxu maris eiusque salsitate, et
in summa de caeli mundique origine ac natura, partim
eadem que ueteres philosophi nostri disserunt, partim,
ut illi inter se dissident, ita hi quoque, dum nouas rerum rationes affe-
runt, ab omnibus illis dissentiunt, nec inter se tamen usque quaque
conueniunt.

[margin: Physica omnium incertissima.]

In ea philosophiae parte qua de moribus agitur, eadem illis dispu- |
103 tantur quae nobis. de bonis animi quaerunt et corporis, et externis, tum utrum boni nomen omnibus his,
an solis animi dotibus conueniat. De uirtute disserunt
ac uoluptate; sed omnium prima est ac princeps con-
trouersia, qua nam in re, una pluribusue sitam hominis
felicitatem putent. At hac in re propensiores aequo

[margin: Ethica. Ordo bonorum. Fines bonorum. Vtopiani felici-tatem honesta]

---

[1] Compare what was said of the
City of the Sun, above, p. lvii.

[2] Ethics, or moral philosophy.

[3] The marginal note 'Fines bonorum' points the reference to Cicero's
treatise. In what follows, frequent
references to the *De Finibus* will appear.

Pleasure.

muche geuen and enclyned to the opinion of them whiche defende pleasure; wherin they determine other all or the chiefyste parte of mans felycytye to reste[1]. And (whyche is more to bee marueled at) the defence of thys soo deyntye and delycate an opynyon they fetche euen from theyre[2] graue, sharpe, bytter, and rygorous relygyon. For they neuer dyspute of felycytye or blessednes, but they ioyne to the reasons of Philosophye certeyne pryncyples taken owte of relygyon; wythoute the whyche, to the inuestygatyon

Reason alone is weak:

of trewe felycytye, theye thynke reason of yt selfe weak and vnperfecte. Thoose pryncyples be thyes and suche

Dogma:
I.

lyke: That the sowle ys immortall, and by the bountifull goodnes of God ordeyned to felicitie: That to our vertues and good deades rewardes be apoynted after this lyfe, and

II.

to our euell deades punyshementes. Though thies be

uoluptate metiuntur.

Principia philosophiae e religione petenda

Theologia Vtopiensium.

Animorum immortalitas, de qua hodie non pauci etiam Christianorum disputant.[b]

uidentur in factionem uoluptatis assertricem, ut qua uel totam, uel potissimam felicitatis humanae partem definiant. Et quo magis mireris, ab religione quoque (quae grauis et seuera est fereque tristis et rigida) petunt tamen sententiae tam delicatae patrocinium. Neque enim de felicitate disceptant unquam, quin principia quaedam ex religione deprompta tum[a] philosophia quae rationibus utitur, coniungant; sine quibus ad uerae felicitatis inuestigationem mancam atque imbecillam per se rationem putant. Ea principia sunt huiusmodi: animam esse immortalem, ac dei beneficentia ad felicitatem natam: uirtutibus ac benefactis nostris praemia post hanc uitam, flagitiis destinata supplicia. Haec tametsi

[a] *Legend.* cum.   [b] Christiani dubitant, B.

[1] This making the people of Utopia to be Epicureans in philosophy is in accordance with what Vesputius had written of some of his newly-discovered tribes:—'Quid vltra dicam? viuunt secundum naturam, et *epycuri* potius dici possunt quam stoici.'—See the *Mundus nouus,* before quoted, fol. 3 verso.

[2] The insertion of this word spoils the sense. The religion of the Utopians was not 'sharpe, bytter and rygorous.' Burnet's rendering is better: 'and, what may seem more strange, they make use of arguments even from religion, notwithstanding its severity and roughness, for the support of that opinion, so indulgent to pleasure.'

Vesputius

perteynyng to religion, yet they thynke it mete that they *Religion &*
shoulde be beleued and graunted by profes of reason. *Reason:*
But if thies principles were condempned and dysanulled,
then without anye delaye they pronounce no man to be so *Epicurean*
folish, whiche woulde not do all hys diligence and en- *philosophy*
deuoure to obteyne pleasure be ryght or wronge, onlye *the*
auoydynge this inconuenience, that the lesse pleasure *second*
should not be a let or hynderaunce to the bygger ; or that *best.*
he laboured not for that pleasure whiche would bryng
after it displeasure, greefe, and sorrowe [1]. For they iudge
it extreame madnes to folowe sharpe and peinful vertue,
and not only to bannyshe the pleasure of lyfe, but also
wyllyngly to suffre grief without any hope of proffyt
thereof [a]. For what proffyt can there be, if a man, when
he hath passed ouer all hys lyfe vnpleasauntly, that is to
say, wretchedlye [b], shall haue no rewarde after hys death ?

[a] therof ensuinge.　　　　　　[b] miserablye.

religionis sint, ratione tamen censent ad ea credenda et concedenda
perduci ; quibus e medio sublatis, sine ulla cunctatione pronunciant
neminem esse tam stupidum, qui non sentiat petendam
sibi per fas ac nefas uoluptatem ; hoc tantum caueret　　Vt non quaeuis [a]
ne minor uoluptas obstet maiori, aut eam persequatur,　　expetenda
quam inuicem retaliet [2] dolor. Nam uirtutem asperam　　uoluptas, ita nec
　　　　　　　　　　　　　　　　　　　　　　　　　　dolor affectandus,
ac difficilem sequi, ac non abigere modo suauitatem　　nisi uirtutis
uitae, sed dolorem etiam sponte perpeti, cuius nullum　　causa.
expectes fructum (quis enim potest esse fructus si
104 post | mortem nihil assequeris, quum hanc uitam totam insuauiter,
hoc est, misere traduxeris) id uero dementissimum ferunt. Nunc
　　　　[a] quiuis, B. *praue.*

---

[1] Epicurus himself taught the necessity of this temperance in the enjoyment of pleasure. It was a boast of
his, Seneca tells us, that he could dine
for less than an *as,* while it cost
Metrodorus the whole of that sum
(about three farthings) for his dinner.
The peculiar pleasure of the feat lay
in the consciousness of being able to
dispense with what lower natures

found necessary to enjoyment. ' Non
enim iucunda res est aqua et polenta,
aut frustum hordacei panis ; sed summa
uoluptas est, posse capere ex his
uoluptatem, et ad id se reduxisse,
quod eripere nulla fortunae iniquitas
possit.' Seneca, *Epist.* xviii.
[2] A post-classical word, found in
Aulus Gellius.

Felicity & pleasure: following nature

Stoic view:

love of divine majesty

But now, syr, they thynke not felicitie to reste in all pleasure, but onlye in that pleasure that is good and honest; and that hereto, as to perfet blessednes, our nature is allured and drawen euen of vertue; wherto only they that be of the contrary opinion) do attribute felicitie. For they define vertue to be a [a] life ordered according to nature [1]; and that we be hereunto ordeined of god; and that he doth followe the course of nature, which in desiering and refusyng thynges is ruled by reason. Furthermore, that reason doth chiefelie and pryncipallye kendle in men the loue and veneration of the deuyne maiestie; of whoes goodnes it is that we be, and that we be impossibilitie [b] to attayne felicite. And that, secondarely, it moueth and prouoketh vs to leade our lyfe out of care [2] in ioye and myrth, and to helpe all other [c], in respecte of the sosiete

[a] a *omitted*.   [b] in possibilitie (*printed as one word*).
[c] [and ... other] and also moueth us to helpe and further all other.

uero non in omni uoluptate felicitatem, sed in bona atque honesta sitam putant. ad eam enim, uelut ad summum bonum, naturam nostram ab ipsa uirtute pertrahi, cui sola aduersa factio felicitatem tribuit. Nempe uirtutem definiunt, secundum naturam uiuere; ad id siquidem a deo institutos esse nos. Eum uero naturae ductum sequi, quisquis in appetendis fugiendisque rebus obtemperat rationi. Rationem porro mortales primum omnium in amorem ac uenerationem diuinae maiestatis incendere, cui debemus et quod sumus, et quod compotes esse felicitatis possumus. secundum id commonet atque excitat nos ut uitam quam licet minime anxiam ac maxime laetam ducamus ipsi, caeterisque omnibus ad idem obtinendum adiutores nos pro naturae societate praebeamus.

Hoc iuxta Stoicos.

---

[1] This is the Stoical definition of virtue. ' Natura enim duce uiuendum est,' wrote Seneca; 'idem est ergo beate uiuere et secundum naturam' (*De Vita beata*, c. viii). Lipsius, in his *Manuductio ad Stoicam Philosophiam* (ed. 1644), p. 177, quotes a number of passages to the same effect. Mr. J. A. St. John, who refers to this passage of Lipsius in his commentary on

the *Utopia*, adds: ' The only difficulty appears to be to determine what it is to live according to nature; for I imagine that every man will be sure to conceive that nature sanctions what he thinks right.'

[2] Lat. *quam ... minime anxiam*, ' as little careful as may be,' in the old sense of *careful* (Phil. iv. 6).

of nature, to obteyne ᵃ the same. For there was neuer man so earnest and paynefull a follower of vertue, and hater of pleasure, that woulde so inioyne you laboures, watchinges, and fastinges¹, but he would also exhort you to ease and lighten to ᵇ your powre the lacke and myserye of others ; praysyng the same as a dede of humanitie and pitie. Then if it be² a poynte of humanitie for man to bryng health and comforte to man, and speciallye (whiche is a vertue moste peculiarlye belongynge to man) to mitigate and assuage the grief of others, and by takyng from them the sorowe and heuynes of lyfe, to restore them to ioye, that is to saye to pleasure ; whye maye it not then be sayd that nature doth prouoke euerye man to doo the same to hymselfe?

For a ioyfull lyfe, that is to saye, a pleasaunt lyfe, is other euell ; and if it be so, then thou shouldest not onlye helpe no man therto, but rather, as muche as in the lieth, helpe ᶜ all men from it, as noysome and hurtefull ; or els, if thou not onlye mayste, but also of dewtie art bounde to

duty to promote pleasure

ᵃ obteyne and enjoye.   ᵇ ease, lighten and relieue to.   ᶜ withdrawe.

Neque enim quisquam unquam fuit tam tristis ac rigidus assecla uirtutis, et osor uoluptatis, qui ita labores, uigilias et squalores indicat
tibi, ut non idem aliorum inopiam atque incommoda leuare te pro tua
uirili iubeat, et id laudandum humanitatis nomine censeat, hominem
homini saluti ac solatio esse, si humanum est maxime (qua uirtute
nulla est homini magis propria) aliorum mitigare molestiam, et sublata tristitia uitae iucunditati, hoc est uoluptati reddere. Quid ni
natura quenquam instiget et sibimet idem praestet?

105   Nam | aut mala est uita iucunda, id est, uoluptaria, quod si est, non
solum neminem ad eam debes adiutare, sed omnibus
utpote noxiam ac mortiferam quantum potes adimere ;   At nunc quidam
aut, si conciliare aliis eam, ut bonam, non licet modo,   accersunt dolores,
uelut in his sita

---

¹ There is an allusion in the English, but not in the Latin, to 2 Cor. vi. 5.
² It will be seen that Robynson, perhaps rightly, makes a different arrangement of the Latin sentences from that in the text. He places a full stop after *censeat*, and only a comma after *reddere*.

procure it to others, why not chiefely to theself, to whome thou art bound to shewe as muche fauour[a] as to other? For when natur biddeth the to be good and gentle to other, she commaundeth the not to be cruell and vngentle to the selfe. Therfore euen very nature[1] (saye they) prescribith to vs a ioyfull lyfe, that is to saye, pleasure, as the ende of all our operations. And they defyne vertue to be lyfe ordered accordyng to the prescrypt of nature[2]. But in that that nature dothe allure and prouoke men one to healpe an other to lyue merilye (whiche suerlye she doth not[3] without a good cause; for no man is so farre aboue the lot of mans state or condicion, that nature doth carke and care for hym only, whiche equallye fauoureth all that be comprehended vnder the communion of one shape, forme, and fassion), verely she commaundeth the to vse diligent circumspection, that thou do not so seke for thine owne commodities, that thou procure others incommodities.

Cicero echoed:

           [a] fauour and gentelnes.

sit religio; cum ferendi potius sint si incidant, ad pietatis officium tendenti, aut naturae necessitate accidant. set etiam debes, cur non tibi in primis ipsi? cui non minus propitium esse te quam aliis decet. neque enim quum te natura moneat uti in alios bonus sis, eadem te rursus iubet in temet saeuum atque inclementem esse. Vitam ergo iucundam, inquiunt, id est uoluptatem, tanquam operationum omnium finem, ipsa nobis natura praescribit; ex cuius praescripto uiuere uirtutem definiunt. At quum natura mortales inuitet ad hilarioris uitae mutuum subsidium (quod certe merito facit: neque enim tam supra generis humani sortem quisquam est, ut solus naturae curae sit, quae uniuersos ex aequo fouet, quos eiusdem formae communione complectitur) eadem te nimirum iubet etiam atque etiam obseruare, ne sic tuis commodis obsecundes, ut aliorum procures incommoda.

Cicero

[1] 'Omne animal, simulatque natum sit, voluptatem appetere, eaque gaudere, ut summo bono; dolorem aspernari, ut summum malum, et, quantum possit, a se repellere: idque facere nondum depravatum, ipsa natura incorrupte atque integre iudicante.' Cic. *De Fin.* I. ix. 30.

[2] See above, p. 190.

[3] Join 'not without.'

Wherfore their opinion is, that not onlye couenauntes
and bargaynes made amonge priuate men ought to be
well and faythfullye fulfylled, obserued, and kept, but also
commen lawes; whiche other a good prince hath iustly
publyshed, or els the people, nother oppressed with
tyranny, nother deceaued by fraude and gyell, hath by
their common consent constitute and ratifyed, concernyng
the particion of the commodities of lyfe,—that is to say, the
matter [1] of pleasure. Thies lawes not offendid, it is wys-
dome that thou looke to thyne own wealthe. And to do
the same for the common wealth is no lesse then thy duetie,
if thou bearest any reuerent loue or any naturall zeale and
affection to thy natiue contrey. But to go about to let an
other man of his pleasure, whiles thou procurest thyne
owne, that is open wrong. Contrary wyse, to withdrawe
somethynge from they selfe to geue to other, that is
a pointe of humanitie and gentylnes; whiche neuer taketh
a waye so muche commoditie, as it bryngeth agayne.
For it is recompensed with the retourne of benefytes;
and the conscience of the good dede, with the remembraunce of the thankefull loue and beneuolence of them

Seruanda igitur censent non inita solum inter priuatos pacta, sed
publicas etiam leges, quas aut bonus princeps iuste
promulgauit, aut populus, nec oppressus [a] tyrannide,   Pacta et leges.
nec dolo circumscriptus, de partiendis uitae commodis, hoc est
materia uoluptatis, communi consensu sanxit. Hiis inoffensis legibus
tuum curare commodum, prudentia [b] est; publicum praeterea, pietatis. Sed alienam uoluptatem praereptum ire, dum consequare tuam,
106 ea uero iniuria est. contra tibi aliquid ipsi | demere, quod addas aliis,
id demum est humanitatis ac benignitatis officium, quod
ipsum nunquam tantum aufert commodi quantum re-   Officia uitae
fert. Nam et beneficiorum uicissitudine pensatur, et   mutua.
ipsa benefacti conscientia, ac recordatio charitatis eorum et beneuo-
lentiae quibus benefeceris, plus uoluptatis affert animo, quam fuisset

     [a] *om.* A.   [b] *Legend.* prudentiæ.

---

[1] That is, the material.

O

Increase of pleasure by creating pleasure:

to whom thou hast done it, doth brynge more pleasure to thy mynde, then that whiche thou hast withholden from thy selfe could haue brought to the[a] bodye. Finallye (which to a godly disposed and a religious mind is easie to be persuaded), God recompenseth the gifte of a short and small pleasure with great and euerlastinge ioye. Therfore, the matter diligentlie wayde and considered, thus they

Virtue & pleasure inseparable

thinke : that all our actions, and in them the vertues themselfes, be referred at the last to pleasure, as theire ende and felicitie.

Pleasure they call euery motion and state of the bodie or mynde, wherin man hath naturally delectation. Appetite they ioyne to nature[1], and that not without a good cause.

recta ratio

For like as not only the senses, but also right reason, coueteth whatsoeuer is naturally pleasaunt ; so that it[b] may be gotten without wrong or iniurie, not letting or debarring a greater pleasur, nor causing painful labour ; euen so those thinges that men by vaine ymagination, do

[a] thy.   [b] for it.

illa corporis qua abstinuisti. Postremo (quod facile persuadet animo libenter assentienti religio) breuis et exiguae uoluptatis uicem ingenti ac nunquam interituro gaudio rependit deus. Itaque hoc pacto censent, et excussa sedulo et perpensa re, omnes actiones nostras, atque in his uirtutes etiam ipsas, uoluptatem tandem, uelut finem felicitatemque, respicere.

Voluptatem appellant omnem corporis animiue motum statumque,
Voluptas quid. in quo uersari natura duce delectet. Appetitionem naturae non temere addunt. Nam ut quicquid natura iucundum est, ad quod neque per iniuriam tenditur, nec iucundius aliud amittitur, nec labor succedit, non sensus modo sed recta quoque ratio persequitur ; ita quae praeter naturam dulcia sibi mor-

---

[1] The sense of the original is here somewhat obscured. More had given the Utopian definition of pleasure as 'every motion or state of body or mind, in which Nature teaches us to find delight.' It is an essential part of this definition that Nature should be the guide. Hence 'they add, with good reason, the appetite (or inclination) of Nature,' without which many things might be taken for pleasures, which were not really so. If this view be right, *naturae* is genitive, not dative.

fayne against nature to be pleasaunt (as though it lay in
their powre to chaunge the thinges as they do the names
of thinges), al suche pleasurs they beleue to be of so small
helpe and furtheraunce to felicitie, that they counte them
great[a] let and hinderaunce ; because that, in whom they
haue ones taken place, all his mynde they possesse with
a false opinion of pleasure ; so that there is no place left
for true and naturall delectacions. For there be manye
thynges, whiche of their owne nature conteyne no
plesauntnes ; yea the moste part of them muche grief and
sorrow ; and yet, through the peruerse and malicious
flickering inticementes of lewde and vnhoneste desyres, be
taken not only for speciall and souereigne pleasures, but
also be counted amonge the chiefe causes of life.

In this counterfeat kinde of pleasure they put them that
I speake of before ; which, the better gown they haue on,
the better men they thynke them selfes. In the whiche
thynge they doo twyse erre. For they be no lesse deceaued in that they thynke their gowne the better, than
they be in that they thinke themselfes the better. For if

Things & names

false pleasures

}*perversity*

Counterfeits

[a] a great.

tales uanissima conspiratione confingunt (tanquam in ipsis esset
perinde res ac uocabula commutare) ea omnia statuunt
adeo nihil ad felicitatem facere, ut plurimum efficiant   *Falsae uoluptates.*
etiam, uel eo quod quibus semel insederunt, ne ueris ac genuinis
oblectamentis usquam uacet locus, totum prorsus animum falsa uoluptatis opinione praeoccupant. Sunt enim perquam multa, quae quum
107 suapte natura nihil contineant sua|uitatis, imo bona pars amaritu-
dinis etiam plurimum, peruersa tum[a] improbarum cupiditatum ille-
cebra, non pro summis tantum uoluptatibus habeantur, uerum etiam
inter praecipuas uitae causas numerentur.

In hoc adulterinae uoluptatis genere eos collocant, quos ante memoraui, qui quo meliorem togam habent, eo sibi meliores   Error eorum qui
ipsi uidentur : qua una in re bis errant. Neque enim   sibi ob cultum
minus falsi sunt, quod meliorem putant togam suam,   placent.
quam quod se. Cur enim si uestis usum spectes, tenuioris fili

[a] *Fortasse legend.* tamen.

O 2

Counterfeits!

garments

yow consider the profitable vse of the garmente, whye
shoulde wulle of a fyner sponne threde be thoughe[a]
better, then the wul of a course sponne threde[1]? Yet
they, as though the one dyd passe the other by nature,
and not by their mistakyng, auaunce themselfes and thinke
the price of their owne persones therby greatly encreased.
And therfore the honoure, whiche in a course gowne they
durste not haue lokyd for, they require as it were of dewtie
for their fyner gownes sake. And if they be passed by
without reuerence, they take it angerlye[b] and disdayn-
fully.

Pride in
honours

cf. Shakesp

And agayne is it not a [c] lyke madnes to take a pride
in vayne and vnprofitable honoures? For what naturall
or trewe pleasure doest thou take of an other mans bare
hede or bowed knees? Will thys ease the payne of thy
knees, or remedye the phrensie of thy heade? In this
ymage of counterfeyte pleasure, they be of a maruelous
madnes, which for the opinion of nobilitie[2] reioyse muche
in their owne conceite, because it was their fortune to
come of suche auncetours, whoes stocke of longe tyme

[a] *So too in the 2nd ed. for* thought.   [b] displeasauntly.   [c] a *omitted.*

lana praestet crassiori? at illi tamen, tanquam natura non errore
praecellerent, attollunt cristas, et sibimet quoque precii credunt
inde non nihil accedere ; eoque honorem, quem uilius uestiti sperare
non essent ausi, elegantiori togae uelut suo iure exigunt, et praeter-
missi neglegentius indignantur.

At hoc ipsum quoque, uanis et nihil profuturis honoribus affici, an
non eiusdem inscitiae est? Nam quid naturalis et uerae
uoluptatis affert nudatus alterius uertex, aut curuati
poplites? hoccine tuorum poplitum dolori medebitur? aut tui capitis phrenesim leuabit? In hac fucatae uoluptatis imagine[a] mirum
quam suauiter insaniunt ii qui nobilitatis opinione sibi blandiuntur
ac plaudunt, quod eiusmodi maioribus nasci contigerit, quorum longa

Stulti honores.

[a] imagine . . . nobilitatis *om.* A.

---

[1] More has used the same comparison before, p. 181.

[2] That is, in fancying themselves
nobly born.

Pride of ancestry & property:

hath bene counted ryche (for nowe nobilitie is nothynge *England*
elles[1]), specially ryche in landes. And though their
auncetours left them not one fote of lande, or els they
themselfes haue pyssed it agaynste the walles[2], yet they   *cf. Wife of Bath prol.*
thynke themselfes not the lesse noble therefore of one
heare[3].

In thys numbre also they counte them that take plea-   *of Gems:*
sure and delyte (as I saide[4]) in gemmes and precious
stones, and thynke themselues almoste goddes, if they
chaunce to gette an excellent one; speciallye of that
kynde whyche in that tyme of their owne contreye men
is had In hyghest estimation. For one kynde of stone
kepeth not hys pryce styll in all contreis, and at all tymes.
Nor they bye them not but taken out of the golde and   *they = people in Europe*
bare; no, nor so nother, before[a] they haue made the
seller to sweare that he wyll warraunte and assure it to

[a] vntyll.

series diues (neque enim nunc aliud est nobilitas) habita sit, praesertim in praediis; nec pilo quidem minus sibi nobiles   Vana nobilitas.
uidentur, etiam si maiores nihil inde reliquerint, aut
108 relictum | ipsi obligurierint.

His adnumerant eos qui gemmis ac lapillis (ut dixi) capiuntur,
ac dii quodammodo sibi uidentur facti, si quando   Stultissima
eximium aliquem consequantur, eius praesertim   uoluptas
generis quod sua tempestate maximo apud suos   ex gemmis.
aestimetur. neque enim apud omnes, neque omni tempore eadem
genera sunt in precio. Sed nec nisi exemptum auro   Opinio hominum
ac nudum comparant. Imo ne sic quidem, nisi adiu-   precium addit aut
rato uenditore, et praestanti cautionem, ueram gem-   adimit gemmis.
mam ac lapidem uerum esse; tam solliciti sunt ne oculis eorum

---

[1] The 'humiliation of the baronage
by exhaustion, impoverishment, and
reduction of numbers,' consequent on
the Wars of the Roses, and the line
of policy followed by Henry VII,
tended to make such of the English
nobility as were left in More's time
follow their sovereign's example, and
seek to repair their fortunes by de-
veloping their estates. Hence one

cause of the inclosures so much complained of. See Bishop Stubbs : *Medieval and Modern History*, p. 390.
[2] 'Squandered it away.'—Burnet.
[3] That is, not a whit the less noble.
[4] See above, p. 181. It is recorded
of Henry VII that 'much of the money
he laid by he appears to have invested
in the purchase of jewels.'—Gairdner,
as before, p. 149.

counterfeit gems.

be a trewe stone and no counterfeyt geme. Suche care they take lest a counterfet stone shoulde deceaue their eyes in the[a] steade of a right stone. But whye shouldest thou not take euen as muche pleasure in beholdynge a counterfette stone, whiche thyne eye cannot discerne from a ryght stone? They should both be of lyke value to the, euen as to a[b] blynde man. What shall I saye of them that kepe superfluous ryches, to take delectacion only in the beholdynge, and not in the vse or occupyenge therof? Do they take trewe pleasure, or els be they de-ceaued with false pleasure? Or of them that be in

hoarding

a contrary vice, hydynge the golde whiche they shall neuer occupie[1], nor peraduenture neuer see more; and, whiles they take care leaste they shall leese it, do leese it in dede? For what is it elles, when they hyde it in the grounde, takynge it bothe from their owne vse, and perchaunce from all other mens also? And yet thou, when thou haste hidde thye treasure, as one out of all care, hoppest for ioye[2]. The whyche treasure if it

[a] the *omitted*.　　　　　　　　　　[b] the.

ueri loco adulterinus imponat. At spectaturo tibi cur minus praebeat oblectamenti factitius, quem tuus oculus non discernit a uero? Vterque ex aequo ualere debet tibi non minus hercle quam caeco. Quid hii qui superfluas opes adseruant, ut nullo acerui usu sed sola contemplatione delectentur; num ueram perci-piunt, an falsa potius uoluptate luduntur? aut hi qui diuerso uitio aurum quo nunquam sint usuri, fortasse nec uisuri amplius, abscon-dunt, et solliciti ne perdant, perdunt. quid enim aliud est, usibus demptum tuis et omnium fortasse mortalium, telluri reddere? et tu tamen abstruso thesauro, uelut animi iam securus, laetitia gestis.

---

[1] See the note above, p. 173.
[2] Dr. Lumby, in the Glossary to his edition of the *Utopia* takes 'hoppest' here as = 'hopest.' But it is plainly what we express by 'jump for joy.'

Compare 'leap for joy' in St. Luke vi. 23, and the use of 'hop' (though in a different sense) in the older version of the Psalms, lxviii. 16.

False pleasures:

vs.
hoarding

shoulde chaunce to bee stoolen, and thou, ignoraunt of
the thefte, shouldest dye tenne yeares after; all that
tenne yeares space that thou lyuedest, after thy money
was stolen, what matter was it to the whether it hadde
bene taken a waye, or els sauffe as thou lefteste it?
Truelye bothe wayes lyke proffyt came to the.

dicing
hunting
&
hawking.

To thyes so foolyshe pleasures they ioyne dycers[1],
whoes madnes they knowe by heare say and not by vse;
hunters also, and hawkers. For what pleasure is there
(saye they) in castynge the dice vpon a table; which
thu[a] hast done so often, that if theire were anyo pleaoure
in it, yet the ofte vse myghte make the werye therof?
Or what delite can there be, and not rather dyspleasure,
in hearynge the barkynge and howlynge of dogges[2]?

cf.
Theseus
&
Hippolyta

[a] thou. *The word is printed* y[u], *i. e.* thu.

Quem si quis furto abstulerit, cuius tu ignarus furti decem post
annis obicris, toto illo decennio, quo subtractae pe-   Mira fictio et
cuniae superfuisti, quid tua retulit surreptum an   aptissima.
saluum fuisset? utroque certe modo tantundem usus ad te peruenit.
   Ad has tam ineptas laetitias aleatores (quorum insa-   Alea.
109 niam auditu non | usu cognouere), uenatores praeterea
atque aucupes adiungunt. Nam quid habet, inquiunt,   Venatio.
uoluptatis talos in alueum proiicere, quod toties fecisti ut si quid
uoluptatis inesset, oriri tamen potuisset ex frequenti usu satietas?
aut quae suauitas esse potest, ac non fastidium potius, in audiendo
latratu atque ululatu canum? aut qui maior uoluptatis sensus est, cum

---

[1] See above, p. 144, and compare
the *Colloquium Senile* of Erasmus:
'EU. In quo mari occurrit iste scopulus? aut quod habet nomen? PA.
Mare non possum dicere, sed scopulus,
plurimorum infamis exitiis, Latine dicitur *Alea*.' It is noticeable that in
the *Praise of Folly* Erasmus places
near together, as More does here,
dice-players and hunters. The madness of the gambler, however, he
assigns 'rather to the furies than to
Folly.'— Kennet's tr., p. 66.
[2] It may seem as if these were not

always More's real sentiments. For
in one of the 'pageauntes' which he
devised in his youth come the lines:
'Manhod I am: therefore I me
   delyght
To hunt and hawke, to nourishe
   vp and fede
The grayhounde to the course, the
   hawke to the flyght,
And to bestryde a good and lusty
   stede:
These thynges become a very man
   in dede.'
English Works, leaf ¶ iij. But the cast

False pleasures: hunting

anti
chase

Or what greater pleasure is there to be felte, when a dogge followeth an hare, then when a dogge followeth a dogge? for one thynge is done in both; that is to saye, runninge; if thou haste pleasure therein. But if the hope of slaughter, and the expectation of tearynge in pieces the beaste dothe please the, thou shouldest rather be moued with pitie to see a seely innocent hare murdered of a dogge; the weake of the stronger; the fearefull of the fearce; the innocente of the cruell and vnmercyfull. Therefore all thys exercyse of huntynge, as a thynge vnworthye to be vsed of free men, the Vtopians haue

butchers:
butchers

reiected to their bochers; to the whiche crafte (as wee sayde before) they appointe ther bondmen. For they

{3 for 1
Latin

counte huntyng the loweste, vyleste [a], and moste abiecte parte of bocherye [1]; and the other partes of it more

[a] the vyleste.

leporem canis insequitur, quam quum canis canem? nempe idem utrobique agitur.   accurritur enim, si te cursus oblectet.   At si te caedis spes, laniatus expectatio sub oculis peragendi retinet, misericordiam potius mouere debet, spectare lepusculum a cane, imbecillum a ualidiore, fugacem ac timidum a feroce, innoxium denique a crudeli discerptum.   Itaque Vtopienses totum hoc uenandi exercitium, ut rem liberis indignam in lanios (quam artem per seruos obire eos supra diximus) reicerunt, infimam enim eius partem esse uenationem statuunt,

At haec hodie ars est deorum aulicorum.

---

of More's mind was too serious, not to say austere, to suffer him long to take pleasure in sports, even of the manlier kind. 'God sent men hither to wake and work,' he wrote later on; ' and as for sleepe and gaming (if any gaming be good in this vale of miserye, in this time of teares), it must serue but for a refreshing of the wearye and forewatched body, to renewe it vnto watche and labour agayne' (*Ib.* p. 1048). The characters seem reversed, when we compare with this the tracts on hunting and hawking

written by a lady abbess, Dame Juliana Berners, and printed during More's childhood. Extracts from them are given in Warton's *English Poetry*, sect. xxvii.

[1] Robynson, after his manner, multiplies his author's epithets by three. Still, the expressions in the Latin are sufficiently strong to make us admire More's courage in thus assailing the favourite pastimes of his age and country. Erasmus, as usual, is at one with him. 'When they have run down their game,' he makes Folly say

profytable and more h̲oneste, as whiche do brynge ᵃ muche more commoditie ; and doo kyll ᵇ beastes onlye f̲o̲r neces- sytie. Where as the hunter seketh nothynge but pleasure of the seely and wofull beastes¹ slaughter and murder. The whiche pleasure in b̲eholdyng d̲eath they thynke dothe ryse in the very b̲eastes, other of a cruell affection of mynde, or els to be chaunged in continuaunce of time into c̲rueltie, by longe vse of so cruell a pleasure. Thies therfore and all suche lyke, which is innumerable, though the c̲ommon sorte of people doth take them for pleasures, yet they, seyng there is no naturall pleasauntnes in them, do playnelye determine them to haue no affinitie with trewe and right pleasure. Far as touchyng that they do commonlye moue the s̲ence with d̲electacion (whiche semeth to be a worke of pleasure) thys doth nothing

ᵃ as bryngynge.   ᵇ in that they kyll.

reliquas eius partes et utiliores et honestiores, ut quae et multo magis conferant ᵃ, et animalia necessitatis duntaxat gratia perimant, quum uenator ab miseri animalculi caede ac laniatu nihil nisi uoluptatem petat. quam spectandae necis libidinem in ipsis etiam bestiis aut ab animi crudelis affectu censent exoriri, aut in crudelitatem denique assiduo tam efferae uoluptatis usu defluere. Haec igitur, et quicquid est huiusmodi (sunt enim innumera) quanquam pro uoluptatibus mortalium uulgus habeat, illi tamen quum natura nihil insit suaue, 110 plane statuunt, cum | uera uoluptate nihil habere commercii. Nam quod uulgo sensum iucunditate perfundunt (quod uoluptatis opus

ᵃ conseruant, A.

---

of the hunters, ' what strange pleasure they take in cutting it up! C̲ows and sheep may be slaughtered by common butchers, but what is killed in hunting must be broken up by n̲one u̲nder a gentleman.' The formalities are then duly described (Kennet's tr., as before, p. 63). G̲ilbert W̲akefield, writing to Fox, who had met with an accident when out shooting, reads him a homily on the text ' indignae homine docto voluptates' (Cic. De Off. ii. 1), in which

he pronounces ' those pleasures to misbecome a man of letters, which consist in mangling, maiming and depriving of that invaluable and irre- trievable blessing, its existence, an inoffensive pensioner on the u̲niversal bounty of the common Feeder and Pro- tector of all his offspring.'—*Correspon- dence of Wakefield and Fox*, 1813, p. 79. ¹ Burnet preserves the force of the diminutive *animalculi*, ' of so *small* and miserable an Animal.'

The true nature of the thing determines its {relation to pleasure;

nature misconceived

diminishe their opinion. For not the nature of the thynge, but there peruerse and lewde custome is the cause hereof; whiche causeth them to accepte bitter or sowre thinges for swete thinges; euen as women with childe, in their viciate and corrupt taste, thinke pitche and tallowe sweter then anye honney. Howbeit no mans iudgement, depraued and corrupte, other by sickenes or by custome, can chaunge the nature of pleasure, more then it can doo the natur of other thinges.

pregnant women

of Soule Body.

They make diuers kyndes of trew[a] pleasures. For som they attribute to the soule, and som to the bodye. To the soule they gyue intellygence, and that delectation that cummeth of the contemplation of truthe. Here vnto is ioyned the pleasaunt remembraunce of the good lyfe past [1].

Soul I.

Body II. A.

The pleasure of the bodye they deuide into ii. partes. The first is when delectation is sensibly felte and perceaued:

[a] trew *omitted.*

uidetur) nihil de sententia decedunt. non enim ipsius rei natura, sed ipsorum peruersa consuetudo in causa est : cuius uitio fit ut amara pro dulcibus amplectantur, non aliter ac mulieres grauidae picem et seuum corrupto gustu melle mellitius arbi-

Citta[2] in grauidis.

trantur. Nec cuiusquam tamen aut morbo aut consuetudine deprauatum iudicium mutare naturam, ut non aliarum rerum, ita nec uoluptatis potest.

Voluptatum quas ueras fatentur species diuersas faciunt. Si-

Verae uoluptatis species.

quidem alias animo, corpori alias tribuunt. Animo dant intellectum, eamque dulcedinem quam ueri contemplatio pepererit. Adhaec suauis additur bene actae uitae

Voluptates corporis.

memoria, et spes non dubia futuri boni. Corporis uoluptatem in duas partiuntur formas, quarum prima sit ea quae sensum perspicua suauitate perfundit ; quod alias earum

---

[1] As Dibdin points out, Robynson omits altogether the concluding words of the Latin, *et spes non dubia futuri boni.* Burnet correctly renders, ' and the assured Hopes of a future Happiness.'

[2] Citta, in Greek κίττα or κίσσα, was a word used to denote a jay or magpie, and then, like Galen's κίττησις, the false appetite or longing referred to in the text.—See Mayne's *Expository Lexicon* (1860), p. 962.

whiche many times chaunceth by the renewing and re-
fresshyng of thoes partes which owre naturall heate
drieth vp : thys cummeth by meate and drynke : and
sumtymes whyles those thynges be [a] voided, wherof is in
the body ouer great abundaunce. This pleasure is felte
when wee doo our naturall easemente, or when we be
doynge the acte of generatyon, or when the ytchynge of
annye parte is eased with rubbynge or stratchinge. Sumtimes pleasure riseth (exhibitinge to) any membre nothing
that it desireth, nor taking from it any payne that it feeleth ;
which for all that [b] tikleth and moueth our senses with
a certein secrete efficacy, but with a manifest motion,
and [c] turneth them to it ; as is that which cummeth of
musicke.

The second part of bodely pleasure they say is that
which consisteth and resteth in the quiete and vpright [1]
state of the body.   And that truelye is euery mans owne

---

    [a] be expulsed and.   [b] neuerthelesse.   [c] and *omitted.*

instauratione partium fit, quas insitus nobis calor exhauserit ; nam
hae cibo potuque redduntur ; alias, dum egeruntur illa quorum copia
corpus exuberat. Haec suggeritur, dum excrementis intestina pur-
gamus, aut opera liberis datur, aut ullius prurigo partis frictu
scalptuue lenitur. Interdum uero uoluptas oritur, nec (redditura)
quicquam quod membra nostra desyderent, nec (ademptura) quo labo-
rent ; caeterum quae sensus nostros tamen in quadam occulta sed
111 illustri motu titillet afficiatque, et in se conuertat ; | qualis ex musica
nascitur.

Alteram corporeae uoluptatis formam eam uolunt esse, quae in
quieto atque aequabili corporis statu consistat ; id est nimirum sua

---

[1] This word appears sometimes to
have been used as simply equivalent
to ' right,' without any idea of erect-
ness. So the Greek *orthos.* But the
Latin rather means ' well balanced,'
with all the humours, &c., in proper
temperament. From this comes what
Paley calls ' that harmonious con-
formation,' which he says ' gives to
the mind its sense of complacency
and satisfaction.' *Moral Philosophy,*
Bk I. ch. vi. Compare also Cic. *De
Off.* I. xi. 37, ' sed maximam illam
voluptatem habemus, quae percipitur
omni dolore detracto.'

II. B.

propre health, entermyngled and dysturbed wyth no grieffe. For thys, yf yt be not letted nor assaulted with no greiffe [1], is delectable of yt selfe, thoughe yt be moued wyth no externall or outwarde pleasure. For though it be not so plain and manyfeste to the sense, as the gredye luste of eatynge and drynckynge, yct neuerthelesse manye take it for the chyefeste pleasure. All the Vtopyans graunte yt to be a ryghte greate [a] pleasure, and as yow wolde saye the foundatyon and grownde of all pleasures; as whyche euen alone ys able to make the state and condytyon of lyffe delectable and pleasaunte; and, yt beynge ones taken awaye, there ys no place lefte for annye pleasure. For to be wythowte greyffe, not hauinge health, that they call vnsensybylyte and not pleasure. The Vtopians haue longe agoo reiected and condempned the opynyon of them, whyche sayde that stedfaste and quyete healthe (for thys questyon also hath bene dylygentelye debated emonge them) owghte not therefore to be cownted a pleasure, bicause they saye yt can not be presentlye and sensyblye perceaued and felte

basis of pleasure

[a] souereigne.

cuiusque nullo interpellata malo sanitas. Haec siquidem, si nihil eam doloris oppugnet, per se ipsa delectat, etiam si nulla extrinsecus adhibita uoluptate moueatur. Quanquam enim sese minus effert, minusque offert sensui, quam tumida illa edendi bibendique libido, nihilo tamen secius multi eam statuunt uoluptatum maximam. omnes fere Vtopienses magnam et uelut fundamentum omnium ac basim fatentur, ut quae uel sola placidam et optabilem uitae conditionem reddat, et qua sublata nullus usquam reliquus sit cuiquam uoluptati locus. Nam dolore prorsus uacare, nisi adsit sanitas, stuporem certe non uoluptatem uocant. Iamdudum explosum est apud eos decretum illorum, qui stabilem et tranquillam sanitatem (nam haec quoque quaestio gnauiter apud eos agitata est) ideo non habendam pro uoluptate censebant, quod prae-

Valeat possessor oportet [2].

---

[1] We should now say 'pain' (*dolor*). See the Glossary.
[2] Hor. *Epist.* I. ii. 49.

by some owtwarde [1] motion.   But, of the contrarye parte,
nowe they agree almoste all in thys, that healthe ys
a moste souereygne pleasure.   For seinge that in syckenes
(saye they) is grieffe, which is a mortal ennemie to pleasure,
euen as sicknes is to health, why shuld not then pleasure
be in the quietnes of health ?   For they say it maketh
nothing to thys matter, whether yow saye that sickenes is
a griefe, or that in sickenes is griefe ;   for all cummeth to
one purpose.   For whether health be a pleasure it selfe,
or a necessary cause of pleasure, as fyer is of heate, truelye
bothe wayes it foloweth, that they cannot be without
pleasure that be in perfyt healthe.   Furthermore, whyles
we eate (saye they), then health, whiche began to be   *allegorical*
appayred, fyghteth by the helpe of foode against hunger.   *fight*
In the whych fighte whyles healthe by lytle and lytle
getteth the vpper hande, that same procedyng [2], and (as
ye would say) that onwardnes to the wonte strengthe

sentem non posse dicerent, nisi motu quopiam contrario, sentiri.
Verum contra nunc in hoc prope uniuersi conspirant, sanitatem uel
in primis uoluptati esse.   Etenim quum in morbo, inquiunt, dolor sit,
qui uoluptati implacabilis hostis est, non aliter ac sanitati morbus,
quidni uicissim insit sanitatis tranquillitati uoluptas ?   nihil enim ad
hanc rem referre putant, seu morbus dolor esse, seu morbo dolor
inesse, dicatur.   Tantundem enim utroque modo effici.   Quippe si
112 sanitas aut uoluptas ipsa sit, aut necessa|rio uoluptatem pariat, uelut
calor igni gignitur, nimirum utrobique efficitur ut, quibus immota sanitas adest, his uoluptas abesse non possit.   Praeterea dum uescimur,
inquiunt, quid aliud quam sanitas, quae labefactari coeperat, aduersus
esurientem (cibo commilitone) depugnat ?   in qua dum paulatim inua-
lescit, ille ipse profectus ad solitum uigorem suggerit illam, qua sic

---

[1] Burnet paraphrases : ' Some have
thought that there was no Pleasure,
but what was excited by some sensible
Motion in the Body.' Both translators
neglect the proper meaning of *contrario*, and Robynson in addition
ignores the presence of *nisi*. It is
literally : ' saying that its presence
could not be felt except by some op-

posite emotion.'   More explains more
fully afterwards what he means by
this. when he speaks of the pleasure
felt in eating, for example, as measured
by the displacement of the opposite
pain of hunger.

[2] In the sense of ' progress ' (*profectus*).

That health is a pleasurable feeling

mynistreth that pleasure, wherbye wee be so refresshed. Health therefore, whiche in the conflycte is ioyfull, shall it not bee merye when it hathe gotten the victory[1]? But as sone as it hathe recouered thee pristynate strengthe, whyche thinge onelye in all the fyghte it coueted, shall it incontinent be astonied? Nor shall it not knowe nor imbrace the owne wealthe and goodnes? For that[a] it is sayed healthe can not be felte, this, they thinke, is nothing trew. For what man wakynge, say they, feleth not hymselfe in health, but he that is not[2]? Is there annye man so possessed wyth stonyshe insensibilitie, or with the sleping sicknes[b], that he wyll not graunt health to be acceptable to hym and delectable? But what other thing is delectation, than that whiche by an other name is called pleasure?

Ⅱ or Ⅰ? They imbrace chiefely[3] the pleasures of the mind. For

[a] where.   [b] the lethargie.

reficimur, uoluptatem. Sanitas ergo quae in conflictu laetatur, eadem non gaudebit adepta uictoriam? sed pristinum robur, quod solum toto conflictu petiuerat, tandem feliciter assecuta, protinus obstupescet, nec bona sua cognoscet atque amplexabitur? Nam quod non sentiri sanitas dicta est, id uero perquam procul a uero putant. Quis enim uigilans, inquiunt, sanum esse se non sentit, nisi qui non est? Quem ne tantus aut stupor aut lethargus adstringit, ut sanitatem non iucundam sibi fateatur ac delectabilem? at delectatio quid aliud quam alio nomine uoluptas est?

Amplectuntur ergo in primis animi uoluptates (eas enim primas

---

[1] Burnet renders: 'And if the Conflict is Pleasure, the Victory must yet breed a greater Pleasure.' But this, though neat, does not give the point of the antithesis, rightly observed by Robynson, between *laetatur* and *gaudebit*. There is in those words the same contrast as between 'joy' and 'gladness;' the latter denoting what Robynson calls 'being merry,' the state of calm cheerfulness when victory is won. Tennyson showed his perception of the difference, when, in his translation of a passage from the *Iliad* (viii. 542–561), he altered 'the hind rejoices at the heart' to 'the shepherd gladdens at his heart.'

[2] Burnet, more clearly, 'for what man is in health, that does not perceive it [is not conscious of it] when he is awake?'

[3] The word 'therefore' (*ergo*) should have been introduced; this being a conclusion from what goes before.

them they cownte the chiefist and most principall of all.
The cheyfe parte of them they thinke doth come of the
exercise of vertue, and conscience of good lyffe. Of thies
pleasures that the boddye ministreth they geue the pre-
emynence to helth. For the delyte of eating and drincking,
and whatsoeuer hath anny like pleasauntnes, they determyne to be pleasures muche to be desiered, but no other
wayes than for healthes sake. For suche thynges of
theyre owne propre nature be not [a] pleasaunte, but in
that they resyste syckenes preuelye stealynge one [1].
Therefore, lyke as yt ys a wyse mans parte rather to
auoyde syckenes, then to wyshe for medycynes, and
rather to dryue away and put to flyghte carefull greyffes [2],
then to call for comforte; so yt ys much better not to
neade thys kynde of pleasure, then in sealynge [3] the contrarye greyffe to be eased of the same [b]. The whyche
kynde of pleasure yf annye man take for hys felycytye,
that man muste nedes graunte, that then he shall be in

[a] not so.   [b] [then in ... same] then thereby to be eased of the contrarie
grief.

omnium principesque ducunt) quarum potissimum partem censent ab
exercitio uirtutum bonaeque uitae conscientia proficisci. Earum
uoluptatem quas corpus suggerit palmam sanitati deferunt. Nam
edendi bibendique suauitatem, et quicquid eandem oblectamenti
rationem habet, appetenda quidem, sed non nisi sanitatis gratia,
statuunt. Neque enim per se iucunda esse talia, sed quatenus
113 aduersae ualetudini clanculum | surrepenti resistunt: ideoque sapi-
enti, sicuti magis deprecandos morbos, quam optandam medicinam,
et dolores profligandos potius quam adsciscenda solatia, ita hoc
quoque uoluptatis genere non egere quam deliniri praestiterit: quo
uoluptatis genere si quisquam se beatum putet, is necesse est fateatur
se tum demum fore felicissimum, si ea uita contigerit, quae in per-

---

[1] That is, stealing on.
[2] The phrase here used might recall
one of the first precepts of the Schola
Salernitana for obtaining health: Curas
tolle graves.' But the Latin has simply
dolores, ' pains.'

[3] Robynson's meaning is: 'than,
by stopping the opposite pain (as of
hunger, when we eat), to gain a
sensation of pleasure.' This is an
expansion of the single word *deliniri*
(*deleniri*), 'to feel the gratification.'

mooste felycytye, yf he lyue that lyffe whyche ys ledde in contynuall honger, thurste, itchynge, eatynge, drynkynge, scratchynge, and rubbynge [1]. The whyche lyffe howe not onlye foule yt is [a], but also myserable and wretched, who perceauethe not? Thyes dowteles be the baseste pleasures of all, as vnpure and vnperfecte. For they neuer cum but accompanied wyth their contrary greiffes. As with the pleasure of eatinge is ioyned hunger, and that after no very egal sort. For of thies ii. the gryeffe is bothe the more vehement, and also of longer continuaunce. For it rysethe [b] before the pleasure, and endeth not vntyll the pleasure dye wyth it.

Wherfore such pleasures they think not greatly to be set by, but in that they be necessary. Howbeit they haue delite also in thies, and thankfully knowledge the tender loue of mother nature, which with most plesaunt delectation allureth her children to that, which of necessitye they be driuen often vse [c]. For how wretched and miserable

---

[a] *The words* yt is *transposed to come after* wretched.   [b] beginneth.

[c] [which ... vse] to the necessarie vse wherof they must from time to time continually be forced and driuen.

---

petua fame, siti, pruritu, esu, potatione, scalptu frictuque traducatur: quae quam non foeda solum, sed misera etiam sit, quis non uidet? Infimae profecto omnium hae uoluptates sunt, ut minime syncerae; neque enim unquam subeunt, nisi contrariis coniunctae doloribus. Nempe cum edendi uoluptate copulatur esuries, idque non satis aequa lege Nam ut uehementior, ita longior quoque dolor est: quippe et ante uoluptatem nascitur, et nisi uoluptate una commoriente non exstinguitur.

Huiusmodi ergo uoluptates, nisi quatenus expetit necessitas, haud magni habendas putant. Gaudent tamen etiam his, gratique agnoscunt naturae parentis indulgentiam, quae foetus suos ad id quod necessitatis causa tam assidue faciendum erat etiam blandissima suauitate pelliceat. Quanto enim in tedio uiuendum erat, si ut

---

[1] This is the horn of the dilemma on which Socrates impales Callicles in the *Gorgias*, § 495. If pleasure consists in counteracting painful sensations, then those sensations must be always present, or the counteraction, in which lies the pleasure, could not go on.

should our liffe be, if thies daily greiffes of hunger and thrust coulde not be dreuen away, but with bitter potions, and sower medicines; as the other deseases be, where with we be seldomer trowbled? But bewtye, strengthe, nemblenes, thies, as peculiare · and pleasaunte giftes of nature, they make muche of. But those pleasures which *3* be receaued by the eares, the iyes, and the nose; which *Senses* nature willeth to be proper and peculiar to man [1] (for no other kind of liuing beastes [a] doth behold the fayrenes and the bewtie of the worlde, or is moued with anny respect of sauours, but only for the diuersity of meates, nother perceaueth the concordaunt and discordante distaunces of soundes and tunes) thies pleasures (I say) they accept and allowe, as certein pleasaunt reioysinges [2] of liffe. But in all thinges thys cautell they vse, that a lesse pleasure hinder not a bigger, and that the pleasur be no cause of dyspleasur; whych they thinke to followe of necessytye, if the pleasure be vnhoneste. But yet to dyspyse the comlynes of bewtye, to waste the bodylye

[a] no other liuinge creature.

caeterae aegritudines quae nos infestaut rarius, ita hii quoque cotidiani famis ac sitis morbi uenenis ac pharmacis amaris essent abigendi? At formam, uires, agilitatem, haec ut propria iucundaque *beauty* naturae dona libenter fouent. Quin eas quoque uoluptates, quae
114 per | aures, oculos, ac nares admittuntur, quas natura proprias ac peculiares esse homini uoluit (neque enim aliud animantium genus aut mundi formam pulchritudinemque suspicit, aut odorum, nisi ad cibi discrimen, ulla commouetur gratia, neque consonas inter se discordesque sonorum distantias internoscit) et has, inquam, ut iucunda quaedam uitae condimenta persequuntur. In omnibus autem hunc habent modum, ne maiorem minor impediat, neu dolorem aliquando uoluptas pariat ; quod necessario sequi censent, si inhonesta sit. At certe formae decus contemnere, uires deterere, agilitatem in pigritiam

---

[1] Cicero developes this argument in *De Nat. Deor.* ii. § 56. Compare also the familiar lines of Ovid, *Met.* i. 85–6.

[2] Burnet's rendering gives the force of *condimenta* better : ' as the pleasant Relishes and Seasonings of Life.'

false pleasures & madness:

strengthe, to tourne nymblenes into sloughishnes, to consume and make feble the boddye wyth fastynge[1], to doo
iniury to health, and to reiect the other[a] pleasaunte motyons
of nature (onles a man neglecte thies hys[b] commodytyes,
whyles he doth wyth a feruent zeale procure the wealth
of others, or the commen proffytte, for the whyche pleasure forborne he is in hope of a greater pleasure of
GOD[c]): els for a vayne shaddowe of vertue, for the wealthe

shadow:

and proffette of no man, to punyshe hymselfe, or to the
intente he maye be able courragiouslye to suffre aduer-
sitye, whyche perchaunce shall neuer come to hym : thys

Truth to Nature in courtly love image:

to doo they thynke it a poynte of extreame madnes, and
a token of a man cruelly minded towardes hymselfe, and
vnkynd towarde nature, as one so dysdaynynge to be in
her daunger[2], that he renounceth and refuseth all her
benefytes.

Thys is theire sentence and opinion of vertue and

    [a] other *omitted.*   [b] hys *omitted.*   [c] at goddes hand.

uertere, corpus exhaurire ieiuniis, sanitati iniuriam facere, et caetera
naturae blandimenta respuere, nisi quis haec sua commoda negligat,
dum aliorum publicamue[a] ardentius procurat, cuius laboris uice
maiorem a deo uoluptatem expectat ; alioquin ob inanem uirtutis
                umbram nullius bono semet affligere, uel quo aduersa
   Annotandum   ferre minus moleste possit, nunquam fortasse uen-
   et hoc   tura : hoc uero putant esse dementissimum, animique
   diligenter.   et in se crudelis, et erga naturam ingratissimi, cui
                tanquam debere quicquam dedignetur, omnibus eius
beneficiis renunciat.

Haec est eorum de uirtute ac uoluptate sententia ; qua nisi sanctius

    [a] *Leg.* publicumue, *sc.* commodum.

---

[1] More doubly guards himself against
any unfair use being made of his words,
(1) by the proviso that such bodily
mortifications are not undergone for
the public good or the welfare of
others ; and (2) by the addition, later
on, of a disclaimer of any approval
of customs and opinions which he is
simply relating. But when every allowance is rightly made, the reader will
judge whether there is not here a
condemnation of the ascetic spirit, as
a thing meritorious in itself. The marginal annotator of the Latin, a little
further on, calls attention to the point
as one deserving careful consideration.

[2] See note above, p. 182.

Virtue thus inseparable from Pleasure:

Raphael excuses himself:

pleasure. And they beleue that by mans reason none
can be fownde trewer then this, onles annye godlyer be
inspyred into man from heauen. (Wherin whether they
belyue well or no, nother the tyme dothe suffer us to
discusse, nother it ys nowe necessarye. For we haue
taken vpon vs to shewe and declare theyr lores and ordenaunces, and not to defende them [1].)

reason
}
revelation

But thys thynge I beleue verely: howe soeuer thies
decrees be, that their is in no place of the wordle nother
a more excellent people, nother a more flouryshynge
commen wealthe. They be lyghte and quycke of boddy,
full of actiuity and nymblenes, and of more strengthe then
a man wold iudge them by theyre stature, whyche for
all that ys not to lowe. And thoughe theyre soyle be
not verye frutefull, nor theyre ayer verye holsome, yet
agaynste the ayer they soo defende them wyth temperate
dyete, and soo order and husbande theyr grounde wyth
dylygente trauayle, that in no contreye ys greatter increase, and plentye of corne and cattell, nor mens bodies
of longer liffe, and subiect or apte to fewer descases.

Utopian excellence

aliquid inspiret homini caelitus immissa religio, nullam inuestigari
credunt humana ratione ueriorem.   qua in re rectene an secus sentiant, excutere nos neque tempus patitur, neque necesse est ; quippe
115 qui narranda eorum instituta, | non etiam tuenda, suscepimus.

Caeterum hoc mihi certe persuadeo, ut ut sese habeant haec
decreta, nusquam neque praestantiorem populum
neque feliciorem esse rempublicam.   Corpore sunt
agili uegetoque, uirium [2] amplius quam statura pro-
mittat. nec ea tamen improcera. et quum neque solo
sint usquequaque fertili, nec admodum salubri caelo,
aduersus aerem ita sese temperantia uictus muniunt, terrae sic
medentur industria, ut nusquam gentium sit frugis pecorisque prouentus uberior, aut hominum uiuaciora corpora, paucioribusque

*Felicitas Vtopi-
ensium ac
descriptio.*

---

[1] This deserves notice, as indicating
the author's own view of his freedom
from responsibility, as a narrator only,

and not an advocate.
[2] A ‘genitiuus qualitatis *sine* epi-
theto.’

P 2

There, therfore, a man maye see well and diligentlye
exploited and furnished, not onlye those thinges whiche
husbandmen doo commenly in other countreys; as by
craft and cunning to remedy the barrennes of the grounde;
transplanting but also a hole wood by the handes of the people plucked
forests vp by the rotes in one place and sett agayne in an other
place [1]. Wherin was hadde regard and consideration not
of plenty but of commodious carriage; that wood and
tymber might be nigher to the sea, or the riuers, or the
cities. For it is lesse laboure and busines to carrye
grayne farre by lande then wood. / The people be gentle,
merye, quycke, and fyne wytted, delytynge in quyetnes,
and, when nede requyreth, able to abyde and suffre muche
bodelye laboure. Elles they be not greatelye desyerous
and fonde of yt; but in the exercyse and studdye of the
of mynde they be neuer werye.
Greek. When they had harde me speake of the Greke [2] lytter-

morbis obnoxia. Itaque non ea modo quae uulgo faciunt agricolae
diligenter ibi administrata conspicias, ut terram natura maligniorem
arte atque opera iuuent; sed populi manibus alibi radicitus euulsam
syluam, alibi consitam uideas: qua in re habita est non ubertatis sed
uecturae ratio; ut essent ligna aut mari, aut fluuiis, aut urbibus ipsis
uiciniora: minore enim cum labore terrestri itinere fruges quam
ligna longius afferuntur. Gens facilis ac faceta, sollers, ocio gaudens,
corporis laborum (quum est usus) satis patiens, caeterum alias haudquaquam sane appetens; animi studiis infatigata.

Qui quum a nobis accepissent de literis et disciplina Graecorum

---

[1] The reader will be reminded of Milton's description:—
. 'They pluck'd the seated hills with all their load,' &c.,
and what critics call the 'magnifica imago' of Claudian : *Gigantomachia*, 66 sqq.

[2] More's fondness for the Greek language, and his proficiency in it, have been spoken of in the Introduction. In this respect the friends of enlightenment could claim him as one of themselves. Nothing can show better the wide difference between his standpoint and that of a defender of things as they were, like Alberto Pio, Count of Carpi, than the way in which they respectively treat the claims of Greek to recognition. More, arguing against Dorp, insists that it contains the most precious treasures of all. ' Quis nesciat,' he asks, ' Graecam esse

arature[a] or learnynge (for in Latyne theyre was nothynge
that I thougthe they wolde greatelye allowe, besydes
hystoryens and Poetes), they made wonderfull earneste
and importunate sute vnto me, that I woldc teache and
instructe them in that tonge and learnynge. I beganne
therefore to reade [1] vnto them; at the fyrste, truelye, more
bycause I wolde not seme to refuse the laboure, then that
I hooped that they wolde annye thyng proffytte therin.
But when I had gone forwarde a lytle, and[b] perceaued
incontynente by theyr dylygence that my labour should
not be bestowed in vayne; for they beganne so easelye
to fassyon theyre letters, so plainly to pronounce the
woordes, so quyckely to learne by harte, and so suerly

Latin Poets & historians

Utopian quickness in Greek

        [a] *sic.*   [b] I.

(nam in latinis praeter historias ac poetas nihil erat quod uidebantur magnopere probaturi) mirum quanto studio
contendcrunt, ut eas liceret ipsis nostra interpre-   Vtilitas linguae
tatione perdiscere. Coepimus ergo legere, magis   graecae.
adeo primum, ne recusare laborem uideremur, quam   Docilitas
116 quod | fructum eius aliquem speraremus. At ubi   Vtopiensium.[a]
paulum processimus, ipsorum diligentia fecit ut nostram haud frustra
impendendam animo statim praeciperemus. Si quidem literarum
formas tam facile imitari, uerba tam expedite pronunciare, tam
celeriter mandare memoriae, et tanta cum fide reddere [2] coeperunt, ut

        [a] *Addit* B. mira.

---

eam quae summopere sit cum ab uniuersis mortalibus, tum uero seorsum
a Christianis amplectenda, utpote
a qua et omnes disciplinae reliquae,
et Nouum Testamentum fere totum
nobis foelicissime successit.' He urges
Dorp, even though late in the day,
to learn it. *Lucubrationes*, p. 415.
Alberto Pio, on the other hand, re-
butting the attacks of Erasmus, the
champion of *bonae literae*, wishes de-
voutly that those *bonae literae* had
never found their way across the Alps.
'Quanto salubrius,' he exclaims, ' ut

illas nunquam didicissent [theologi],
quam ut earum occasione tam vastum
incendium excitassent, quo fere vni-
uersa Germania conflagrauit? Quanto
commodius Germaniae, vt hae bonae
literae alpes nunquam transcendissent,
vt et Germani contenti materna lingua,
vel vtcunque latina, tam atrocia dissidia non concitassent?' *Tres et uiginti
libri in . . . Erasmi*, &c., 1531, leaf
10 verso.

[1] Lat. *legere*, the technical term for
oral instruction.

[2] This was the regular term for the

to rehearse the same, that I marueled at it; sauynge that
the most parte of them were fyne and chosen wittes, and
of rype age, pyked oute of the companye of the learned
men, whyche not onlye of theyr owne faee ᵃ and volun-
tarye wyll, but also by the commaundemente of the
cowncell, vndertoke to learne thys langage. Therfore
in lesse than iii. yeres space their was nothing in the
Grekc tonge that they lackede. They were able to reade
good authors wythout anny staye, if the booke were not
[false 1.) defective.

Thys kynde of learnynge, as I suppose, they toke so
muche the souner, bycause it is sumwhat allyaunte to
them. For I thynke that thys nation tooke their begin-
ninge of the Grekes, bycause their speche, which in all
other poyntes is not muche vnlyke the persian tonge 2,
kepeth dyuers signes and tookens of the greke langage in
the names of their cityes and of theire magystrates. They
haue of me (for, when I was determyned to entre into my

ᵃ *Misprint for* free.

nobis miraculi esset loco, nisi quod pleraque pars eorum, qui non
At nunc stipites   sua solum sponte accensi, uerum senatus quoque
et caudices   decreto iussi, ista sibi discenda sumpserunt, e nu-
dicantur literis : mero scholasticorum selectissimis ingeniis et matura
felicissima
ingenia uolupta-   aetate fuerunt. Itaque minus quam triennio nihil erat
tibus corrum-   in lingua quod requirerent; bonos autores, nisi obstet
puntur.   libri menda, inoffense perlegerent.

Eas literas, ut equidem coniicio, ob id quoque facilius arripuerunt,
quod nonnihil illis essent cognatae. Suspicor enim eam gentem
a graecis originem duxisse, propterea quod sermo illorum, caetera
fere Persicus, non nulla graeci sermonis uestigia seruet in urbium ac
magistratuum uocabulis. Habent ex me (nam librorum sarcinam

scholar's *repetition* of what he had   Et quaecumque mihi reddis, dis-
learnt by heart. So in Lily's *Carmen*   cantur ad unguem,
de moribus :—   Singula et abiecto uerbula redde
' Incumbens studio, submissa uoce   libro.'
     loqueris ;   1 That is, unless the text were
  Nobis dum reddis, uoce canorus   defective. Burnet avoids the clause.
     eris.   2 See note above, p. 135.

.iiii. voyage[1], I caste into the shippe in the steade of marchandyse a pretye fardell of bookes, bycause I intended to
come agayne rather neuer than shortelye) the [a] mooste
parte of Platoes woorkes; more of Aristotles; also Theophrastus[2] of Plantes, but in diuers places (which I am
sorye for) vnperfecte. For whyles wee were saylynge [b],
a mormosett chaunced vpon the booke, as yt was negly-
gentlye layde by; whyche, wantonlye playinge therewyth,
plucked owte certeyne leaues, and toore them in pieces[3].
Of them that haue wrytten the grammer, they haue onelye
Lascaris[4].   For Theodorus I caried not wyth me; nor

Plato etc

the monkey of More

Theod. Gaza

<hr>

[a] they haue, I saye, of me the.   [b] a shipborde.

<hr>

mediocrem loco mercium quarto nauigaturus in nauem conieci, quod
mecum plane decreueram nunquam potius redire quam cito) Platonis
opera pleraque, Aristotelis plura ; Theophrastum item de plantis, sed
pluribus, quod doleo, in locis mutilum.   In librum enim, dum naviga-
bamus negligentius habitum, cercopithecus inciderat; qui lasciuiens
ac ludibundus paginas aliquot hinc atque hinc euulsas lacerauit. Ex
117 hiis qui scripsere grammati|cam, Lascarem habent tantum ; Theodo-

<hr>

[1] See the Introduction, p. xxxvii.

[2] The works of Theophrastus had
been published at Venice, in 1497.
Why More should give so prominent
a place to this treatise, as to mention
it next after Plato and Aristotle, is
uncertain. It may have been a favourite
of his own, or one which seemed a
natural companion for a traveller in
foreign lands. Theophrastus was often
included in the same edition with
Aristotle, as in the great Venice edition
of 1493-8.

[3] Besides the Rabelaisian *vraisemblance* which this little touch gives to
the description, there is no doubt that
More is calling up some actual reminiscence of the tricks of his own pet
monkey. This animal, more famous
than the one which is said to have
carried the infant Cromwell up in its

paws to the roof of the house, is
immortalized in Erasmus's Colloquy
Amicitia, and has its place in Holbein's
picture of the household of Sir Thomas
More.

[4] The first edition of the *Grammatica
Graeca* of Constantine Lascaris appeared at Milan in 1476, after which
editions appeared frequently. Theo-
dore Gaza's *Introductiuae Grammatices
Libri iv.*, mentioned just afterwards,
first appeared from the press of Aldus
in 1495. Gaza's work was recognized
by competent judges ' as superior to
all other manuals of the kind.' Budaeus
' praised it as a masterpiece of the
grammarian's art.' Erasmus translated
it to his class at Cambridge, and
Richard Croke to his class at Leipsic.
—See Mullinger's *University of Cambridge*, i. p. 430.

Plutarch

Lucian

companion

Tricius

Apinatus:
figure of
Triviality

neuer a dyctyonarye, but Hesichius [1] and Dioscorides. They sett greate stoore by Plutarches bookes. And they be delyted wyth Lucianes merye conceytes and iestes. Of the Poettes they haue Aristophanes, Homer, Euripides, and Sophocles in Aldus small prynte. Of the Historyans they haue Thucidides, Herodotus, and Herodian. Also my companion, Tricius Apinatus [2], caried with him phisick bokes, certein smal woorkes of Hippocrates, and Galenes

rum enim non aduexi mecum, nec dictionarium [3] aliquem praeter Hesychium ac Dioscoridem. Plutarchi libellos habent charissimos, et Luciani quoque facetiis ac lepore capiuntur. Ex poetis habent Aristophanem, Homerum atque Euripidem, tum Sophoclem minusculis Aldi formulis; ex historicis Thucydidem atque Herodotum, necnon Herodianum. Quin in re medica quoque sodalis meus Tricius Apinatus aduexerat secum parua quaedam Hippocratis opuscula, ac

---

[1] The *Glossarium Graecum* of Hesychius had only recently been issued from the press when More wrote; the first edition being that brought out under the care of Musurus at Venice, in 1514. Pedanius Dioscorides, of Anazarbus near Tarsus, was a medical writer in the time of Nero. Vives, in his *De tradendis disciplinis* (ed. 1636, p. 553), mentions his *De Herbis* as a treatise to be studied, along with Theophrastus's *De stirpibus*, named by More just above. The works of Dioscorides had been printed at Venice in 1499.

No special notice is needed of the common authors that are next mentioned in the text, who, as it will be observed, are all Greek. It may be remarked, however, that Herodian was a very favourite author after the revival of letters. He and Sallust are among those most frequently prescribed in the statutes of early grammar schools in this country. Vives (*ubi sup.* p. 530) says that the student ' ad historiam praeleget *Herodianum*, ut cum versione conferat Angeli Politiani.

Est author ille candidus ex se ac facilis; sed ea gratia Politianus transtulit, ut non ab homine Graeco videatur genitus sed a Latino.'

[2] This is a name evidently formed from the 'apinae tricaeque' of Martial, xiv. 1. 7:

'Sunt apinae tricaeque et si quid
    vilius istis.'

So also in I. cxiv. 1, 2:

' Quaecumque lusi juvenis et puer
    quondam,
    Apinasque nostras;'

lines which More may often have had in his mind, as reflecting youthful occupations of his own. Perotti in his *Cornucopiae*, 1513, col. 466, gives the explanation of the phrase. Apina and Trica, he says, were two small towns in Apulia, captured (according to Pliny) by Diomede; the names of which passed into a proverb for anything trivial—mere bagatelles. Much to the same effect Erasmus in his *Adagia*, 1629, p. 134.

[3] A late Latin word for *glossarium*, though that is not much better.

Microtechne [1]: the whyche boke they haue in greate estymatyon. For thoughe there be almost no nation vnder
heauen that hath lesse nede of Phisick [2] then they, yet, this
notwithstandyng, Phisicke is no where in greater honour;
bycause they count the knowledge of yt emonge the good-
lieste, and mooste profytable partes of Philosophie. For
whyles they by the helpe of thys Philosophie searche owte
the secrete mysteryes of nature, they thynke that they not
onlye receaue therby [a] wonderfull greate pleasur, but also [b]
obteyn great thankes and fauour of the auctoure and
maker therof. Whome they thynke, accordynge to the

Scientific Interests

cf. Bacon New Atlantis

[a] [that . . . therby] themselfes to receaue therby not onlye.
[b] also to.

Microtechnen Galeni, quos libros magno in precio habent. Siquidem
et si omnium fere gentium re medica minime egent,
nusquam tamen in maiore honore est, uel eo ipso quod   Medicina
eius cognitionem numerant inter pulcherrimas atque   utilissima.
utilissimas partes philosophiae; cuius ope philo-
sophiae dum naturae secreta scrutantur, uidentur sibi non solum
admirabilem inde uoluptatem percipere, sed apud autorem quoque
eius atque opificem summam inire gratiam; quae [a] caeterorum more

[a] *Sic etiam* A.; B. *recto* quem.

[1] No collected edition of Galen's
works in Greek had appeared at the
time when More wrote; the earliest
being that of Aldus at Venice, in 1525.
But separate treatises had been already
published, as the *Therapeuticorum
Libri xiv*, in 1500. The *Microtechne*,
'Little art,' was a name given to
Galen's Τέχνη ἰατρική, which, as
Donaldson says, 'was the text-book
and chief subject of examination for
medical students in the middle ages,
when it was known in barbarous Latin
as the *Tegnum* or *Microtegnum* (*Micro-
technum*) of Galen'— *Literature of
Ancient Greece* (1858), ii. p. 274. This
was in contradistinction to the *Megalo-*

tegnum, or Θεραπευτικῆς μεθόδου βιβλία
ιδ'.
[2] By 'Phisicke' here is meant medicine, not physical science, as seen by
the Latin. But in what follows More
is plainly thinking of physical, or
natural, science in general. As a contrast to the picture he draws, may be
compared the description of Erasmus,
in which the medical practitioner alone
thrives, while the professors of other
sciences starve :—' Esuriunt theologi,
frigent physici, ridentur astrologi, neg-
liguntur dialectici; solus ἰατρὸς ἀνὴρ
πολλῶν ἀντάξιος ἄλλαν.' *Encomium
Moriae*, ed. 1668, p. 82.

fassyon of other artyfycers, to haue sett furthe the maruelous and gorgious frame of the worlde for man to [a]
beholde; whome onelye he hathe made of wytte and
capacytye to consydre and vnderstand the excellencye of
so greate a woorke. And therefore, saye they, dothe
he beare [b] more good wyll and loue to the curyous and
diligent beholder and vewere of his woorke, and mar-
uelour at the same, then he doth to him, whyche lyke
a very beaste [c] wythowte wytte and reason, or as one
wythowte sense or mouynge, hath no regarde to soo greate
and soo wonderfull a spectacle [1].

Admiration
The wyttes therefore of the Vtopians, inurede and exercysed in learnynge, be maruelous quycke in the inuentyon
of feates, helpynge annye thynge to the aduantage and
for
wealthe of lyffe. Howebeyt, ii. feates theye maye thanke
printing
vs for; that is, the scyence of imprintyng, and the crafte
of makynge paper : and yet not onelye vs but chyefelye
and pryncypallye themselfes. For when wee shewede to
of
Aldus.
them Aldus [2] hys prynte in bookes of paper, and told them

[a] with great affeccion intentiuely to.
[b] [saye . . . beare] he beareth (say they).   [c] brute beast.

artificum arbitrantur mundi huius uisendam machinam homini (quem
solum tantae rei capacem fecit) exposuisse spectandam,
Contemplatio   eoque chariorem habere curiosum ac sollicitum in-
naturae.   spectorem, operisque sui admiratorem, quam eum qui,
uelut animal, expers mentis, tantum ac tam mirabile
spectaculum stupidus immotusque neglexerit.
Vtopiensium itaque literis ingenia mire ualent ad inuentiones
artium, quae faciant aliquid | ad commodae uitae compendia. Sed 118
duas tamen debent nobis, Chalcographorum et faciendae chartae;
nec solis tamen nobis sed sibi quoque bonam eius partem. Nam quum
ostenderemus eis libris chartaceis impressas ab Aldo literas, et de

---

[1] Mr. St. John aptly compares with
this the fine passage in Cicero, *De
Nat. Deor.* ii. §§ 37, 38, in which,
after translating from Aristotle, he
continues, in a similar strain to More :
'Licet enim . . . oculis quodammodo

contemplari pulchritudinem earum
rerum, quas divina providentia dicimus
constitutas.'
[2] The recent death of Aldus Manutius the elder, in April 1515, was
probably fresh in More's recollection

The Utopians conceive printing though not fully explained:

of the stuffe wher of paper is made, and of the feat of
grauynge letters, speakynge sumwhat more[1] then wee
colde playnlye declare (for there was none of vs that
knewe perfectlye other the one or the other), they furthwyth verye wyttelye coniectured the thynge. And where
as before they wrote onelye in skynnes, in barkes of tryes,
and in rides[2], now they haue attempted to make paper
and to imprint letters. And thoughe at the fyrste yt
proued not all of the beste, yet by often assayinge the
same they shortelye gott the feate of bothe ; and haue so
broughte the matter abowte, that yf they had copyes of
Greeke authores, they coulde lacke no bookes. But
nowe they haue no moore then I rehearsed before ;
sauynge that by pryntynge of bookes they haue multy-
plyed and increased the same into manye thowsande of
copyes.

Who soeuer cummeth thether to see the lande, beynge
excellente in annye gyfte of wytte, or throughe muche and
longe iournyenge well experiensed and sene in the know-

language / difficulty

Utopians receive strangers well: curiosity

chartae faciendae materia, ac literas imprimendi facultate loqueremur
aliquid magis quam explicaremus (neque enim quisquam erat nostrum
qui alterutram calleret), ipsi statim acutissime coniecerunt rem ; et
quum ante pellibus, corticibus, ac papyro tantum scriberent, iam
chartam ilico facere et literas imprimere tentarunt : quae quum primo
non satis procederent, eadem saepius experiendo breui sunt utrumque consecuti ; tantumque effecerunt, ut, si essent Graecorum
exemplaria librorum, codices deesse non possent. At nunc nihil
habent amplius quam a me commemoratum est. id uero quod
habent impressis iam libris in multa exemplariorum millia propa-
gauere.

Quisquis eo spectandi gratia uenerit, quem insignis aliqua dos
ingenii, aut longa peregrinatione usum multarum cognitio terrarum

---

when he wrote this.—See Renouard,
Annales de l'Imprimerie des Alde, 1803,
i. p. 123 n.
  [1] If this were the meaning, it would
be a genuine touch of human nature—

ignorance seeking to veil itself under
a cloud of words. But the Latin
simply means 'talking something about
it, rather than explaining.'
  [2] That is, reeds, such as the papyrus.

ledge of manye countreys (for the whyche cause wee were
verye welcome to them), hym they receyue and interteyne
wonders gentyllye and louynglye ; for they haue delyte to
heare what ys done in euerye lande. Howebeyt, verye
few marchaunte men come thythere. For what shoulde
they brynge thither ? onles yt were Iron, or els golde and
syluer ; whiche they hadde rathere carrye home agayne.
Also suche thynges as arre to be caryed owte of their
lande, they thynke yt more wysedome to carrye that geer
furthe themselfes, then that othere shoulde come thether
to fetche yt[1] ; to thentente they maye the better knowe the
owte landes of euerye syde[a] them, and kepe in vre[2] the
feat and knouledge of saylinge.

[a] syde of.

commendet (quo nomine gratus fuit noster appulsus) pronis animis
excipitur. Quippe libenter audiunt quid ubique terrarum geratur.
Caeterum mercandi gratia non admodum frequenter appellitur. Quid
enim ferrent, nisi aut ferrum, aut, quod quisque referre mallet, aurum
argentumue? Tum quae ex ipsis exportanda sint, ea consultius
putant ab se efferri quam ab aliis illinc peti ; quo et caeteras undique
gentes | exploratiores habeant, neque maritimarum rerum usum ac 119
peritiam oblitum eant.

---

[1] That is, the Utopians prefer to ship their exports in their own bottoms,
rather than wait for foreigners to come and take them.

[2] Use. See the Glossary.

Of Bonde=

men, sicke persons, wedlocke, and dyuers other matters.

They nother make bondemen of prysoners taken in
battayll, oneles yt be in battaylle that the fowghte
themselfes, nor [a] bondemens chyldren, nor, to be shorte [b],
annye man whome [c] they canne gette owte of an othere
countreye [d], thoughe he were theyre a bondeman; but
other suche as amonge themselfes for heynous offences be
punnyshed wyth bondage, or elles suche as in the Cytyes
of other landes for greate trespasses be condempned to
deathe [1]. And of thys sorte of bondemen they haue
mooste stoore. For manye of them they brynge home,
sumtymes payinge very lytle for them; yea, mooste commonlye gettynge them for gramercye [2]. Thyes sortes
of bondemen they kepe not onelye in contynuall woorke

[a] nor of.   [b] shorte of.   [c] annye suche as.
[d] forreine countries.

DE SERVIS.

PRo seruis neque bello captos habent, nisi ab ipsis gesto, neque
seruorum filios, neque denique quenquam quem apud alias
gentes seruientem possent comparare, sed aut si cuius apud se
flagitium in seruitium uertitur, aut quos apud exteras
urbes (quod genus multo frequentius est) admissum   Mira huius gentis
facinus destinauit supplicio. Eorum enim multos,   aequitas.
interdum aestimatos uili, saepius etiam gratis impe-
tratos auferunt. Haec seruorum genera non in opere solum perpetuo,

---

[1] See the Introduction, p. li.
[2] That is, gratuitously. See the Glossary.

and laboure, but alsoo in bandes. But theyre owne men they handle hardeste, whome they judge more desperate, and to haue deseruede greater punnysshemente; bycause they, beynge so godlye broughte vp to vertue, in soo excellente a common wealthe, cowlde not for all that be refreyned from mysdoynge.

An other kynde of bondemen they haue, when a vyle drudge, beynge a poore laborer in an other cowntreye, dothe chewse of hys owne free wyll to be a bondeman amonge them. Thyes they handle [a] and order honestelye, and enterteyne almooste as gentyllye, as theyre owne free cytyzeyns; sauynge that they put them to a lytle more laboure, as thereto accustomede. Yf annye suche be dysposed to departe thens (whyche seldome ys seene) they nother holde hym agaynste hys wyll, nother sende hym awaye wyth emptye handes.

The sycke (as I sayde[1]) they see to wyth greate affectyon, and lette nothynge at all passe, concernynge other Physycke or good dyete, wherby they may be restored agayne to theyre healthe. Them that be sycke of incurable dyseases they comforte wyth syttynge by them,

[a] intreate.

uerum etiam in uinculis habent; sed suos durius: quos eo deploratiores, ac deteriora meritos exempla censent, quod tam praeclara educatione ad uirtutem egregie instructi contineri tamen ab scelere non potuerint.

Aliud seruorum genus est, quum alterius populi mediastinus quispiam laboriosus ac pauper elegerit apud eos sua sponte seruire. Hos honeste tractant, ac nisi quod laboris, ut pote consuetis, imponitur plusculum, non multo minus clementer ac ciues habent. uolentem discedere (quod non saepe fit) neque retinent inuitum neque inanem dimittunt.

Egrotantes, ut dixi, magno cum adfectu curant, nihilque prorsus omittunt, quo sanitati eos, uel medicinae uel uictus obseruatione, restituant. Quin insanabili mor|bo laborantes assidendo, colloquendo, adhibendo demum quae

De aegrotis.   120

---

1 See above, p. 159.

Euthenasia

wyth talkynge wyth them, and, to be shorte, wyth all maner of helpes that maye be. But yf the dysease be not onelye vncurable, but also full of contynuall payne and anguyshe, then the priestes and the magistrates exhort the man, seynge he ys not able to doo annye dewtye of lyffe, and by ouerlyuing hys owne deathe is noysome and yrke-some to other, and greuous to hymself; that he wyll determyne with hymselfe no longer to cheryshe that pestilent and peynefull dysease: and, seynge hys lyfe ys to hym but a tourmente, that he wyll nott bee vnwyllynge too dye, but rather take a good hope to hym, and other dyspatche hymselfe owte of that payntull lytte, as owte of a pryson or a racke of tormente, or elles suffer hym selfe wyllynglye to be rydde owte of yt by other[1]. And in so doynge they tell hym he shal doo wyselye, seynge by hys deathe he shall lyse no commodytye, but ende hys payne.

Suicide

possunt leuamenta, solantur. Caeterum si non immedicabilis modo morbus sit, uerumetiam perpetuo uexet atque discruciet, tum sacer-dotes ac magistratus hortantur hominem, quandoquidem omnibus uitae muniis impar, aliis molestus ac sibi grauis, morti iam suae cuperuiuat, ne secum statuat pestem diutius   Mors spontanea. ac lucem alere, neue, quum tormentum ei uita sit, mori dubitet; quin bona spe fretus acerba illa uita uelut carcere atque aculeo uel ipse semet eximat, uel ab aliis eripi se sua uoluntate patiatur. hoc illum, quum non commoda sed supplicium abrupturus

---

[1] The words of More to his daughter Margaret, when in the Tower: 'I be-lieve, Meg, that they that have put me here ween that they have done me a high displeasure : but I assure thee on my faith, mine own good daughter, if it had not been for my wife and ye that be my children, I would not have failed long ere this to have closed myself in as strait a room, and straiter too,' were taken by Warner to imply that he would have been prepared, under certain circumstances, to carry out the recommendation in the text. The true reference, however, can only be, as Father Bridgett points out (*Life*, pp. 25, 367) to the cell of a Carthusian monastery. A similar misinterpreta-tion of the 'lowly bed' of Gray's *Elegy* is sometimes met with. It must be admitted, in Warner's defence, that the stoical doctrine of suicide, under certain limitations. is here presented in as attractive a form as it well could be. For the Christian view of the subject, see the authorities collected by Bishop Wordsworth in his note on Acts xvi. 27.

And bycause in that acte he shall followe the cownsell of the pryestes, that is to saye of the interpreters of goddes wyll and pleasure, they shewe hym that he shall do lyke a godly and a vertuouse man. They that be thus persuaded fynyshe theyre lyues wyllynglye, othere wyth hunger, or elles dye in theyre slcape[1] wythowte annye fealnige of deathe. But they cause none suche to dye agaynste hys wyll; nor they vse no lesse dilygence and attendaunce about hym; beleuynge[2] thys to be an honorable deathe. Elles he that kylleth hym selfe before that the pryestes and the cownsell haue allowed the cause of hys deathe, hym, as vnworthy both of the earth and of fyer[a], they cast vnburied into some stinkyng marrish.

⌈The woman is not maried before she be xviii. yeres olde. The man is[b] iiii. yeres elder before he mary[3]. If other the man or the woman be proued to haue bodely[c] offended, before their marriage, with an other[4], he or she

sopiti: drugged with opium.

unapproved suicides

of Women

---

a [both . . . fyer] either to be buryed, or with fier to be consumed.
b is *omitted*.   c actually.

---

morte sit, prudenter facturum; quoniam uero sacerdotum in ea re consiliis, id est, interpretum dei, sit obsecuturus, etiam pie sancteque facturum. Haec quibus persuaserint, aut inedia sponte uitam finiunt, aut sopiti sine mortis sensu soluuntur. Inuitum uero neminem tollunt, nec officii erga eum quicquam imminuunt. persuasos hoc pacto defungi honorificum. Alioqui qui mortem sibi consciuerit causa non probata sacerdotibus et senatui, hunc neque terra neque igne dignantur; sed in paludem aliquam turpiter insepultus abiicitur.

    Foemina non ante annum duodeuicesimum nubit. Mas non nisi expletis quatuor etiam amplius. Ante coniugium mas aut foemina si conuincatur furtiuae libidinis, grauiter

De coniugiis.

---

1 This would rather suggest a natural death. But the Latin, *sopiti*, implies that they would be sent to sleep, or, as Burnet plainly words it, 'take Opium.'

2 Robynson apparently took *persuasos* as if *persuasi*, and connected it with the preceding clause. It is

literally: 'for men to die in this way upon persuasion (that is, convinced by proper authority) is honourable.'

3 Compare the remarks on premature marriages in the Introduction, p. xxxiii.

4 This is an uncalled for addition by the translator.

Women & marriage:

Virginity enforced.

whether it be[a] is sharpely punyshed; and both the offenders be forbydden euer after in all their lyfe to marrye,
oneles the faulte be forgeuen by the princes pardone.
But bothe the good man and the good wyfe of the house
where that offence was done[b], as beyng slacke and neg-
lygent in lokyng to there chardge, be in daunger of great
reproche and infamye. That offence is so sharpelye
punyshed, bicause they perceaue, that onles they be
diligentlye kept from the lybertie of this vice, fewe wyll
ioyne together in the loue of marriage[1]; wherin all the
lyfe must be led with one, and also all the griefes and
displeasures that come[c] therewith must paciently be taken
and borne.

Furthermore, in cheusyng wyfes and husbandes they
obserue earnestly and straytelye a custome whiche semed
to (vs) very fonde and folysh. For a sad and an honest
matrone sheweth the woman, be she maide or widdowe,
naked to the wower. And lykewyse a sage and discrete
man exhibyteth the wowere naked to the woman. At

[a] [he or . . . be] the partye that so hathe trespaced.
[b] committed.   [c] comming.

in eum eamue animaduertitur, coniugioque illis in totum inter-
121 dicitur, nisi uenia principis noxam remiserit. sed et | pater et ma-
terque[a] familias cuius in domo admissum flagitium est, tanquam
suas partes parum diligenter tutati, magnae obiacent infamiae. id
facinus ideo tam seuere uindicant, quod futurum prospiciunt, ut rari
in coniugalem amorem coalescerent[2], in quo aetatem omnem cum uno
uideant exigendam, et perferendas insuper quas ea res affert molestias,
nisi a uago concubitu diligenter arceantur.

Porro in deligendis coniugibus ineptissimum ritum (uti nobis
uisum est) adprimeque ridiculum, illi serio ac seuere   Etsi parum
obseruant. Mulierem enim, seu uirgo seu uidua sit,   uerecunde haud
grauis et honesta matrona proco nudam exhibet; ac   tamen incaute.
probus aliquis uir uicissim nudum puellae procum sistit. Hunc

[a] _Sic etiam_ A.; B. _omittit_ que.

---

[1] This argument is enforced by   Plato's, did not extend to community
Paley: _Moral Philosophy_, Bk. iii. ch. 2.   of wives.
The Utopian communism, unlike   [2] Should be _coalescant_.

Q

this custome we laughed and disalowed it as foolyshe[1]. But they on the other part doo greatlye wonder at the follye of all other nations, whyche in byinge a colte, where as a lytle money is in hassarde, be so charye and circumspecte, that though he be almoste all bare, yet they wyll not bye hym, oneles the saddel and all the harneys be taken of, leaste vnder those couerynges be hydde som galle or soore; and yet in chewsynge a wyfe, whyche shalbe other pleasure or dyspleasure to them all theire lyfe after, they be so recheles, that, all the resydewe of the wooman's bodye beinge couered wyth cloothes, they esteme here scaselyc be one handebredeth (for they can se no more but her face); and so do[a] ioyne her to them not without great ieoperdie of euell agreing together, if any thynge in her body afterwarde do offende[b] and myslyke them. For all men be not so wyse as to haue respecte to the vertuous condicions of the partie; and the endowmentes of the bodye cause the vertues of the mynde more

     ᵃ to.   ᵇ should chaunce to offende.

morem quum uelut ineptum ridentes improbaremus, illi contra caeterarum omnium gentium insignem demirari stultitiam, qui quum in equuleo comparando, ubi de paucis agitur nummis, tam cauti sint, ut, quamuis fere nudum, nisi detracta sella tamen omnibusque reuulsis ephippiis, recusent emere, ne sub illis operculis hulcus aliquod delitesceret; in deligenda coniuge, qua ex re aut uoluptas aut nausea sit totam per uitam comitatura, tam negligenter agant, ut, reliquo corpore uestibus obuoluto, totam mulierem uix ab unius palmae spatio (nihil enim praeter uultum uisitur) aestiment, adiungantque sibi non absque magno (si quid offendat postea) male cohaerendi periculo. Nam neque omnes tam sapientes sunt ut solos mores respiciant, et in ipsorum quoque | sapientum coniugiis ad 122

---

[1] Burton, in his *Anatomy of Melancholy* (Part III, sec. 3, mem. 4, subs. 2), quotes this fancy of More's, and compares it with one of the institutions of Lycurgus (Plutarch's *Lives*, tr. by the Langhornes, 1805, i. p. 139). Bacon, in his *New Atlantis* (ed. by St. John, p. 248), also refers to it, and devises what he thinks a better expedient.

to be estemed and regarded, yea, euen in the mariages of
wyse men. Verely so fowle deformitie may be hydde
vnder thoes coueringes, that it maye quite alienate and
take awaye the mans mynde from his wyfe, when it shal
not be lawfull for their bodies to be seperate agayne. If
suche deformitie happen by any chaunce after the mariage
is consumate and finyshed; well, there is no remedie
but patience. Euery man must take his fortune, well
a worthe.[1] But it were well done that a lawe were made,
wherebye all suche deceytes myghte be eschewed and
aduoyded before hand. And thys were they constreyned
more earnestlye to looke vpon, because they onlye of the
nations in that parte of the worlde bee contente euerye
man wyth one wyfe a piece; and matrymoney is there
of divorce
neuer broken, but by death; excepte adulterye breake the
bonde, or els the intollerable waiward maners of eyther
partie. For if either of them fynde themselfe for any
suche cause greued; they maye by the licence of the
councell chaunge and take an other. But the other partie
lyueth euer after in infamye and out of wedlocke. But

animi uirtutes non nihil additamenti corporis etiam dotes adiciunt.
certe tam foeda deformitas latere sub illis potest inuolucris, ut alienare
prorsus animum ab uxore queat, quum corpore iam seiungi non
liceat. Qualis deformitas si quo casu contingat post contractas nup-
tias, suam quisque sortem necesse [a] ferat: ante uero ne quis capiatur
insidiis legibus caueri debet; idque tanto maiore studio fuit curandum [b],
quod et soli illarum orbis plagarum singulis sunt contenti coniugibus,
et matrimonium ibi haud saepe aliter quam morte soluitur, nisi adulterium in causa fuerit, aut morum non   Diuortium.
ferenda molestia. Nempe alterutri sic offenso facta ab
senatu coniugis mutandi uenia: alter infamem simul ac caelibem
perpetuo uitam ducit. Alioquin inuitam coniugem, cuius nulla sit

[a] necesse est, A.

[b] *om.* A.

---

[1] There is nothing in the Latin to
show in what sense this exclamation
was meant to be used. On the analogy
of 'wellaway,' and 'woe worth,' it
will be an exclamation of sorrow:
'alas! that it should be so.'

Divorce:

for the [a] husbande to put away his wyfe for no [b] faulte, but
for that some myshappe is fallen to her bodye, thys by no
meanes they wyll suffre. For they iudge it a greate
poynte of crueltie that any body in their moste nede of
helpe and comforte, shoulde be cast of and forsaken ; and
that olde age, whych both bryngeth sycknes with it, and
is a syckenes it selfe [1], should vnkyndlye and vnfaythfullye
be delte withall. But nowe and then it chaunseth, where
as the man and the woman cannot well agree betwene
themselfes, bothe of them fyndynge other with whome
they hope to lyue more quyetlye and meryly, that they by
the full consent of them both be diuorsed a sonder and
newe maried to other [2] ; but that not without the aucthoritie of the councell ; which agreeth to no dyuorses, before
they and their wyfes haue diligently tried and examyned
the matter. Yea and then also they be loth to consent to

of incompatibles

[a] Howbeit the.   [b] no other.

noxa, repudiare, quod corporis obtigerit calamitas, id uero nullo pacto
ferunt. nam et crudele iudicant tum quenquam deseri, cum maxime
eget solatio, et senectuti, quum et morbos afferat et morbus ipsa sit,
incertam atque infirmam fidem fore. Caeterum accidit interdum ut
quum non satis inter se coniugum conueniant mores, repertis utrique
aliis quibus cum sperent se suauius esse uicturos, amborum sponte
separati noua matrimonia contrahant, haud absque senatus auctoritate
tamen, qui nisi causa per se atque uxores suas diligenter cognita
diuortia non admittit. Imo ne sic quidem facile, quod rem minime

---

[1] The thought is from Terence, *Phormio*, iv. 1 :
' CH. Pol me detinuit morbus. DE. Unde? aut qui? CH. Rogas? *Senectus ipsa est morbus.*'

[2] Milton contended in earnest for what More here makes the Utopians allow, protesting vehemently against the law which continued to bind together a married couple, although ' through their different tempers, thoughts, and constitutions, they can neither be to one another a remedy against loneliness, nor live in any union or contentment all their days.' He is careful to guard against its being thought ' that licence, and levity, and unconsented breach of faith should herein be countenanced ; but that some conscionable and tender pity might be had of those who have unwarily, in a thing they never practised before, made themselves the bondmen of a luckless and helpless matrimony.' See the Preface to *The Doctrine and Discipline of Divorce.*

it, bicause they knowe thys to be the nexte waye to breke
loue betwene man and wyfe, to be in easye hope of
a newe mariage.

Breakers of wedlocke be punyshed with moste greuous
bondage. And if both the offenders were maried, then
the partyes whiche in that behalfe haue suffered wronge
be diuorsed from the auoutrers if they wyll, and be
maried together[a], or els to whom they luste. But if
eyther of them both do styll contynewe in loue towarde
so vnkynde a bedfellowe, the vse of wedlocke is not to
them forbydden, if the partie[b] be disposed to followe in
toylinge and drudgerye the person, which for that offence
is condempned to bondage. And very ofte[1] it chaunceth
that the repentaunce of the one, and the earnest diligence
of the other, dothe so moue the prince with pytie and
compassion, that he restoreth the bonde persone from
seruitude to libertie and fredom again. But if the same
partie be taken eftsones in that faulte, there is no other
way but death.

To other trespaces there is[c] no prescript punyshment
appoynted by anye lawe. But accordinge to the hey-

---

[a] [be diuorsed . . . together] beinge diuorsed from the auoutrers, be maried
together, if they will.

[b] partie faulteles.   [c] [there is no] no . . . is.

---

123 utilem sciunt firmandae | coniugum charitati, facilem nouarum nup-
tiarum spem esse propositam.

Temeratores coniugii grauissima seruitute plectuntur ; et, si neuter
erat caelebs, iniuriam passi (uelint modo) repudiatis adulteris coniugio
inter se ipsi iunguntur, alioquin quibus uidebitur. At si laesorum
alteruter erga tam male merentem coniugem in amore persistat, tamen
uti coniugii lege non prohibetur, si uelit in opera damnatum sequi :
acciditque interdum ut alterius poenitentia, alterius officiosa sedulitas,
miserationem commouens principi, libertatem rursus impetret. Caeterum ad scelus iam relapso nex infligitur.

Caeteris facinoribus nullam certam poenam lex ulla praestituit,

---

[1] Lat. *interdum*, not so much as ' very ofte ; ' but rather, ' now and then.'

Punishments:

nousenes of the offence, or contrarye, so the punyshemente is moderated by the discretion of the councell.
The husbandes chastice theire wyfes[1]; and the parentes
theire chyldren; oneles they haue done anye so horryble
an offence, that the open punyshemente thereof maketh
muche for the aduauncemente of honeste maners. But
moste commenlye the moste heynous faultes be punyshed
with the incommoditie of bondage. For that they suppose

Bondage

to be to the offenders no lesse griefe, and to the common
wealth more profitable[a], then if they should hastely put
them to death, and make them[b] out of the waye. For
there cummeth more profite of theire laboure, then of
theire deathe; and by theire example they feare other the
lenger from lyke offences. But if they, beinge thus vsed,

death penalty.

doo rebell and kicke agayne, then forsothe they be slayne
as desperace[c] and wilde beastes, whom nother pryson nor
chayne could restraine and kepe vnder. But they whiche
take theire bondage patientlye be not left all hopeles.
For after they haue bene broken and tamed with longe

    [a] profit.   [b] and so make them quite.   [c] *so, for* desperate.

sed ut quodque atrox aut contra uisum est, ita supplicium senatus decernit. Vxores mariti castigant, et parentes
liberos; nisi quid tam ingens admiserint, ut id publice
puniri morum intersit. sed fere grauissima quaeque
scelera seruitutis incommodo puniuntur; id siquidem
et sceleratis non minus triste et reipublicae magis commodum arbitrantur, quam si mactare noxios et protenus amoliri festinent. Nam
et labore quam nece magis prosunt, et exemplo diutius alios ab simili
flagitio deterrent. quod si sic habiti rebellent atque recalcitrent, tum
demum uelut indomitae beluae, quos cohercere carcer et catena non
potest, trucidantur. At patientibus non adimitur omnis omnino spes.
quippe longis domiti | malis si eam poenitentiam prae se ferant, quae 124

Aestimatio supplicii penes magistratum.

---

[1] In England it was long supposed
to be the law that a man might chastise
his wife, so it be in moderation, and
with a stick no thicker than his thumb.
See Dalton: *The Countrey Justice*, ed.
1705, p. 284. But 'modern law recog-
nizes no such right, and a husband is
not justified in beating his wife, even
though she be drunk or insolent.' See
*The American and English Encyclo-
paedia of Law*, vol. ix. (1889), p. 815,
and the authorities there quoted.

myseries, yf then they shewe suche repentaunce, wherebye[a] it maye be perceaued that they be soryer for theire
offence then for theire punyshemente, sumtymes by the
Prynces prerogatyue, and sumtymes by the voyce and *prerogative*
consent of the people, theire bondage other is mitigated, or
els cleane remytted and forgeuen[1]. | He that moueth to[2]
aduoutrye is in no lesse daunger and ieoperdie, then yf he
hadde committed aduoutrye in dede.   For in all offences
they counte the intente and pretensed purpose as euell as *intent:*
the acte or dede it selfe[3].   For they thynke[b] that no lette *cf.*
owghte to excuse hym, that dyd hys beste too haue no lette. *Measure*
    They sette greate store by[c] fooles[4]. And as it is[d] *for Meas.*
greate reproche to do to[e] annye of them hurte or iniury, *I*
so they prohibite not to take pleasure of foolyshnes.   For *_Love of*
that, they thynke, doth muche good to the fooles.   And *Fools*
if any man be so sadde and sterne, that he cannot laughe
nother at their wordes nor at their dedes, none of them

[a] as therebye.   [b] Thinking.
[c] [sette . . . by] haue singular delite and pleasure in.
[d] is a.   [e] to *omitted*.

peccatum testetur magis eis displicere quam poenam, principis interdum praerogatiua, interdum suffragiis populi, aut mitigatur seruitus
aut remittitur. Sollicitasse ad stuprum nihilo minus
quam stuprasse periculi est. In omni siquidem flagitio   *Stupri sollicitati*
certum destinatumque conatum aequant facto. neque   *poena.*
enim id quod defuit ei putant prodesse debere, per quem non stetit
quominus nihil defuerit.
    Moriones in delitiis habentur, quos ut affecisse contumeliis magno
in probro est, ita uoluptatem ab stultitia capere non   *Voluptas e*
uetant. Siquidem id morionibus ipsis maximo esse   *morionibus.*
bono censent, cuius[5] qui tam seuerus ac tristis est ut nullum

[1] See the note above, p. 71.   the family of Sir Thomas More. See
[2] Not in the sense of inciting others Jortin's *Erasmus*, i. p. 175, and
to, but of attempting.   Bridgett's *Life*, p. 126.
[3] St. Matt. v. 28.   [5] *Cuius* appears to refer, by a
[4] The reader will at once recall   rather harsh change of number, to
More's own fancy for a *morio*, in the   *morionis*, supplied from the preceding
person of Henry Pattinson, who is   *morionibus*.
introduced into Holbein's sketch of

Fools

be commytted to his tuition; for feare lest he would not ordre^a them gentilly and fauorably enough, to whom they should brynge no delectation (for other goodnes in them is none); muche lesse any proffyt shoulde they yelde hym.

Mockery

To mocke a man for hys deformitie, or for that he lacketh anye parte or lymme of hys bodye, is counted greate dishonestie and reproche, not to hym that is mocked, but to hym that mocketh[1]; which vnwysely doth imbrayde[2] any man of that as a vice, whiche was not in his powre to eschewe. Also as they counte and reken very lyttell wytte to be in hym that regardeth not

anti cosmetics

naturall bewtie and comlines, so to helpe the same with payntinges is taken for a vayne and a wanton pryde, not without great infamye[3]. For they knowe euen by verye experience, that no comelines of bewtie doth so hyghly commende and auaunce the wyues in the conceyte of there husbandes, as honest conditions and lowlines. For as loue is oftentimes wonne with bewtie, so it is not kept, preserued, and continued[4], but by vertue and obedience.

^a intreate.

neque factum neque dictum rideat, ei tutandum non credunt, ueriti ne non satis indulgenter curetur ab eo, cui non modo nulli usui, sed ne oblectamento quidem (qua sola dote ualent) futurus esset.

     Irridere deformem aut mutilum turpe ac deforme non ei qui ridetur habetur, sed irrisori, qui cuiquam, quod in eius potestate non erat ut fugeret, id uitii loco stulte exprobret. Vt enim formam naturalem non tueri segnis atque inertis ducunt, sic adiumentum
Fucata forma.   ab fucis quaerere infamis apud illos insolentia est.
Vsu enim ipso sentiunt, quam non ullum formae decus uxores, aeque ac morum probitas et reuerentia, commendet maritis. Nam ut forma nonnulli sola capiuntur, ita nemo nisi uirtute atque obsequio retinetur.

---

[1] Such a one as Persius describes :   fucis frustra utentem,' ending 'num-
. . . 'lusco possit qui dicere lusce.'   quam Hecuben haec facient Helenen.'
[2] Upbraid. See the Glossary.   [4] All this is for *retinetur*. For the sen-
[3] More has an epigram 'In anum   timent, compare More's charming lines

They do not only feare theire people from doinge euell
by punyshmentes, but also allure them to vertue with
rewardes of honoure.   Therfore they set vp in the market
place the ymages of notable men[1], and of such as· haue
bene great and bounteful benefactors to the common
wealth, for the perpetual memorie of their good actes;
and also that the glory and renowme of the auncetors
may sturre and prouoke theire posteritie to vertue.   He
that inordinatlie and ambitiously desireth promotions, is
lefte all hopeles for euer atteynyng any promotion as
longe as he liueth.   They lyue together louingly.   For
no magistrate is other hawte or ferefull.   Fathers they
be called, and lyke fathers they vse themselfes.   The
citezens (as it is their dewtie) do[a] willingly exhibite vnto
them dewe honoure, without any compulsion.   Nor the
prince hymselfe is not knowen from the other by his
apparel, nor by a crown or diademe[b] or cappe of main-

Rewards:

Fathers

a lowly Prince.

---

[a] do *omitted*.   [b] [by his ... diademe] by princely apparel, or a robe of
state, nor by a crown or diademe roial.

---

125   Non poenis tantum deterrent a flagitiis, sed | propositis quoque
honoribus ad uirtutes inuitant.   Ideoque statuas uiris
insignibus et de republica praeclare meritis in foro   Et praemiis
collocant, in rerum bene gestarum memoriam, simul   inuitandi ciues
ut ipsorum posteris maiorum suorum gloria calcar et   ad officium.
incitamentum ad uirtutem sit.   Qui magistratum ullum   Damnatus
ambierit, exspes omnium redditur.   Conuiuunt ama-   ambitus. Honor
biliter, quippe nec magistratus ullus insolens aut   magistratuum.
                                                              Dignitas
terribilis est.   patres appellantur et exhibent[2].   iisdem   principis.
defertur, ut debet, ab uolentibus honor, non ab inuitis
exigitur.   Ne principem quidem ipsum uestis aut diadema, sed

---

'Ad Candidum: qualis uxor deligenda.'   [1] The 'image' of More himself has
'That is true love,' he says, 'which   of late years been so set up in his
   Virtutis inclytae   native city, though not yet in a manner
   (Quae certa permanens   worthy of him.   See the Introduction,
   Non febre decidit,   p. xviii. n.
   Annisue deperit)   [2] An ellipse of *se*.
   Respectus efficit.'

Prince's sign:

sheaf of wheat

tenaunce [1], but by a littell sheffe of corne caried before hym. And so a taper of wax is borne befor the byshop [2], whereby onely he is knowen.

Few Laws: Thei haue but few lawes. For to people so instructe and institute very fewe do suffice. Yea this thynge they

anti

law &

lawyers

chieflye reproue amonge other nations, that innumerable bokes of lawes and expositions vpon the same be not sufficient [3]. But they thinke it against al right and iustice, that men shuld be bound to thoes lawes, whiche other be in numbre mo then be able to be readde, or els blinder and darker, then that any man can well vnderstande them. Furthermore they vtterly exclude and bannyshe all [a] proctours and sergeauntes at the lawe [4], which craftely handell matters, and subtelly dispute of the lawes. For they

[a] all attorneis.

gestatus frumenti manipulus discernit, ut pontificis insigne est praelatus cereus.

Leges habent perquam paucas, sufficiunt enim sic institutis paucissimae. Quin hoc in primis apud alios improbant
Leges paucae.   populos, quod legum interpretumque uolumina non
infinita sufficiunt. Ipsi uero censent iniquissimum,
ullos homines his obligari legibus, quae aut numerosiores sint quam
ut perlegi queant, aut obscuriores quam ut a quouis possint intel-
ligi. porro causidicos, qui causas tractent callide ac leges uafre

---

[1] The 'cap of maintenance,' or 'cap of dignity,' was a cap of crimson velvet, lined with ermine, originally assigned only to dukes. The name is said to be derived from its having been 'borne in the hand' by a distinguished captive, in the train of the victorious general who owned it. See the Dictionaries. In the Latin text, however, there is nothing but *diadema* to answer to Robynson's triplet.

[2] See below, p. 294.

[3] This is a stock complaint. The jurisconsults have their share in the

Praise of Folly, as those who 'sexcentas leges eodem spiritu contexunt, nihil refert quam ad rem pertinentes;' and who 'glossematis glossemata, opiniones opinionibus cumulantes, efficiunt ut studium illud omnium difficillimum esse videatur.'—*Moriae Encom.*, ed. 1668, p. 144.

[4] This is Robynson's expansion of the single term *causidicos*. 'Proctor' is Chaucer's 'procuratour:'—

'May I not axe a libel, sire sompnour,
    And answer there by my procuratour?'

thinke it most mete, that euery man shuld pleade his
owne matter, and tell the same tale before the iudge,
that he would tel to his man of lawe. So shall there be
lesse circumstaunce of wordes, and the trewth shal soner
cum to light; whiles the iudge with a discrete iudgement
doth waye the wordes of hym whom no lawier hath in-
struct with deceit; and whiles he helpeth and beareth
out simple wittes agaynst the false and malicious circumuertions of craftie chyldren[1]. This is harde to be obserued in other countreis, in so infinitie a numbre of
blynd and intricate lawes. But in Vtopia euery man is
a cunnyng lawier. For, as I sayde, they haue verye fewe
lawes; and the playnner and grosser that anye interpretation is, that they allowe as most iuste. For all lawes
(saye they) bee made and publysshed onelye to thenthente,
that by them euerye man shoulde be put in remembraunce
of hys dewtye. But the craftye and subtyll interpretation

Lawyers exiled:

distrust of words:

Everyman a lawyer

disputent, prorsus omnes excludunt. censent enim ex usu esse
ut suam quisque causam agat, eademque referat indici
quae narraturus patrono fuerat. Sic et minus am-
bagum fore et facilius elici ueritatem, dum, eo dicente
quem nullus patronus fucum docuit, iudex solerter expendit singula,
et contra uersutorum calumnias simplicioribus ingeniis opitulatur.

Aduocatorum inutilis turba.

126 haec apud | alias gentes in tanto perplexissimarum aceruo legum
difficile est obseruari. Caeterum apud eos unusquisque est legis
peritus. Nam et sunt (ut dixi) paucissimae; et interpretationum
praeterea ut quaeque est maxime crassa, ita maxime aequam censent.
Nempe quum omnes leges (inquiunt) ea tantum causa promulgentur,
ut ab hiis quisque sui commonefiat officii, subtilior interpretatio pau-

---

[1] That is, 'people,' as constantly in
the Bible. Comp. 'obedient children'
(1 Pet. i. 14), &c. More elsewhere
recommends trusting to the summary
jurisdiction of a judge. 'Though
maister More saye, that he neuer saw
the day yet, but that he durst as well
trust the truth of one iudge as of two
iuries,' is a statement in *The Debellacion
of Salem and Byzance.* See also Father
Bridgett's note in *Wisdom and Wit*,
p. 179; and for one cause of the
corruption of juries, see the *Discourse
of the Common Weal*, before quoted,
Appendix to Introduction, p. lix:
'Somme founde the meanes to haue
ther seruantes sworne in the Juryes,
to thyntent to haue them hasarde ther
soules to saue ther gredynes.'

vs.
Laws:

of them can ^a put verye fewe in that remembraunce (for they be but fewe that do perceaue them); where as the simple, the plaine, and grosse meaning of the lawes is open to euerye man. Els as touchynge the vulgare sorte of the people, whiche be bothe moste in numbre, and haue moste neade to knowe theire dewties, were it not as good for them that no lawe were made at all, as, when it is made, to brynge so blynde an interpretacion vpon it, that without greate witte and longe arguynge no man can discusse it ? to the findinge out whereof nother the grosse iudgement of the people can attayne, nother the hole lyfe of them that be occupied in woorkynge for theire lyuynges can suffyse therto [1].

Loan of
magistrates
to
neighbors:

Thies vertues of the Vtopians haue caused theire nexte neyghbours and borderers, whiche lyue fre and vnder no subiection (for the Vtopians longe agoo haue delyuered manye of them from tyrannye), to take magistrates of them, some for a yeare, and some for fyue yeares space. Whiche, when the tyme of theire office is expired, they brynge home agayn with honoure and prayse ; and take newe ons ^b agayne wyth them into theire countrey. Thies

---

^a [them can] them (for as muche as few can atteyne therto) canne.
^b ons *omitted.*

cissimos admonet (pauci enim sunt qui assequantur), quum interim simplicior ac magis obuius legum sensus omnibus in aperto sit. alioquin, quod ad uulgus attinet, cuius et maximus est numerus et maxime eget admonitu, quid referat utrum legem omnino non condas, an conditam in talem interpreteris sententiam, quam nisi magno ingenio et longa disputatione nemo possit eruere, ad quam inuestigandam neque crassum uulgi iudicium queat attingere, neque uita in comparando uictu occupata sufficere.

Hiis eorum uirtutibus incitati finitimi, qui quidem liberi sunt et suae spontis (multos enim ipsi iam olim tyrannide liberauerunt) magistratus sibi ab illis, alii quotannis, alii in lustrum impetrant ; quos defunctos imperio cum honore ac laude reducunt, nouosque secum rursus in patriam reuehunt. Atque hi quidem populi optime profecto

---

[1] See Budé s letter, above, pp. lxxx—xcii.

nations haue vndowtedlye verye well and holsomlye prouyded for theire common wealthes. For seynge that
bothe the makyng and the marrynge of the weale publique doth depende and hange of ᵃ the maners of the
rulers and magistrates, what officers coulde they more
wyselye haue chosen, then thoes whiche cannot be ledde
from honestye by brybes [1] (for to them that shortlye
after shall departe thens into theyre owne countreye
money shoulde be vnprofytable); nor yet be moued other
with fauour or malyce towardes annye man, as beynge
straungers and vnaquainted with the people? The which
twoo vices of affection [2] and auryce where they take place
in iudgementes, incontynente they breake iustice, the
strongeste and suereste bonde of a common wealthe [3].
Thies peoples, whiche fetche theire officers and rulers
from them, the Vtopians cal theire fellowes; and other,
to whome they haue bene beneficiall, they call theire
frendes.

ᵃ vpon.

ac saluberrime reipublicae suae consulunt : cuius et salus et pernicies
quum ab moribus magistratuum pendeat, quos nam potuissent ele-
127 gisse [4] prudentius, quam qui | neque ullo precio queant ab honesto
deduci (utpote quod breui sit remigraturis inutile) ignoti ciuibus, aut
prauo cuiusquam studio aut simultate flecti. Quae duo mala, affectus
atque auaritiae [5], sicubi incubuere iudiciis, illico iustitiam omnem,
fortissimum reipublicae neruum, dissoluunt. Hos Vtopiani populos,
quibus qui imperent ab ipsis petuntur, appellant socios, caeteros quos
beneficiis auxerunt amicos uocant.

---

[1] For More's own practice in this respect see the anecdotes in Roper's *Life* (ed. 1822, pp. 61, 62).

[2] 'Affection' here denotes the 'being moved with favour or malice' towards anyone, just described; in other words, partiality or bias. The Latin *affectus* sometimes has the same sense, as in Quintil. vi. 2, 'inducere iudicem in affectus.' Shakspere uses the word similarly in *Merchant of Venice*, iv. 1:—

'For affection,
Master of passion, sways it to the mood
Of what it likes or loathes.'

[3] The second title of Plato's *Republic*, it will be remembered, is *Concerning Justice*.

[4] For *eligere*. See note above, p 111.

[5] Should rather have been the nominative, in apposition to *mala*.

Irony on Christian Europe:

of Treaties:

As towchynge leages, which in other places betwene countrey and countrey be so ofte concluded, broken, and made agayne [a], they neuer make none with anye nacion [1]. For to what purpose serue leagues ? saye they ; as though nature had not set sufficient loue betwene man and man. And who so regardeth not nature, thynke yowe that he wyll passe for wordes ? They be brought into thys opinion chiefely bicause that in thoes parties of the wordle leagues betwene princes be wont to be kept and

Europe

obserued very slenderly. For here in Europa, and espe-ciallye in thies partes, where the faythe and religion of Christe reygneth, the maiestie of leagues is euerye where estemed holly and inuiolable ; partlye through the iustice and goodnes of princes, and partelye through the reue-

Pope

rence of great byshoppes [b] [2]. Whyche, lyke as they make

[a] renewed.   [b] [through . . . byshoppes] at the reuerence and motion of the head byshoppes.

Foedera, quae reliquae inter se gentes toties ineunt, frangunt ac renouant, ipsi nulla cum gente feriunt. Quorsum enim
De foederibus.   foedus, inquiunt, quasi non hominem homini satis natura conciliet ; quam qui contempserit, hunc uerba scilicet putes curaturum ? In hanc sententiam eo uel maxime tra-huntur, quod in illis terrarum plagis foedera pactaque principum solent parum bona fide seruari. Etenim in Europa, idque his potissi-mum partibus quas CHRISTI fides et religio possidet, sancta est et inuiolabilis ubique maiestas foederum, partim ipsa iustitia et bonitate principum, partim summorum reuerentia metuque pontificum, qui ut

[1] On this subject, see the Introduc-tion, p. xxxii.

[2] Robynson seems to have stuck at the words ' *metuque pontificum*,' as will be seen from the reading of his second edition, where he evidently took *metu* for *motu*. In a former passage (*sup.* p. 8) he appears in like manner to have hesitated about rendering *ponti-fices* by Popes, which is a common use of the word in More. So Burnet : ' Which is partly owing to the Justice and Goodness of the Princes them-selves, and partly to the Reverence they pay to the Popes : Who, as they are most religious Observers of their own Promises, so they exhort all other Princes to perform theirs.' On the part taken by Pope Julius II in the League of Cambray and afterwards, which is probably what More had most in view, see Tytler : *History of Scotland*, 1864, ii. p. 281, and Brewer : *Reign of Henry VIII*, i. p. 12.

no promysse themselfes, but they doo verye religiouslye
perfourme the same, so they exhorte all prynces in any
wyse to abyde by theyre promisses ; and them that refuse
or denye so to do, by theire pontificall powre and auctho-
rytie they compell therto[1]. And surely they thynke well
that it myght seme a verye reprochefull thynge, yf in the
leagues of them, whyche by a peculiare name be called
faythfull, faythe shoulde haue no place.

But in that newefonnde parte of the worlde, whiche
is scaselye so farre from vs beyonde the lyne equinoctiall,   *Equator*
as owre lyfe and manners be dissidente from theirs, no
truste nor confydence is in leagues. But[2] the mo and
holyer cerymonies the league is knytte vp with, the soner
it is broken, by some cauillation founde in the woordes ;
whyche manye tymes of purpose be so craftelye put in
and placed, that the bandes can neuer be so sure nor
so stronge, but they wyll fynde some hole open to crepe

nihil in se recipiunt ipsi, quod non religiosissime praestant, ita caeteros
omnes principes iubent ut pollicitis omnibus modis immorentur, tergi-
uersantes uero pastorali censura et seueritate compellunt. Merito
sane censent turpissimam rem uideri si illorum foederibus absit fides
qui peculiari nomine fideles appellantur.

128 At in illo nouo orbe terrarum, quem circulus aequator uix tam
longe | ab hoc nostro orbe semouet, quam uita moresque dissident,
foederum nulla fiducia est ; quorum ut quoque[a] plurimis ac sanctissi-
mis ceremoniis innodatum fuerit, ita citissime soluitur, inuenta facile
in uerbis calumnia, quae sic interim de industria dictant callide, ut
nunquam tam firmis adstringi uinculis queant, quin elabantur aliqua,

[a] quodque, A. recte.

---

[1] With this sarcastic contrast of
the ideal with the real, compare the
strictures of Erasmus, in a similar
strain, on the conduct of Christian
Kings and Popes, in his *Adagia,* under
the headings *Imperitia* and *Simulatio et
Dissimulatio* (ed. 1629, pp. 301, 655).

[2] This way of beginning a fresh
sentence dislocates the meaning, by
appearing to make the conduct here
described to be the practice of the Utopians ; as if they broke treaties the
more quickly, the more solemnly they
were concluded. Burnet's rendering
gives what I take to be the same
wrong impression. The Latin simply
means : 'there is no confidence in
treaties ; which are speedily broken,'—
that is, which in the old world are so
broken.

owte at[1], and to breake bothe league and trewthe. The
whiche crafty dealynge, yea, the whiche fraude and de-
ceyte, yf they shoulde knowe it to bee practysed amonge
pryuate men in theire bargaynes and contractes, they
woulde incontinent crye owte at it with a[a] sower countenaunce, as an offence most detestable, and worthie to be
punnyshed with a shamefull death ; yea, euen verye they[2]
that auaunce themselfes authours of like councel geuen to
princes. Wherfore it maye well be thought other that all
iustice is but a basse and a lowe vertue, and whiche
aualeth it self[3] farre vnder the hyghe dignitie of kynges ;
or, at the least wyse, that there be two iustices ; the one
mete for the inferioure sorte of the people, goinge a fote
and crepynge by lowe on the[b] grounde, and bounde
downe on euery side with many bandes, because it shall
not run at rouers : the other a pryncely vertue, whiche
lyke as it is of muche hygher maiestie then the other
poore iustice, so also it is of muche more lybertie, as to
the whiche nothinge is vnlawful that it lusteth after.

cf.
Machiavelli

     [a] with an open mouth and a.   [b] lowe by the.

foedusque et fidem pariter eludant. Quam uafriciem, imo quam
fraudem dolumque, si priuatorum deprehenderent interuenisse con-
tractui, magno supercilio rem sacrilegam et furca dignam clamitarent
hi nimirum ipsi, qui eius consilii principibus dati semet gloriantur
autores. Quo fit ut iustitia tota uideatur aut non nisi plebea uirtus et
humilis, quaeque longo interuallo subsidat infra regale fastigium, aut
uti saltem duae sint, quarum altera uulgus deceat, pedestris et humi-
repa, neue usquam septa transilire queat, multis undique restricta
uinculis ; altera principum uirtus, quae sicuti sit quam illa popularis
augustior, sic est etiam longo interuallo liberior, ut cui nihil[a] non
liceat nisi quod non libeat.

     [a] *om.* A.

---

[1] Here again, Robynson and Burnet
('but they will find some Loophole,'
&c.) convey the impression that this
is what the Utopians do. The metaphor in the Latin is taken from tying
up a parcel, which in such hands can
never be so securely fastened, 'but
that some things slip out, and baffle
alike treaty and trust.'

[2] Latin, *hi ipsi.* Compare the French
même eux.

[3] That is, sinks. See the Glossary.

Thies maners of princes (as I sayde) whiche be there [1]
so euyll kepers of leagues cause the Vtopians, as I suppose, to make no leagues at all : whiche perchaunce
woulde chaunge theire mynde if they lyued here. Howebeit they thynke that thoughe leagues be neuer so faythfully obserued and kept, yet the custome of makinge
leagues was verye euel begonne. For this causeth men
(as though nations which be separate a sondre by the
space of a lytle hyl or a ryuer, were coupled together by
no societe or bonde of nature), to thynke them selfes
borne aduersaryes and enemyes one to an other ; and that
it is [a] lawfull for the one to seke the death and destruction
of the other, if leagues were not ; yea, and that, after the
leagues be accorded, fryndeshyppe dothe not growe and
encrease ; but the lycence of robbynge and stealynge doth
styll remayne, as farfurthe as, for lacke of forsight and
aduisement in writinge the woordes of the league, anny
sentence or clause to the contrary is not therin suffycyentlye comprehended.   But they be of a contrary
opinion : that is, that no man ought to be counted an

[a] were.

Hos mores, ut dixi, principum illic foedera tam male seruantium
puto in causa esse ne ulla feriant Vtopienses, mutaturi fortasse sententiam si hic uiuerent. Quanquam illis uidetur, ut optime seruentur,
male tamen inoleuisse foederis omnino sanciendi consuetudinem ; qua
fit ut (perinde ac si populum populo, quos exiguo spacio collis tantum
129 aut riuus discriminat, nulla naturae societas copularet) | hostes atque
inimicos inuicem sese natos putent, meritoque in mutuam grassari
perniciem, nisi foedera prohibeant : quin his ipsis quoque initis non
amicitiam coalescere sed manere praedandi licentiam, quatenus per
imprudentiam dictandi foederis nihil quod prohibeat satis caute com-
prehensum in pactis est.   At illi contra censent, neminem pro inimico
habendum, a quo nihil iniuriae profectum est ; naturae consortium

---

[1] Namely, in the old world. The
use of *illic* and *hic* in the same sentence
of the Latin, both denoting Europe
from different points of view, is a little
confusing.

enemy, whyche hath done no iniury; and that the felow-
shyppe of nature is a stronge league; and that men
be better and more surely knitte togethers by loue and beneuolence, then
by couenauntes of leagues; by
hartie affection of minde,
then by woor-
des.

foederis uice esse; et satius ualentiusque homines inuicem beneuo-
lentia quam pactis, animo quam uerbis, connecti.

Hythloday accepts war as a natural tide of things: p. 45.

Of Warfare,

WArre or battel as a thinge very beastelye[1], and yet to
no kynde of beastes in so muche vse as it is[a] to
man, they do detest and abhorre; and, contrarye to the
custome almost of all other natyons, they cownte nothinge
so much against glorie, as glory gotten in warre. And
therefore, though they do daily practise and exercise
themselfes in the discypline of warre, and that[b] not only
the men, but also the women, vpon certeyne appoynted
dayes, leste they shoulde be to seke in the feat of armes
yf nead should requyre; yet they neuer to[c] goo to
battayle, but other in the defence of thcir owne cowntreye, or to dryue owte of theyr frendes lande the enemyes
that be comen in[d], or by their powre to deliuer from the

a it is *omitted.*   b that *omitted.*   c to *omitted.*
d that haue inuaded it.

DE RE MILITARI.

BEllum utpote rem plane beluinam—nec ulli tamen beluarum
formae in tam assiduo, atque homini, est usu—summopere
abominantur, contraque morem gentium ferme omnium nihil
aeque ducunt inglorium atque petitam e bello gloriam. eoque, licet
assidue militari sese disciplina exerceant, neque id uiri modo, scd
foeminae quoque statis diebus, ne ad bellum sint, quum exigat usus,
inhabiles, non temere capessunt tamen, nisi quo aut suos fines tuean-
tur, aut amicorum terris infusos hostes propulsent, aut populum

---

[1] Lat. *plane beluinam.* This derivation is given in the *Cornucopiae*: '*Bellua,*
immanis fera, quasi *bellum* gerens, a
quo *belluinus* adiectivum,' &c. Pace, in
his *De Fructu* (p. 32), plays similarly, though not with the same etymology
in view, on the word *bellum*: 'Cae-
terum, ut verum dicam, *bellis* invita
intersum, ideo quod minime *bella* sunt'
(Musica loq.).

Revenge:

yocke and bondage of tyrannye some people that be
oppressed wyth tyranny[a]. Whyche thynge they doo
of meere pytye and compassion. Howebeit they sende
healpe to theyre fryndes ; not euer[1] in theire defence, but
sumtimes also to requyte and reuenge iniuries before to
them done. But thys they do not, onles their counsell
and aduise in the matter be asked, whyles yt ys yet newe
and freshe. For yf they fynde the cause probable, and yf
the contrarye parte wyll not restore agayne suche thynges
as be of them iustelye demaunded, then they be the
chyeffe auctores and makers of the warre. Whyche they
do not onlye as ofte as by inrodes and inuasions of soldiours prayes and booties be dreuen away, but then also
much more mortally, when their frindes marchauntes in
any land, other vnder the pretence of vniust lawes, or els
by the wresting and wronge vnderstonding of good lawes,
do sustaine an vniust accusation vnder the colour of iustice. Nother the battel which the vtopians fowghte for
the Nephelogetes against the Alaopolitanes[2], a lytle before
oure time, was made for annye other cause, but that the

[for revenge: new & fresh]

[Lucian]

    [a] [that be ... tyrannye] that be therewith oppressed.

quempiam tyrannide pressum miserati (quod humanitatis gratia
faciunt) suis uiribus Tyranni iugo et seruitute liberent. Quanquam
auxilium gratificantur amicis, non semper quidem quo se defendant,
sed interdum quoque illatas retalient, atque ulciscantur iniurias. 130
uerum id ita demum faciunt, si re adhuc integra consulantur ipsi, et
probata causa, repetitis ac non redditis rebus, belli autores inferendi
sint ; quod non tunc solum decernunt, quoties hostili incursu abacta
est praeda, uerum tum quoque multo infestius, quum eorum negotiatores usquam gentium, uel iniquarum praetextu legum, uel sinistra
deriuatione bonarum, iniustam subeunt, iustitiae colore, calumniam.
Nec alia fuit eius origo belli, quod pro Nephelogetis aduersus Alaopolitas, paulo ante nostram memoriam, Vtopienses gessere, quam apud

---

    [1] That is, not always.
    [2] The names here devised, Νεφελό-
γεται, 'Cloudlanders,' and Ἀλαοπολῖτα,

    'men of Blindville,' are suggestive of
the *Verax Historia* of Lucian.

Nephelogete marchaunte men, as the vtopians thought,⟩ *Venpeance*
suffred wrong of the Alaopolitanes, vnder the pretence of⟩
righte. But whether it were righte or wrong, it was with⟩
so cruell and mortal warre reuenged, the countreis round
about ioyning their healpe and powre to the puisaunce and
malice of bothe parties, that most florishing and wealthie
peoples beyng some of them shrewedely shaken, and some
of them sharpely beaten, the mischeues were not finished
nor ended, untill the Alaopolitanes at the last were yelded
vp as bondmen into the iurisdiction of the Nephelogetes.
For the vtopians foughte not this warre for themselfes.
And yet the Nephelogetes before the warre, when the
Alaopolitanes flourished in wealth, were nothyng to be
compared with them.

So egerly the Vtopians prosequute the iniuries done to
ther frindes, yea, in moncy matters; and not their owne
likewise.   For if they by coueyne or gyle be⟨wiped beside⟩ *cheated of*
their gooddes[1], so that no violence be done to their bodies,
they wreake their anger by absteining from occupieng
with that nation, untill they haue made satisfaction. Not

Alaopolitas Nephelogetarum mercatoribus illata praetextu iuris (ut
uisum est ipsis) iniuria.   certe, siue illud ius, siue ea iniuria fuit, bello
tam atroci est uindicata, quum ad proprias utriusque partis uires
odiaque circumiectarum etiam gentium studia atque opes adiungeren-
tur, ut florentissimis populorum aliis concussis, aliis uehementer
afflictis, orientia ex malis mala Alaopolitarum seruitus demum ac
deditio finierit, qua in Nephelogetarum (neque enim sibi certabant
Vtopienses) potestatem concessere; gentis, florentibus Alaopolitarum
rebus, haud quaquam cum illis conferendae.

Tam acriter Vtopienses amicorum, etiam in pecuniis, iniuriam
persequuntur, suas ipsorum non item; qui sicubi circumscripti bonis
excidant, modo corporibus absit uis, hactenus irascuntur uti, quoad

---

[1] That is, cheated out of their goods.
In Cooper's *Thesaurus*, ed. 1584, the
sentence from Terence (*Phorm.* iv.
4. 1) 'emunxi argento senes' is rendered 'I have ⟨wipte the old fooles
from ⟩al their money.' The use of

'beside' for 'out of' may be illustrated
from a passage in Foxe: *Acts and
Mon.* ii. 384 (quoted in the *New
English Dictionary*)—'He put the new
Pope Alexander beside the cushion,
and was made pope himself.'

for bicause they set lesse stoore by their owne cytyzeyns,
then by theire frindes; but that they take the losse of
their fryndes money more heuely then the losse of theyr
owne: bicause that their frindes marchaunte men, forasmuche as that they leise is their owne priuate gooddes,
susteyne great damage by the losse; but their owne
citizeyns leise nothing but of the commen gooddes, and of
that which was at home plentifull and almost superfluous,
elles hadde it not bene sent furth. Therfore no man
feeleth the losse. And for this cause they thynke it to
cruell an acte to reuenge that losse wyth the death of
many; the incommoditie of the whiche losse no man
feeleth nother in his liffe, nother [a] in his liuinge. But if
it chaunce that any of their men in any other countreye
be maymed or kylled, whether it be done by a commen
or a priuate councell; knowing and trying out the treuth
of the matter by their ambassadours, onles the offenders
be rendered vnto them in recompence of the iniury, they
will not be appeased; but incontinent they proclayme
warre against them. The offenders yelded they punnishe
other with death or with bondage.

[a] nor yet.

satisfactio fiat, eius commercio gentis absti|neant. Non quod minoris 131
sibi curae ciues quam socii sint, sed horum tamen pecuniam intercipi
aegrius quam suam ferunt; propterea quod amicorum negotiatores,
quoniam de suo perdunt priuato, graue uulnus ex iactura sentiunt; at
ipsorum ciuibus nihil nisi de republica perit, propterea quod abunda-
bat domi, ac ueluti supererat, alioqui non emittendum foras. Quo fit
ut intertrimentum [1] citra cuiusquam sensum accidat. Quo circa nimis
crudele censent id damnum multorum ulcisci mortibus, cuius damni
incommodum nemo ipsorum aut uita aut uictu persentiscat. Caeterum
si quis suorum usquam per iniuriam debilitetur, aut occidat [a], siue id
publico factum consilio siue priuato sit, per legatos re comperta, nisi
deditis noxiis placari non possunt quin ilico bellum denuncient. Noxae
deditos aut morte aut seruitio puniunt.

[a] Sic quoque A. Legend. occidatur.

---

[1] A rarer word than detrimentum, but used once by Cicero.

trickery

They be not only sorye, but also ashamed to atchieue the victory with much ^a bloodshed [1]; cowntinge it greate follye to bye pretyous wares to dere. They reioyse and auaunte themselfes, yf they vaynquyshe and oppresse theire enemyes by crafte and deceyt. And for that act they make a generall tryumphe; and as yf the matter were manfullye handeled, they sett vp a pyller of stone [2] in the place where they so vanquysshed theyre ennemyes, in token of the vyctory. For then they glorye, then they booste and cracke that they haue plaied the men in dede, when they haue so ouercommen, as no other lyuynge creature but onely man coulde; that ys to saye, by the myghte and pusyaunce ^b of wytte. For wyth boddelye strengthe (saye they) beares, lyons, boores, wulffes, dogges, and other wylde beastes doo fyghte [3]. And as the mooste

^a much *omitted*.   ^b puisance.

Cruentae uictoriae non piget modo eos, sed pudet quoque, reputantes inscitiam esse, quamlibet preciosas merces nimio emisse. arte doloque uictos, oppressos hostes impendio gloriantur, triumphumque ob eam rem publice agunt, et uelut re strennue gesta tropheum erigunt. tunc enim demum uiriliter sese iactant et cum uirtute gessisse, quoties ita uicerint, quomodo nullum animal praeter hominem potuit, id est, ingenii uiribus. Nam corporis ^a inquiunt, ursi, leones, apri, lupi,

Magno empta uictoria.

^a *Sic quoque* A. *Legend.* corporibus.

---

[1] See the Introduction, p. xlvii; and compare the remarks of Erasmus on the proverb 'incruentum statuit trophaeum' (*Adagia*, ed. 1629, p. 481 b). A saying of Pittacus is quoted, 'oportere victorias citra sanguinem fieri.'

[2] Lat. *tropheum*, a trophy.

[3] With this compare what Erasmus wrote to the Abbot of St. Bertin, in a letter dated London, March 14, 1513-14: 'We are worse than the dumb animals, for among them it is only the wild beasts that wage war,

and even they do not fight among themselves, but with beasts of a different species, and that with the weapons with which nature has furnished them.' Drummond's *Life of Erasmus*, i. p. 236. In a similar strain, but in language blending argument and satire together with a power seldom met with, the 'timid' Erasmus attacks the bellicose potentates of his day, in his *Adagia*. See the long disquisition headed *Imperitia.* (*Adag.* ed. 1629, pp. 295-298).

parte of them doo passe vs in strengthe and fyerce courage, so in wytte and reason wee be muche stronger than they all.

Theyre chyefe and princypall purpose in warre ys to obteyne that thynge, whyche yf they had before obteyned, they wolde not haue moued battayle. But if that be not possible, they take so cruell vengeaunce of them whych be in the fault, that euer after they be aferde to doo the lyke. Thys ys theyre cheyffe and pryncypall intente, whyche they immedyatelye and fyrste of all prosequute and sette forewarde; but yet so, that they be more cyr-cumspecte in auoydynge and eschewynge ieopardyes, then they be desyerous of prayse and renowne. Therfore immediatly after that warre is ones solemply denounced, they procure manye proclamations, signed with their owne commen seale, to be sett up preuilie at one time in their ennemyes lande, in places mooste frequented. In thyes proclamatyons they promysse greate rewardes to hym that will kyll their enemies prince; and sumwhat lesse gyftes, but them verye greate also, for euerye heade of them, whose names be in the sayde proclamacions conteined. They be those whome they count their chieffe aduersaries, next vnto the prince. What soeuer is pre-

paid

assassination

canes, caeteraeque beluae dimicant ; quarum ut pleraeque nos robore ac ferocia uincunt, ita cunctae ingenio et ratione superantur.

Hoc unum illi in bello spectant, uti id obtineant, quod si fuissent 132 ante consecuti, bellum non fuerant illaturi ; aut, si id res uetet, tam seueram ab his uindictam expetunt, ut idem ausuros in posterum terror absterreat. Hos propositi sui scopos destinant, quos mature petunt ; at ita tamen uti prior uitandi pericula cura quam laudis aut famae consequendae sit. Itaque protinus indicto bello schedulas ipsorum publico signo roboratas locis maxime conspicuis hosticae terrae clam uno tempore multas appendi procurant, quibus ingentia pollicentur praemia, si quis principem aduersarium sustulerit ; deinde minora, quanquam illa quoque egregia, decernunt, pro singulis eorum capitibus, quorum nomina in iisdem literis proscribunt. hii sunt quos secundum principem ipsum autores initi aduersus se consilii ducunt.

scribed vnto him that killeth any of the proclamed persons, that is dobled to him that bringeth any of the same to them aliue : yea, and to the proclamed persones them selfes, if they wil chaunge their mindes and come into them, takinge their partes, they profer the same greate rewardes with pardon, and suerty of their liues.

Therfore it quickely cummeth to passe that they[a] haue al other men in suspicion, and be vnfaithfull and mistrusting emong themselfes one to another ; liuing in great feare and in no lese ieopardye. For it is well knowen that dyuers times the most part of them, and specially the prince him selfe, hath bene betraied of them in whome they put their most hoope and trust. So that[1] there is no maner of acte nor dede, that giftes and rewardes do not enforce men vnto. And in rewardes they kepe no measure ; but, remembring and considering into howe great hasard and ieopardie they call them, endeuoure themselfes[2] to recompence the greatenes of the daunger

[a] their enemies.

Quicquid percussori praefiniunt, hoc geminant ei qui uiuum e proscriptis aliquem ad se perduxerint, quum ipsos quoque proscriptos praemiis iisdem, addita etiam impunitate, contra socios inuitant.

Itaque fit celeriter ut et caeteros mortales suspectos habeant, et sibi inuicem ipsi neque fidentes satis neque fidi sint, maximoque in metu et non minore periculo uersentur. Nam saepenumero constat euenisse uti bona pars eorum et princeps in primis ipse ab his proderentur, in quibus maximam spem reposuerunt. Tam facile quoduis in facinus impellunt munera. quibus illi nullum exhibent 133 mo|dum : sed memores in quantum discrimen hortantur, operam dant uti periculi magnitudo beneficiorum mole compensetur ; eoque

---

[1] This should not be so worded as to express a consequence. The Latin is *Tam facile*, &c., ' so easily are men incited by gifts to any deed whatever.' In the edition of 1624 ' that ' is omitted. Burnet connects the sentence with what follows : ' For the Rewards that the *Utopians* offer are so unmeasurably great, that there is no Sort of Crime to which Men cannot be drawn by them.'

[2] This is the reflexive use of the verb, as it occurs in the Collect for the Second Sunday after Easter. So in *Twelfth Night*, iv. 2, ' Malvolio . . . endeavour thyself to sleep.' A large

with lyke great benefites. And therfore they promisse not only wonderfull greate abundaunce of golde, but also landes of greate reuenues, lyenge in moost sauffe places emonge theire fryndes. And theyre promysses they perfourme faythfully, wythowte annye fraude or couyne.

Thys custome of byinge and sellynge aduersaryes amonge other people ys dysallowed, as a cruell acte of a basse and a cowardyshe mynde. But they in thys behalfe thynke themselfes muche prayse woorthye, as who lyke wyse men by thys meanes dyspatche greate warres wyth owte annye battell or skyrnyshe. Yea, they cownte yt also a dede of pyty and mercye, bycause that by the deathe of a fewe offenders the lyues of a greate numbre of ynnocentes, as well of their own men as also of their enemies, be raunsomed and saued, which in fighting shoulde haue bene sleane. For they doo no lesse pytye the basse and commen sorte of theyr enemyes people, then they doo theyre owne; knowynge that they be dryuen to ᵃ warre agaynste theyre wylles by the furyous madnes of theyre prynces and heades.

Yf by none of thies meanes the matter go forwarde as

ᵃ and enforced to.

non immensam modo auri uim, sed praedia quoque magni reditus in locis apud amicos tutissimis propria ac perpetua pollicitantur, et summa cum fide praestant.

Hunc licitandi mercandique hostis morem, apud alios improbatum, uelut animi degeneris crudele facinus, illi magnae sibi laudi ducunt, tanquam prudentes, qui maximis hoc pacto bellis sine ullo prorsus praelio defungantur ; humanique ac misericordes etiam, qui paucorum nece noxiorum numerosas innocentium uitas redimant, qui pugnando fuerint occubituri, partim e suis, partim ex hostibus ; quorum turbam uulgusque non minus ferme quam suos miserantur, gnari non sua sponte eos bellum capessere, sed principum ad id furiis agi.

Si res hoc pacto non procedat, dissidiorum semina iaciunt aluntque ;

---

collection of examples will be found in the *New English Dictionary*, and in the *Clerical Journal*, May 15, 1862, and May 14, 1864.

they wolde haue yt, then they procure occasyons of debate and dyssentyon to be spredde emonge theyre enemyes; as by bryngynge the prynces brother, or some of the noble men, in hoope to obtayne the kyngedome[1]. Yf thys way preuayle not, then they reyse vp the people that be nexte neyghboures and borderers to theyr enemyes, and them they sette in theyre neckes[2] vnder the coloure of some olde tytle of ryghte, suche as kynges doo neuer lacke. To them they promysse theire helpe and ayde in theyre warre. And as for moneye they gyue them abundance; but of theyre owne cytyzeyns they sende to them fewe or none. Whome they make so much of, and loue so intyerlye, that they wolde not be willing to chaung anye of them for their aduersaries prince. But their gold and siluer, bycause they kepe yt all for thys

fratre principis aut aliquo e nobilibus in spem potiundi regni perducto. Si factiones internae languerint, finitimas hostibus gentes excitant committuntque, eruto uetusto quopiam titulo, quales nunquam regibus desunt. Suas ad bellum opes polliciti pecuniam affluenter suggerunt, ciues parcissime ; quos tam unice habent charos, tantique sese mutuo faciunt, ut neminem sint e suis cum aduerso principe libenter com-mutaturi. At aurum argentumque, quoniam unum hunc in usum

---

[1] More may have been thinking of the intrigues carried on by his own sovereign in Scotland in the very year (1515) in which this was written. Since the battle of Flodden, in 1513, which left a mere child inheritor of the throne, Henry had been trying by every crooked means to get the boy and his mother (Henry's own sister, Margaret) into his power. The comments of the Scotch historian on his conduct will illustrate what is said in the text: ' By means of his indefatigable agent, Lord Dacre, he had not only corrupted some of its leading nobility, but so successfully fomented dissensions amongst them, that every effort of the regent to re-establish the control of the laws was rendered abortive

by the prevalence of private war.'— Tytler, as before, ii. p. 305. ' He must be dull indeed,' writes Professor Brewer,' who does not perceive that Utopia, when following out these principles, is removed but a few miles from the English Channel; and that a practice, which seems the more odious in these upright and wise Uto-pians, was tenfold more unjustifiable in those who, professing the doctrines of Christ, never scrupled to employ the same means against their own enemies.' —Reign of Henry VIII, i. p. 289. The wonder is that More, even under cover of a learned language, should have had the boldness to expose these proceed-ings so unmistakeably.

[2] See note above, p. 103.

only purpose, they laye it owte frankly and frely ; as who
shoulde lyue euen as wealthely, if they hadde bestowed it
euerye pennye.   Yea, and besydes theyre ryches, whyche
they kepe at home, they haue also an infynyte treasure
abrode, by reason that (as I sayde before) manye natyons

mercenaries

_cf. p. 48_

_motive
p. 255_

be in their debte.   Therefore they hyere soldyours oute of
all countreys, and sende them to battayle ; but cheiflye of
the Zapoletes [1].   Thys people is .500. myles from Vtopia
eastewarde.   They be hydeous [2], sauage, and fyerce,
dwellynge in wild woodes and high mountaines, where
they were bredde and brought vp.   They be of an harde
nature, able to abide and susteine heate, cold, and labour ;
abhorrynge from all delycate deyntyes, occupyenge no
husbandrye nor tyllage of the ground, homelye and rude
both in the [a] buildinge of their houses and in their apparrell ; geuen vnto no goodnes, but onelye to the breede [b]

a the *omitied*.   b breedinge.

omne seruant, haud grauatim erogant, utpote non mi|nus commode 134
uicturi, etiam si uniuersum impenderent.   Quin praeter domesticas
diuitias est illis foris quoque infinitus thesaurus, quo plurimae gentes,
uti ante dixi, in ipsorum aere sunt.   ita milites undique conductos ad
bellum mittunt, praesertim ex Zapoletis.   Hic populus quingentis
passuum millibus ab Vtopia distat, orientem solem uersus, horridus,
agrestis, ferox ; syluas montesque asperos, quibus sunt innutriti,
praeferunt.   Dura gens, aestus frigoris et laboris patiens, delitiarum
expers omnium, neque agriculturae studens, et cum aedificiorum tum

---

[1] The edition of 1517 has a marginal
note at this point : ' Gens haud ita
dissimilis eluetiis.' But even without
this the allusion to the Swiss would
be obvious. They were the great mercenaries of the period.—See Oman's
Art of War in the Middle Ages, 1885,
pp. 62–95. Their tactics resembled
those of the Macedonian phalanx.

It is strange that the derivation of
' Zapoletes' should have perplexed
commentators. We cannot be sure

whether More meant the nominative
to represent Ζαπωλῆται or Ζαπωλητοί ;
but in either case, whether as ' ready
sellers' (of themselves), or ' readily
sold,' the word would naturally express mercenaries.

[2] The Latin *horridus* was probably
used by More to express only ' rough.'
Robynson seems to have taken it in the
sense (a legitimate one) of ' dreadful,'
which ' hideous' in his time would
still express. See the Glossary.

Zapoletes.

and bringynge vp of cattell. The mooste parte of theire lyuynge is by huntynge and stealynge. They be borne onelye to warre, whyche they dylygentlye and earnestlye seke for. And when they haue gotten yt, they be wonders gladde therof. They goo furthe of theyre countreye in greate companyes together. and who soeuer lacketh souldyours, there they proffer theyre seruyce for small wages. Thys ys onely the crafte that ᵃ they haue to gette theyre lyuynge by. [They maynteyne theyr lyfe by sekyng ⟩ *epigram* theyre deathe.] For them, whomewyth they be in wayges, they fyghte hardelye, fyerslye, and faythefullye. But they bynde themselfes for no certeyne tyme. But vpon thys condytion they entre into bondes, that the nexte daye they wyll take parte wyth the other syde for greatter ⟩ wayges; and the nexte daye after that they wyll be readye to come backe agayne for a lytle more moneye[1]. There be fewe warres there awaye, wherin is not a greate

ᵃ that *omitted*.

uestitus indiligens, pecorum duntaxat curam habent. Magna ex parte uenatu et raptu uiuunt, ad solum bellum nati, cuius gerendi facultatem studiose quaerunt, repertam cupide amplectuntur, et magno numero egressi cuiuis requirenti milites uili semet offerunt. [Hanc unam uitae⟩ artem nouerunt, qua mors quaeritur.] Sub quibus merent, acriter pro iis et incorrupta fide dimicant. Verum in nullum certum diem sese obstringunt, sed ea lege in partes ueniunt, ut posteriore die uel ab hostibus oblato maiore stipendio sint staturi ; iidem perendie rursus inuitati plusculo remigrant. Rarum oritur bellum, in quo non bona

[1] It will be noticed how much space More devotes to the ways and doings of this people. This may have been due to the prominent part played by the Swiss in European affairs about the time he wrote. At the great battle of Marignano, in October, 1515, they fought on the side of Ferdinand and the Pope against the King of France, and were defeated. In that same year More's friend Richard Pace, was sent to Zürich, to negotiate for their help. His letter to Wolsey is dated at the end of November, 1515, and gives a striking picture of the state of the country, and the exorbitant demands of the Swiss mercenaries The letter is preserved in Cotton MSS.. Vitell. B. xviii. p. 222, from which it was printed in Planta's *History of the Helvetic Confederacy*, 1807, ii. pp. 424-434. See also Brewer: *Letters and Papers*, vol. ii. pt. i., p. liii, and no. 553.

numbre of them in bothe partyes. Therefore yt daylye chauncethe that nye kynsefolke, whyche were hiered together on one parte, and there verye fryndelye and famylyerly vsed themselfes one wyth an other, shortely after, beynge separate into[a] contrarye partes, runne one agaynste an other enuyouslye and fyercelye ; and for-gettynge bothe kyndred and frendeshyp, thruste theyre swordes one in another : and that for none other cause, but that they be hyered of contrarye prynces for a lytle moneye. Whyche they doo so hyghelye regarde and esteame, that they will easelye be prouoked to chaunge partes for a halfpenye more waygcs by the daye. So quyckelye they haue taken a smacke in couetesenes ; whyche for all that ys to them no proffyte. For, that they gette by fyghtynge, ymmedyatelye they spende vnthryftelye and wretchedlye in ryott.

Thys people fyghte for the Vtopyans agaynste all natyons, bycause they giue them greatter wayges, then annye other natyon wyll. For the Vtopians, lyke as they seke good men to vsc wel, so they seke thyes euell and vycyous men to abuse. Whome, when neade requyreth,

^a in.

pars illorum in utroque sint exercitu. itaque accidit quotidie ut san-guinis necessitudine coniuncti, qui et iisdem in partibus conducti familiarissime semet inuicem utebantur, paulo post in contrariis[a] distracti copias, hostiliter concurrant, et infestis ani|mis, obliti generis, 135 immemores amicitiae, mutuo sese confodiant, nulla alia causa in mutuam incitati perniciem, quam quod a diuersis principibus exigua pecuniola conducti ; cuius tam exactam habent rationem, ut ad diurnum stipendium unius accessione assis facile ad commutandas partes impellantur. Ita celeriter imbiberunt auaritiam, quae tamen nulli est eis usui. Nam quae sanguine quaerunt, protinus per luxum, et eum tamen miserum, consumunt.

Hic populus Vtopiensibus aduersus quosuis mortales militat, quod tanti ab hiis eorum conducatur opera quanti nusquam alibi. Vtopienses si quidem ut bonos quaerunt quibus utantur, ita hos quoque homines pessimos quibus abutantur. quos quum usus postulat, magnis im-

^a contrarias, A. *recte.*

wyth promisses of greate rewardes they putt furthe into
greate ieopardyes; from whens the mooste part of them
neuer cummeth againe to aske their rewardes. But to
them that remain on liuc [a] they paye that which they
promissed faithfully, that they may be the more willinge
to put themselfes in like daungers another time. Nor the
Vtopians passe not how many of them they bring to
distruction. For they beleue that they should doo a very
good deade for all mankind, if they could ridde out of the
wordle all that fowle, stinkinge denne of that most wicked
and cursed people [1].

Next vnto thies they vse the soldiours of them whom
they fight for [b]. And then the help of their other frindes.
And last of al they ioyne to [2] their owne citizeins. Emong
whome they gyue to one of tried vertue and prowes the
rewle, goouernaunce, and conductyon of the hole armye.
Vnder hym they appoynte ii. other, whyche whyles he ys
sauffe be bothe pryuate and owte of offyce; but yf he be

[a] aliue.   [b] for whom they fight.

pulsos pollicitationibus maximis obiiciunt periculis, unde plerunque
magna pars nunquam ad exigenda promissa reuertitur. superstitibus,
quae sunt polliciti, bona fide persoluunt, quo ad similes ausus incen-
dantur. Neque enim pensi quicquam habent quam multos ex eis
perdant, rati de genere humano maximam merituros gratiam se, si
tota illa colluuie populi tam tetri ac nepharii orbem terrarum purgare
possent.

Secundum hos eorum copiis utuntur, pro quibus arma capiunt;
deinde auxiliaribus caeterorum amicorum turmis. Postremo suos
ciues adiungunt, e quibus aliquem uirtutis probatae uirum totius
exercitus summae praeficiunt. Huic duos ita substituunt, uti eo
136 incolumi | ambo priuati sint; capto aut interempto, alter e duobus

[1] Robynson's epithets are vigorous,
but in this case hardly surpass More's
own. I do not know whether Erasmus
is referring to the same people, when
he writes: ' Quin est apud Germanos
populus, cuius haec praecipua gloria,
quam plurimos mortales ferro truci-

dasse: quod cum per se immane est,
tum hoc etiam foedius, quod hoc faciunt mercede conducti; veluti carnifex
quispiam ad lanienam precio emptus.'
Adagia, as before p. 482 a.

[2] ' Join to;' that is, add or asso-
ciate.

taken or slayne, the one of the other .ii. succedeth hym, as yt were by inherytaunce [1]. And if the second miscarry, then the third taketh hys rowme; leaste that (as the chaunce of battell ys vncerteyne and dowtefull), the yeopardye or deathe of the capytayne shoulde brynge the hole armye in hasarde. They chuse soldyers owte of euerye cytye those whyche putt furthe themselfes wyl-lynglye. For they thruste no man furthe into warre agaynste hys wyll; bycause they beleue, yf annye man be fearefull and faynte harted of nature, he wyll not onelye doo no manfull and hardye act hym selfe, but also by[a] occasyon of cowardenes to hys fellowes. But yf annye battell be made agaynste theyre owne countreye, then they putt thyes cowardes, so that they be stronge bodyed, in shyppes emonge other bolde harted men. Or elles they dyspose them vpon the walles, from whens they maye not flye. Thus, what for shame that theyre enne-myes be at hande, and what for bycause they be withowt hope of runnynge awaye, they forgette all feere. And manye tymes extreame necessytye turneth cowardnes into prowes and manlynes.

But as none of them ys thrust forthe of his countrey

[a] be.

uelut haereditate succedat; eique ex euentu tertius, ne (ut sunt bellorum sortes uariae) periclitante duce totus perturbetur exercitus. E quaque ciuitate delectus exercetur ex his qui sponte nomen profi-tentur. neque enim inuitus quisquam foras in militiam truditur; quod persuasum habeant, si quis sit natura timidior, non ipsum modo nihil facturum strennue, sed metum etiam comitibus incussurum. Caeterum si quod bellum ingruat in patriam, ignauos huiusmodi, modo ualeant corpore, in naues mixtos melioribus collocant, aut in moenibus sparsim disponunt, unde non sit refugiendi locus. ita suorum pudor, hostis in manibus, atque adempta fugae spes, timorem obruunt, et saepe extrema necessitas in uirtutem uertitur.

At sicuti ad externum bellum ex ipsis nemo protrahitur nolens, ita

---

[1] This was the Lacedaemonian custom. Thucyd. iv. 38.

into warre agaynste hys wyll, so women that be wyllynge
to accompanye their husbandes in times of warre be not
prohybyted or stopped ª. Yea, they prouoke and exhorte
them to yt wyth prayses. And in sett fylde the wyues doo
stande euerye one by here owne husbandes syde. Also
euery man is compassed nexte abowte wyth hys owne
chyldren, kins folkes, and alliaunce; that they, whom
nature chiefelye moueth to mutuall succoure, thus stondynge together, maye helpe one an other¹. It is a great
reproche and dishonestie for the husbande to come home
wythowte hys wiffe, or the wiffe withoute her husband, or
the sonne without his father. And therfore, if the other
part sticke so harde by it, that the battell come to their
handes, it is fought with great slaughter and bloodshed,
euen to the vtter destruction of both partes. For as they
make all the meanes and shyftes that maye be, to kepe
themselfes from the necessitye of fyghtynge, so that they
may dispatche the battell by their hiered soldyours, so,
when there is no remedy but that they muste neades
fyghte themselfes, then they do as corragiouslye fall to

ª letted.

foeminas uolentes in militiam comitari maritos adeo non prohibent, ut
exhortentur etiam et laudibus incitent. profectas cum suo quamque
uiro pariter in acie constituunt. tam sui quemque liberi, affines, cog-
nati circumsistunt, ut hi de proximo sint mutuo sibi subsidio, quos
maxime ad ferendas inuicem suppetias natura stimulat. In maximo
probro est coniux absque coniuge redux, aut amisso parente reuersus
filius. quo fit uti si ad ipsorum manus uentum sit, modo perstent
hostes, longo et lugubri praelio ad internitionem usque decernatur.
137 Nempe, ut omnibus cu|rant modis ne ipsis dimicare necesse sit, modo
bello possint uicaria conductitiorum manu defungi; ita, quum uitari
non potest quin ipsi ineant pugnam, tam intrepide capessunt quam

---

¹ Such was the custom of the Ger-
mans in ancient times: ' Memoriae
proditur quasdam acies inclinatas iam
et labantes a feminis restitutas con-
stantia precum et obiectu pectorum et
monstrata comminus captivitate,' &c.
Tac., *Germ.* c. viii. Compare also
Caesar, *Bell. Gall.* vii. 51. It was
the same, to a great degree, with the
ancient Gauls and Britons.

S

it, as before, whyles they myght, they dyd wyselye auoyde it[a]. Nor they be not moste fierce at the fyrst bronte. But in continuaunce by litle and lytle theire fierce corrage encreaseth, with so stubborne and obstynate myndes, that they wyll rather die then gyue backe an ynche. For that suertye of lyuynge, whiche euery man hath at home, beynge ioyned with noo carefull anxietye or remembraunce how theire posteritie shall lyue after them (for this [b] pensifenes oftentymes breaketh and abateth couragious stomakes) maketh them stowte and hardy, and dysdaynful to be conquered. Moreouer, theire knowledge in cheualrye and feates of armes putteth them in a good hope. Finally, the holsome and vertuous opinions, wherin they were brought vp euen from theire childhode, partely through learnyng, and partelye throughe the good ordenaunces and lawes of theire weale publique, augmente and encrease theire manfull currage. By reason whereof they nother set so litle store by theire liues, that they will rasshely and vnaduisedlye cast them away; nor they be not so farre in lewde and fond loue therewith, that they will shamefully couete to kepe them, when honestie biddeth leaue them.

When the battel is hottest and in al places most fierce

[a] and refuse it.   [b] his.

quoad licuit prudenter detrectabant: nec tam primo ferociunt impetu, quam mora sensim et duratione inualescunt, tam offirmatis animis ut interimi citius quam auerti queant. Quippe uictus illa securitas, quae cuique domi est, ademptaque de posteris anxia cogitandi cura (nam haec solitudo[a] generosos ubique spiritus frangit) sublimem et uinci dedignantem facit. Ad haec militaris disciplinae peritia fiduciam praebet. postremo rectae opiniones (quibus et doctrina et bonis reipublicae institutis imbuti a pueris sunt) uirtutem addunt; qua neque tam uilem habent uitam ut temere prodigant, neque tam improbe charam ut, quum honestas ponendam suadeat, auare turpiterque retineant.

Dum ubique pugna maxima feruet, lectissimi iuuenes coniurati

[a] Sic et B. Solicitudo, recte, ed. 1563.

and feruent, a bende of chosen and picked yong men, whiche be sworne to liue and dye togethers, take vpon them to destroye theire aduersaries capitaine[1]. Hym[a] they inuade, now with preuy wyeles, now by open strength. At hym they strike both nere and farre of. He is assayled with a long and a continewal assault[2] ; freshe men styll commyng in the weried mens places. And seldome it chaunceth (onles he saue hymselfe by flying) that he is not other slayne, or els taken prysoner, and yelded to his enemies alyue. If they wynne the fyelde, they persecute not theire enemies with the violent rage of slaughter. For they had rather take them aliue then kyll them. Nother they do so followe the chase and pursute of theire enemies, but they leaue behynde them one parte of theire hoste in battayl arraye vnder theire standardys. In so muche that, if all theire hole armie be discumfetyd and ouercum, sauing the rerewarde, and that they therewith achieue the victory, then they had rather lette all theire enemies scape, then to followe them owt of array. For they remembre it hath chaunced vnto them-

[a] whome.

deuotique ducem sibi deposcunt aduersum. hunc aperte inuadunt, hunc ex insidiis adoriuntur. idem eminus idem co-minus petitur, longoque ac perpetuo cuneo, summissis assidue in fatigatorum locum recentibus, oppugnatur ; raroque accidit (ni sibi fuga prospiciat) ut non in-tereat, aut uiuus in hostium potestatem ucniat. Si ab ipsis uictoria sit, haud quaquam caede grassantur ;

Dux potissimum impetendus, quo citius finiatur bellum.

fugatos enim comprehendunt quam occidunt libentius ; neque un-
138 quam ita persequuntur fugientes, ut non unam | interim sub signis instructam aciem retineant : adeo uisi[a] caeteris superati partibus, postrema acie sua uictoriam adepti sint, elabi potius hostes uniuersos sinant quam insequi fugientes perturbatis suorum ordinibus insues-cant ; memores sibimet haud semel usu uenisse ut, mole totius

[a] nisi, A. vt si *recte* B.

---

[1] Tactics not unheard of in modern football matches.

[2] In the Latin, *cuneo* ; a wedge-shaped, or compact, body of assailants.

S 2

selfes more then ones : the hole powre and strength of theyre hoste being vanquished and put to flight, whiles theire enemies, reioysing in the victory, haue persecuted them flying, some one way and some an other ; fewe [a] of theire men lying in an ambusshe, there reddy at all occasions [1], haue sodaynly rysen vpon them thus dispersed and scattered owt of array, and through presumption of safetye vnaduisedly pursuynge the chase, and haue incontinent changed the fortune of the hole battayll ; and spyte of there tethes wrestynge owt of theire handes the sure and vndowted victory, being a litle before conquered, haue for theire parte conquired the conquerers.

It is hard to say whether they be craftier in laynge an ambusshe, or wittier in auoydynge the same. Yowe woulde thynke they intende to flye, when they meane nothing lesse. And contrary wise, when they go about that purpose, yow wold beleue it were the least part of their thoughte. For if they perceaue themselfes other ouermatched in numbre, or closed in to narrowe a place,

Ambush

[a] a small companye.

cxercitus uicta profligataque, quum hostes uictoria gestientes hac atque illac abeuntes persequerentur, pauci ipsorum in subsidiis collocati, ad occasiones intenti, dispersos ac palantes illos et praesumpta securitate negligentes derepente adorti totius euentum praelii mutauerunt [2], extortaque e manibus tam certa et indubitata uictoria uicti uictores inuicem uicerunt.

Haud facile dictu est, astutiores instruendis [3] insidiis an cautiores ad uitandas sient [4]. fugam parare credas, quum nihil minus in animo habent : contra, quum id consilii capiunt, nihil minus cogitare putes. Nam si nimium sese sentiunt aut numero aut loco premi, tunc aut

---

[1] That is, watching their opportunity. For the subject of laying ambuscades, see Polyaenus, *Stratag.* I. xi. 2 ; II. xii.

[2] As *usu uenisse ut* precedes, this should have been *mutauerint*, and *uicerint* just after. The error, due to the length of the sentence, is left uncorrected in later editions.

[3] This should probably be two words, *in struendis*.

[4] A form common in Plautus and Terence, whence probably More took it.

then they remoue their campe other in the nyght season
with silence, or by some pollicie they deceaue theire enemies; or in the daye time they retiere backe so softely[1],
that it is no lesse ieoperdie to medle with them when they
gyue backe then when they preese on. They fence and
fortifie theire campe sewerlye with a deape and a brode
trenche. The earth therof is cast inward[2]. Nor they do
not set drudgeis and slaues a worke about it. It is doone
by the handes of the souldiours them selfes. All the hole
armye worketh vpon it, except them that watche[a] in harneis before the trenche for sodeyne auentures. Therefore,
by the labour of so manye, a large trenche closinge in
a great compasse of grounde is made in lesse tyme then
any man wold beleue.

Theire armoure or harneis whiche they weare is sure   *armour.*
and stronge to receaue strokes, and handsome for all
mouinges and gestures of the bodye; in so muche that
it is not vnweldy to swymme in. For in the discipline

[a] kepe watche and warde.

noctu agmine silente castra mouent, aut aliquo stratagemate eludunt,
aut interdiu ita sensim sese referunt, tali seruato ordine, ut non minus
periculi sit cedentes quam instantes adoriri. Castra diligentissime
communiunt fossa prealta lataque, terra quae egeritur introrsum
reiecta; nec in eam rem opera mediastinorum utuntur. ipsorum
manibus militum res agitur, totusque exercitus in opere est, exceptis
qui pro uallo in armis ad subitos casus excubant. Itaque tam multis
139 adnitentibus, magna | multumque amplexa loci munimenta omni fide
citius perficiunt.

Armis utuntur ad excipiendos ictus firmis, nec ad motum gestumue
quemlibet ineptis, adeo ut ne natando quidem molesta   Formae
sentiant. Nam armati natare inter militaris disciplinae   armorum.

---

[1] For this use of the word ' softly,'
Lat. *sensim*, see the Glossary. Robynson leaves out the clause, *tali seruato
ordine*, 'keeping such good order,'
and so makes it difficult to see the
reason for what is stated.

[2] This was the regular custom. See

the article *Castra* in Smith's *Dict. of
Antiquities.* It was a necessary proceeding, in order that the *agger*, formed
by the earth thrown out, might be
itself protected by the trench, and
more completely under the control of
the defenders.

Swimming in armor :

long-bow.

of theire warefare, amonge other feates thei lerne to swimme in harneis[1]. Their weapons be arrowes afarre of[a], which they shote both strongely and suerly[2]; not onelye fotemen but also horsemen. At hande strokes they vse not swordes but pollaxes, whiche be mortall, aswel in sharpenes as in weyghte, bothe for foynes and downe strokes. Engines for warre they deuyse and inuente wonders wittely. Whiche, when they be made, they kepe very secret; leaste if they should be knowen before neade requyre, they should be but laughed at, and serue to no purpose. But in makynge them, hereunto they haue chiefe respecte; that they be both easy to be caried, and handsome to be moued and turned about.

     [a] aloufe.

rudimenta consuescunt. tela sunt eminus sagittae, quas acerrime simul et certissime iaculantur, non pedites modo sed ex equis etiam ; cominus uero non gladii, sed secures uel acie letales uel pondere, seu caesim seu punctim feriant. Machinas excogitant solertissime, factas accuratissime caelant, ne ante proditae quam res postulet ludibrio magis quam usui sint. in quibus fabricandis hoc in primis respiciunt, uti uectu faciles et habiles circumactu sint.

---

[1] In this suggestion, as in many others, More was in advance of his own age, or even of ours. The soldiers of Charles XII of Sweden were trained to cross rivers by swimming. The subject may have been freshly brought to the minds of English people, a short time before More wrote, by the conflict between the English and French fleets off Brest, Aug. 10, 1512, in which the two flagships grappled together and both took fire, when 'the captain of the English ship (being the *Regent*), and of the French (call'd the *Cordeliere*), together with the soldiers in them, perished all, save only a few French, who saved themselves with swimming.' See Lord Herbert of Cherbury's *Hist. of England under Henry VIII*, ed. 1683, p. 25.

[2] In this description, and in that of the bills or poleaxes just after, we easily see a reminiscence of the English archers and infantry. ' In times past,' writes Harrison, in a well-known passage, 'the cheefe force of England consisted in their long bowes. But now we haue in maner generallie giuen ouer that kind of artillerie, and for long bowes in deed doo practise to shoot compasse for our pastime.'— *Description of England*, ed. 1877, p. 279. (For shooting 'compasse,' that is, at an angle or elevation, see the examples given in the *New English Dict.*) Compare also the extracts from Sir John Smythe's *Discourses on the forms and effects of divers sorts of Weapons*, quoted in *Letters of eminent Literary Men* (Camden Society), 1843, pp. 54, 55.

Truce taken with theire enemies for a shorte time they
do so fermelye and faythfully keape, that they wyll not
breake it ; no not though they be theire vnto prouoked[1].
They do not waste nor destroy there enemies lande with
forraginges, nor they burne not vp theire corne. Yea, they
saue it as muche as maye be from beinge ouerrune and
troden downe, other with men or horses ; thynkynge that
it groweth for theire owne vse and proffyt. They hurt no
man that is vnarmed, onles he be an espiall. All cities
that be yelded vnto them, they defende. And suche as
they wynne by force of assaute they nother dispoyle nor
sacke ; but them that withstode and dyswaded the yeld-
ynge vp of the same they put to death ; the other souldiours they punnyshe with bondage. All the weake
multitude they leaue vntouched. If they knowe that anye
cytezeins counselled to yelde and rendre vp the citie, to
them they gyue parte of the condempned mens goodes.
The resydewe they distribute and gyue frely amonge
them, whose helpe they had in the same warre. For none
of them selfes taketh anye portion of the prayc.

But when the battayll is fynyshed and ended, they put

Initas cum hostibus inducias tam sancte obseruant, ut ne lacessiti
quidem uiolent. Hostilem terram non depopulantur,
neque segetes exurunt ; imo ne hominum equorumue   De induciis.
pedibus conterantur, quantum fieri potest, prouident,
rati in ipsorum usus crescere. Inermem neminem laedunt, nisi idem
speculator sit. Deditas urbes tuentur, at nec expugnatas diripiunt, sed
per quos deditio est impedita eos enecant, caeteris defensoribus in
seruitutem addictis. Imbellem turbam omnem relinquunt intactam.
Si quos deditionem suasisse compererint, his e damnatorum bonis
aliquam partem impartiunt ; reliqua sectione[3] auxiliares donant. Nam
ipsorum nemo quicquam de praeda capit.

140   Caeterum confecto | bello non amicis impensas in quos insumpsere,

---

[1] Compare the Introduction, p. xxxii.
[2] Burnet, more correctly, ' When
a *War* is ended.'

[3] *Sectio* is the regular term for distribution of booty by auction, and the
like. See Cic. *De Invent.* i. 45.

theire frendes to neuer a penny coste of al the chardges that they were at, but laye it vpon theire neckes that be conquered. Them they burdeyne with the hole chardge of theire expenceis; which they demaunde of them partelye in money, to be kept for lyke vse of battayll, and partelye in landes of greate reuenues, to be payde vnto them yearlye for euer. Suche reuenues they haue nowe in manye countreis; whiche by litle and lytle rysyng, of dyuers and sondry causes, be encreased aboue vii. hundreth thousand ducates[1] by the yere. Thither they sende furth some of their citezeins as Lieuetenauntes[2], to lyue theire sumptuously lyke men of honoure and renowne. And yet, this notwithstanding, muche money is saued, which commeth to the commen treasory; onles it so chaunce, that thei had rather truste the countrey with the money. Which many times thei do so long vntil they haue neade to occupie it. And it seldome happeneth, that thei demaund al. Of thies landes thei assigne part vnto them, which at their request and exhortacion put

sed uictis imputant, exiguntque eo nomine partim pecuniam, quam in similes bellorum usus reseruant, partim praedia, quae sint ipsis apud eos perpetua non exigui census. Huiusmodi reditus nunc apud multas gentes habent, qui uariis ex causis paulatim nati supra septingenta ducatorum millia in singulos annos excreuere; in quos e suis ciuibus aliquos emittunt quaestorum nomine, qui magnifice uiuant, personamque magnatum illic prae se ferant. at multum tamen superest quod inferatur aerario, nisi malint eidem genti credere, quod saepe tantisper faciunt, quoad[3] uti necesse sit: uixque accidit unquam ut totam reposcant. Ex his praediis partem assignant illis qui ipsorum

At hodie uictores maximam partem dependunt.

---

[1] Taking the gold ducat, which is the one usually meant, at 9s. 4d., this would be about £327,000.

[2] The English by itself might seem to suggest such an instance as that of William, Lord Mountjoy, Erasmus's friend and pupil, who was appointed governor of Hammes Castle in Picardy, near the frontiers of Calais. But the Latin, *quaestorum nomine*, points rather to officials sent out, as Burnet words it, 'to receive these Revenues.'

[3] *Tantisper* followed by *quoad* is a post-classical construction.

themselfes in such ieoperdies as I spake of before. If
anye prynce stirre vp warre agaynst them, intendyng to
inuade theire lande, they mete hym incontinent owt of
thcire owne borders with great powre and strengthe. For
they neuer lyghtly make warre in their owne countrei.
Nor

*cf.
Machiavelli.*

> they be neuer brought into so ex-
> treme necessitie, as to take
> helpe out of forreyne
> landes into thire
> owne Ilande.

hortatu tale discrimen adeunt, quale ante monstraui. Si quis princeps, armis aduersus eos sumptis, eorum ditionem paret inuadere,
magnis illico uiribus extra suos fines occurrunt. nam neque temere
in suis terris bellum gerunt, neque ulla necessitas tanta est, ut eos
cogat aliena auxilia in insulam suam admittere.

Of the reli=

gyons in Vtopia.

Many religions

THere be dyuers kyndes of religion, not only in
sondry partes of the Ilande, but also in dyuers places
of euerye citie. Some worshyp for God the sunne;
some the mone; some some other of the planetes[1].
There be that gyue worshyp to a man that was ones of
excellente vertue or of famous glory[2], not only as God,
but also as the chiefest and hyghest God. But the moste
and the wysest parte (reiectynge all thies) beleue that
there is a certayne Godlie powre unknowen, euerlastyng,

DE RELIGIONIBVS
VTOPIENSIVM.

RELIGIONES sunt non per insulam modo uerum singulas etiam
urbes uariae, aliis Solem, Lunam aliis, aliis aliud errantium
syderum dei uice | uenerantibus. sunt quibus homo quispiam, 141
cuius olim aut uirtus aut gloria enituit, non pro deo tantum, sed pro
summo etiam deo suspicitur. At multo maxima pars, eademque
longe prudentior, nihil horum, sed unum quoddam numen putant,

---

[1] These various opinions are discussed by Lactantius, *Op.* ed. 1660,
pp. 162 sqq. 'Non est astrorum motus
voluntarius, sed necessarius; quia
praestitutis legibus officiisque deser-
viunt.' They therefore cannot be gods.
The opinion that the Deity was 'numen
quoddam, per mundum diffusum' (referred to just afterwards) was akin to
that of Pythagoras : 'Pythagoras ita

definivit quid esset Deus: Animus, qui
per universas mundi partes omnemque
naturam commeans atque diffusus' (*Ib.*
p. 24). Comp. also Cicero, *De Nat.
Deor.* i. § 11.

[2] As Gaudama the Buddha, Con-
fucius, or Zoroaster. But the expressions which follow would be too
strong to apply to these.

The Majority religion

incomprehensible, inexplicable, farre aboue the capacitie
and retche of mans witte, dispersed through out all the
worlde, not in bygnes, but in vertue and powre[1]. Hym
they call the father of all. To hym allone they attrybute
the begynnynges, the encreasynges, the procedynges, the
chaunges, and the endes of all thynges. Nother they
gyue deuine ^a honours to any other then to him.

One God:

Yea, all the other also, though they be in diuers
opinions, yet in this pointe they agree all togethers with
the wisest sort, in beleuynge that there is one chiefe and
pryncipall God, the maker and ruler of the hole worlde;
whome they all commonly in theire countrey language call
Mythra[2]. But in this they disagre, that amonge some he
is counted one, and amonge some an other. For euery
one of them, whatsoeuer that is whiche he taketh for the
chiefe God, thynketh it to be the very same nature, to
whose onlye deuyne myght and maiestie the som and
soueraintie of al thinges, by the consent of all people, is

Mythra (Persian)

_a any deuine.

incognitum, aeternum, immensum, inexplicabile, quod supra mentis
humanae captum sit, per mundum hunc uniuersum uirtute non mole
diffusum : hunc parentem uocant. Origines, auctus, progressus, uices,
finesque rerum omnium, huic acceptos uni refcrunt ; nec diuinos
honores alii praeterea ulli applicant.

Quin caeteris quoque omnibus, quanquam diuersa credentibus, hoc
tamen cum istis conuenit, quod esse quidem unum censent summum,
cui et uniuersitatis opificium et prouidentia debeatur ; eumque com-
muniter omnes patria lingua Mythram appellant, sed eo dissentiunt,
quod idem alius apud alios habetur ; autumante quoque, quicquid
id sit quod ipse summum ducit, eandem illam prorsus esse naturam,
cuius unius numini ac maiestati rerum omnium summa omnium

---

[1] This seems a reminiscence of Vir-
gil's 'totamque infusa per artus | mens
agitat molem ;' though the use of the
word *uirtute*, in the Latin, may rather
point to the imitation of that passage
by Statius, *Theb*. i. 416.

[2] More had before remarked, that
the old language of the Utopians
was 'not unlike the Persian tongue.'
Hence the name of the Persian Sungod is appropriately used here. See
the note above, p. 148.

Present changes:

attributed and geuen. Howe be it, they al begynne by litle and litle to forsake and fall from thys varietie of superstitions, and to agree togethers in that religion whiche semethe by reason to passe and excell the resydewe. And it is not to be dowted but all the other would longe agoo haue bene abolyshed; but that, whatsoeuer vnprosperous thynge happened to any of them as he was mynded to chaunge his religion, the fearefulnes of people dyd take it not as a thynge cummynge by chaunce, but as sente frome God owt of heauen[1]; as thoughe the God, whose honoure he was forsakynge, woulde reuenge that wicked purpose against him.

us: Hythloday (& Apinatus?)

But after they harde (vs) speake of the name of Christe, of his doctryne, lawes, myracles, and of the no lesse wonderful constancie of so manye martyrs, whose bloude wyllynglye shedde brought a great numbre of nations throughe out all partes of the worlde into theire secte; yowe wyll not beleue with howe gladde myndes they agreed vnto the same; whether it were by the secrete

consensu gentium tribuitur. Caeterum paulatim omnes ab ea superstitionum uarietate desciscunt, atque in unam illam coalescunt religionem, quae reliquas ratione uidetur antecellere. Neque dubium est quin caeterae iam pridem euanuissent, nisi quicquid improsperum[a] cuiquam inter mutandae religionis consilia fors obiecisset, non id accidisse casu, sed caelitus immissum inter|pretaretur timor; tan- 142 quam numine, cuius relinquebatur cultus, impium contra se propositum uindicante.

At posteaquam acceperunt a nobis CHRISTI nomen, doctrinam, mores, miracula, nec minus mirandam tot martyrum constantiam, quorum sponte fusus sanguis tam numerosas gentes in suam sectam longe lateque traduxit, non credas quam pronis in eam affectibus

[a] in posterum, A.

---

[1] Compare what was said in the Introduction, p. xlix, about the origin of the *De Civitate Dei*, and St. Augustine's own statement in the first chapter of his great work: 'Sic evaserunt multi, qui nunc Christianis temporibus detrahunt, et mala quae illa civitas pertulit Christo imputant.'

inspiration of God, or els for that they thought it next[a] vnto that opinion which amonge them is counted the chiefest. Howe be it, I thynke this was no smal healpe and furtheraunce in the matter, that they harde vs saye that Christ instytuted[1] amonge hys/all thynges commen ; and that the same communitie dothe yet remayne amongest the rightest Christian companies[2]. Verely, howe soeuer it came to passe, manye of them consented togethers in oure religion, and were wasshed in the hollye water of baptisme[3].

  But because amonge vs foure (for no moo of vs was left alyue ; two of oure companye beynge deade[4]) there was no prieste, whiche I am ryghte sorye for, they, beinge entered and instructed in all other poyntes of oure relygion, lacke onelye those sacramentes, whyche here none but priestes do minister. Howe be it, they vnderstande and perceyue them, and be verye desierous of the same. Yea, they reason and dispute the matter earnestly amonge

        [a] nieghest.

Christian communism.

4 men left of 6:

no priest

sacraments wanted.

ctiam ipsi concesserint, siue hoc secretius inspirante deo, siue quod eadem ei uisa est haeresi proxima, quae est apud ipsos potissima : quanquam hoc quoque fuisse non paulum momenti crediderim, quod CHRISTO communem suorum uictum audierant placuisse, et apud germanissimos Christianorum conuentus adhuc in usu esse. Certe, quoquo id momento accidit, haud pauci   Coenobia. nostram in religionem coierunt, Lymphaque sacra sunt abluti.

  Verum quoniam in nobis quatuor (totidem enim duntaxat supereramus, nam duo fatis concesserant) nemo, id quod doleo, sacerdos erat, caeteris initiati, ea tamen adhuc sacramenta desyderant, quae apud nos non nisi sacerdotes conferunt. intelligunt tamen, optantque ita ut nihil uehementius. quin hoc quoque sedulo iam inter se disputant, an

---

[1] This is too strong a rendering of *Christo placuisse*: 'that Christ approved of a community of living among his followers.'

[2] The marginal note in the Latin points the allusion to monasteries.

[3] As to the lawfulness of lay baptism in exceptional cases, which must be understood here, see Bingham, *Antiquities*, Bk. II. ch. xx. § 9.

[4] The party had originally consisted of Hythloday and five companions. See above, p. 29.

on choosing a bishop:

themselfes, whether, without the sendyng of a christian bysshoppe, one chosen out of theire owne people may receaue the ordre of priesthode. And truly they were mynded to chuse one : but at my departure from them they hadde chosen none. They also, whiche do not agree to Christes religion, (feare [1]) no man frome it, nor speake agaynste anye man that hath receyued it. Sauing that one of oure companye in my presence was sharpely punyshed. He, as sone as he was baptised, began against

a zealot :

our willes, with more earnest affection then wisdome, to reason of Christes religion ; and began to waxe so hotte in his matter, that he dyd not only preferre oure relygion before all other, but also dyd vtterlye despise an condempne al other, callynge them prophane, and the followers of them wicked and deuelishe [2], and the chyldren of euerlasting dampnation. When he had thus longe reasoned the matter, they layde holde on hym, accused

exiled :

hym, and condempned hym into exyle ; not as a despyser of religion, but as a sedicious persone, and a rayser vp of dissention amonge the people. For this is one of the

sine Christiani pontificis missu quisquam e suo numero delectus sacerdotii consequatur characterem. Et electuri sane uidebantur ; uerum quum ego discederem nondum elegerant. Quin hi quoque, religio|ni 143 Christianae qui non assentiunt, neminem tamen absterrent, nullum oppugnant imbutum ; nisi quod unus e nostro coetu me praesente cohercitus est. Is quum recens ablutus, nobis contra suadentibus, de CHRISTI cultu publice maiore studio quam prudentia dissereret, usque adeo coepit incalescere, ut iam nostra [a] modo caeteris anteferret, sed reliqua protenus uniuersa damnaret ; prophana ipsa, cultores impios

Laude trahendi sunt homines ad religionem.

ac sacrilegos aeterno plectendos igni uociferaretur. Talia diu concionantem comprehendunt, ac reum non spretae religionis, sed excitati in populo tumultus agunt peraguntque [3] ; damnatum exilio mulctant : siquidem hoc

[a] non nostra, A. *recte.*

---

[1] That is, deter.
[2] The Latin is not quite so strong, being literally, as Burnet renders it,

'impious and sacrilegious Persons.'
[3] *Peragere*, as a law term, meant 'to prosecute to conviction.'

Toleration: (handwritten)

auncientest lawes amonge them : that no man shalbe
blamed for reasonynge in the mayntenaunce of his owne
religion [1].

For kyng Vtopus, euen at the first begynning, hearing   *King
that the inhabitauntes of the lande were before his com-   Utopus:* (handwritten)
myng thether at contynuall dissention and stryfe among
themselfes for their religions ; perceyuing also that this
common dissention, whyles euerye seuerall secte tooke
seuerall partes in fyghting for theire countrey, was the
only occasion of hys conquest ouer them all ; assone as
he had gotten the victory, first of all he made a decrie,
that it shoulde be lawfull for euery man to fauoure and   *freedom
followe what religion he would, and that he myght do the   to
beste he cold to bryng other to his opinion ; so that he   believe
dyd it peaccably, gentelye, quyetly, and soberlye, without   &
hastye and contentious rebuking and inuehyng against   persuade* (handwritten)

interim [a] antiquissima instituta numerant, ne sua cuiquam religio
fraudi sit.

Vtopus enim iam inde ab initio, quum accepisset incolas ante suum
aduentum de religionibus inter se assidue dimicasse, atque animad-
uertisset eam rem, quod in commune dissidentes singulae pro patria
sectae pugnabant, occasionem praestitisse sibi uincendarum omnium,
adeptus uictoriam in primis [b] sanxit uti quam cuique religionem libeat
sequi, liceat ; ut uero alios quoque in suam traducat, hactenus niti
possit, uti placide ac modeste suam rationibus astruat ; non ut acerbe

[a] inter, A. *recte.*   [b] A. *om.* in primis.

---

[1] As the sentence is an important
one, it should be more exactly rendered. It is literally : ' For they
reckon this among their most ancient
(or, most important) institutions, that
no one's religion should be an injury
to him ;' that is, that no one should be
worse off for it. *Antiquissima,* which
Burnet also renders ' most ancient,'
may mean ' of most importance ;' and
I should have thought that was the
sense here, but for the mention of
Utopus's enactment *inde ab initio,*
which follows. The passage is one
to be noted, not only as bearing on
More's own views of religious toleration, but as laying down a distinction,
significant as coming from him, between punishing an act as an offence
against religion, and as an offence
against the public peace of the realm.
See the next note.

other. If he coulde not by fayre and gentle speche induce them vnto his opinion, yet he should vse no kinde of violence, and refrayne from displeasaunt and seditious woordes. To him that would vehemently and feruently in this cause striue and contend, was decreid bannishment or bondage.

Toleration for the good of religion

This lawe did kynge Vtopus make, not only for the maintenaunce of peace, which he sawe through continuall contention and mortal hatred vtterly extinguished, but also because he thought this decrye shuld make for the furtheraunce of religion. Wherof he durst define and determine nothing vnaduisedly; as dowting whether god, desieryng manifolde and diuers sortes of honoure, would inspire sondrie men with sondrie kyndes of religion. And this suerly he thought a very vnmete and folishe thing, and a pointe of arrogant presumption, to compell all other by violence and threatenynges to agre to the same that thou beleuest to bee trewe[1]. Furthermore though there

caeteras destruat, si suadendo non persuadeat; neque uim ullam adhibeat, et conuiciis temperet. pe|tulantius hac de re contendentem exilio aut seruitute mulctant.   141

Haec Vtopus[a] instituit, non respectu pacis modo, quam assiduo certamine atque inexpiabili odio funditus uidit euerti, sed quod arbitratus est, uti sic decerneretur, ipsius etiam religionis interesse : de qua nihil est ausus temere definire ; uelut incertum habens, an uarium ac multiplicem expetens cultum deus aliud inspiret alii. certe ui ac minis exigere et[b] quod tu uerum credis idem omnibus uideatur, hoc uero et insolens et ineptum censuit. tum si maxime una uera sit,

     [a] Vtopienses, A.   [b] *Sic quoque* A. *Legend.* ut *cum* B.

---

[1] More's tone is too serious, and the arguments he makes Utopus employ too solid and convincing, to allow us to regard all this as merely proper to the romance. On the other hand, if the words express to us the author's own thoughts on the subject of religious toleration, how are we to reconcile them with his avowed principles at a later period ? The question is a difficult one. It is, of course, easy to offer as a solution a change of opinions, or a revulsion of feeling, caused by the Lutheran outbreak. *Dissimiles hic vir et ille puer.* But that is only partially satisfactory. There is an oft-quoted passage in Roper's *Life* (ed. 1822, p. 34), which

be one religion whiche alone is trewe, and all other vayne
and superstitious, yet did he well forsee (so that the matter
were handeled with reason and sober modestie), that the

caeterae omnes uanae, facile tamen praeuidit (modo cum ratione ac
modestia res agatur) futurum denique ut ipsa per se ueri uis emergat

shows that, with the spread of 'heretical' opinions fully before his eyes,
he at least doubted the wisdom of
suppression of them by force. 'Troth
it is indeed, son Roper,' said More
(referring to the outward security of
the Church in England at the time) ;
'and yet, son Roper, I pray God, said
he, that some of us, as high as we
seem to sit upon the mountains treading heretics under our feet like ants,
live not the day that we gladly would
wish to be at league and composition
with them, to let them have their
churches quietly to themselves, so
that they would be contented to let
us have ours quietly to ourselves.'
And on these tolerant principles More
himself, in the day of his power—if
we accept his own statement—would
seem to have acted. 'Dyuers of
theym,' he says in one place, referring to Protestants, 'haue saide that
of suche as were in my house, while I
was chauncellour, I vsed to examine
theym with tormentes, causinge theym
to bee bounden to a tree in my gar-
deine, and their pituously beaten.'
But after explaining the cases (two
only) which gave any shadow of justi-
fication to these reports, he declares
emphatically that ' of al that euer came
in my hand for heresye, as helpe me
God, sauing as I said the sure keeping
of them, and yet not so sure neither
but that George Constantine could
stele awaye : els had neuer any of
them any stripe or stroke giuen them,
so muche as a fylyppe on the fore-
head ' (English Works, p. 901).
So far, all would be consistent.

But this picture of More has to be
brought into harmony with another,
and seemingly very different one. In
his epitaph, composed by himself, he
is described as 'furibus, homicidis,
haereticisque molestus.' Erasmus
testifies that he fully bore out this
description. While he himself professed (Works, p. 925) to hate only
the vice of heresy, and not the persons
of heretics, his language towards these
is harsh and violent, and betokens the
strongest personal antipathy. (Ib.,
pp. 348, 361, c. d., 366 c., 423, &c.).
As regards the special cases of Bainham and Tewksbury, alleged by some
against More (Foxe : Acts and Monuments, ed. 1846, iv. p. 698 , I for one
could not discredit More's solemn
asseveration, quoted above. But
when his biographer pleads that 'in
the administration of those laws'
(against heresy) 'he was not only
rigidly upright, but as tender and
merciful as is compatible with the
character and office of a judge,' while
yet affirming that, 'he held strongly
that the dogmatizing heretics of those
days, in the then circumstances of
England and Christendom, should be
forcibly repressed, and, if necessary
punished even by death, according to
the existing laws' (Bridgett : Life,
p. 271) — many people will feel a
difficulty in harmonizing the two pic-
tures. The description of England as
'a country hitherto in perfect peace
and unity in religious matters' (ib.
263), is too imaginary a one to contribute much to our enlightenment.—
See, for further views of the subject,

T

faith in Truth

trewthe of the owne powre[1] woulde at the laste issue owte and come to lyght. But if contention and debate in that behalfe shoulde continuallye be vsed, as the woorste men be moste obstynate and stubburne, and in theire euell opynion moste constante; he perceaued that then the beste and holyest religion woulde be troden vnder foote and destroyed by moste vayne superstitions; euen as good corne is by thornes and weydes ouergrowen and choked. Therfore al this matter he lefte vndiscussed, and gaue to euery man free libertie and choyse to beleue what he *Necessary beliefs* woulde; sauinge that he earnestly and straytelye chardged them, that no man shoulde conceaue so vile and base an opinion of the dignitie of mans nature, as to thinke that the sowles do dye and perishe with the bodye; or that the worlde runneth at al auentures, gouerned by no diuine prouidence. And therfore thei beleue that after this lyfe vices bc extreamely punyshed, and vertues bountyfully rewarded. Hym that is of a contrary opinion they counte *not a man* not in the numbre of men, as one that hath aualed[2] the hyghe nature of his sowle to the vielnes of brute beastes

aliquando atque emineat; sin armis et tumultu certetur, ut sint pessimi quique maxime peruicaces, optimam ac sanctissimam religionem ob uanissimas inter se superstitiones, ut segetes inter spinas ac frutices, obrutum iri. Itaque hanc totam rem in medio posuit, et quid credendum putaret liberum cuique reliquit: nisi quod sancte ac seuere uetuit, ne quis usque adeo ab humanae naturae dignitate degeneret, ut animas quoque interire cum corpore, aut mundum temere ferri sublata prouidentia putaret. atque ideo post hanc uitam supplicia uitiis decreta, uirtuti praemia constituta credunt; contra sentientem ne in hominum quidem ducunt numero, ut qui sublimem animae suae naturam ad pecuini corpusculi uilitatem deiecerit: tan-

---

Mr. Sidney Lee's article in the *Dict. of National Biography*, vol. xxxviii. p. 436; Froude's *Erasmus*, p. 373; Gairdner: *Letters and Papers*, v. p. 772; W. S. Lilly, *Claims of Christianity*, p. 215; Prescott: *Ferdinand and Isabella*, as before, pp. 593, 594;

Miss Taylor: *Memoir of Sir Thomas More*, 1834, p. 81: Bishop Creighton: *Persecution and Tolerance*, 1895, pp. 104–8.

[1] That is, 'that Truth, by its innate force.'

[2] Lowered, or debased.

Loss of humanity

bodies; muche lesse in the numbre of their citiziens, whoes lawes and ordenaunces, if it were not for feare, he wold nothing at al esteme. For yow may be suer that he wil study other with crafte preuely to mock, or els vio- lently to breake, the commen lawes of his countrey, in whom remayneth no further feare then of the lawes, nor no further hope then of the bodye. Wherefore he that is thus mynded is depryued of all honours, excluded from all offices, and reiecte from all ᵃ common administrations in the weale publyque. And thus he is of all sorte ᵇ despysed as of an vnprofitable and of a base and vile nature. Howe be it they put hym to no punyshemente [1], because they be perswaded that it is in no mans powre to beleue what he lyst. No, nor they constrayne hym not with threatninges to dissemble his minde, and shewe countenaunce contrary to his thoughte. For deceite, and falshed, and all maner of lyes, as next vnto fraude, they do meruelouslye deteste and abhorre [2]. But they suffre him not to dispute in his

ᵃ [offices . . . all] *omitted.*   ᵇ sortes.

145 tum abest ut inter ciues ponant, quorum | instituta moresque (si per metum liceat) omnes floccifacturus sit. Cui enim dubium esse potest, quin is publicas patriae leges aut arte clam eludere, aut ui nitatur infringere, dum suae priuatim cupiditati seruiat, cui nullus ultra leges metus, nihil ultra corpus spei superest amplius? Quamobrem sic animato nullus communicatur honos, nullus magistratus committitur, nullo publico muneri praeficitur. Ita passim uelut inertis ac iacentis naturae despicitur. Caeterum nullo afficiunt supplicio, quod persua- sum habeant, nulli hoc in manu esse ut quicquid libet sentiat. sed nec minis adigunt ullis, animum ut dissimulet suum; nec fucos admittunt et mendacia, quae uelut proxima fraudi mirum quam habent inuisa.

---

[1] Exclusion from civil offices, to which a man is otherwise entitled to aspire, is itself a punishment. But More no doubt refers to severe or capital punishment (*supplicium*) in its positive form.

[2] Compare what More says in his *Treatise vpon the Passion* (*Works*, p. 1384, F.): 'Among al sortes of mischiefe, none can there lightly be fownden more odious vnto God, than whan we abuse thinges that be of their owne nature good, and turne them contrariwise to serue vs in our lewdenes. And for this consideracion dothe God much mislike lieng, for that

Unbelievers not allowed general freedom of Speech:

opinion, and that onlye[1] among the commen people. For elles a parte, among the pryestes and men of grauity, they doo not only suffre but also exhorte him to dispute and argue; hoopinge that at the laste that madnes will giue place to reason.

Other heretics:

There be also other, and of them no small numbre, whych be not forbidden to speake their mindes, as grounding their opinion vpon some reason; being in their gliuine[a] nother euell nor vitious. Their heresye is much contrary to the other. For they beleue that the soules of brute beastes be immortall and euerlasting[2]; but nothinge to be compared with owers in dignitie, nother ordeyned and[b] predestinate to like felicitie. For all they[3] beleue certeinly and sewerly, that mans blesse shall be so greate, that they doo morne and lamente euerye mans sicknes, but no mans death; oneles it be one whom they see depart from his liffe carfully, and agaynst his will. For this they take for a very euell token, as though the sowle, beinge

[a] *i.e.* livinge.   [b] nor.

Verum ne pro sua disputet sententia prohibent, atque id dumtaxat apud uulgus. Nam alioquin apud sacerdotes grauesque uiros seorsum non sinunt modo, sed hortantur quoque, confisi fore ut ea tandem uesania rationi cedat.

Sunt et alii, nec hii sane pauci, nempe improhibiti, ueluti neque racione penitus pro se carentes, neque mali, qui, uitio longe diuerso, brutorum quoque aeternas esse animas opinantur, at nostris tamen neque dignitate comparandas, neque ad aequam natas felicitatem. hominum enim cuncti fere tam immensam fore beatitudinem pro certo atque explorato habent, ut morbum lamententur omnium, mortem uero nullius, nisi quem uident anxie e uita inuitumque diuelli. Nempe hoc | pro pessimo habent augurio, tanquam anima exspes 146

Mira opinio de animabus brutorum.

---

the wordes which wer by him ordeined truely to expresse our myndes by, wee falsely peruerte to a quite contrary vse.'

[1] That is, the prohibition only applies to disputing, &c.

[2] For some modern successors of this school, among whom it would seem that John Wesley must be included, see the Rev. Edward White's *Life in Christ*, ed. 1878, p. 73 *n.*

[3] That is, 'they all.'

in dyspayre and vexed in conscience, through some preuy *Unhappy* and secret forefeilyng [1] of the punnishment now at hande, *deaths an* were aferde to depart. And they thinke he shall not be *evil omen:* welcome to God, whyche, when he ys called, runneth not [2] to hym gladly, but ys drawen by force and sore agaynste hys wyll. They therfore that see thys kynde of deathe doo abhorre it, and them that so die they burye wyth sorrow and silence. And when they haue prayed God to be mercifull to the sowle, and mercifully to pardon the infirmities therof, they couer the dead coorpe with earthe.

Contrarye wise, all that depart merely [3] and ful of good *Happy* hoope, for them no man mournethe, but followethe the *deaths:* heerse with ioyfull synging, commending the soules to god with great affection. And at the last not with mourning sorrow, but with a great reuerence, they bourne the bodies [4]; and in the same place they set vp a piller of

ac male conscia occulto quopiam imminentis poenae praesagio reformidet exitum. Ad hoc haudquaquam gratum deo eius putant aduentum fore, qui quum sit accersitus non accurrit libens, sed inuitus ac detrectans pertrahitur. Hoc igitur mortis genus qui intuentur horrent, itaque defunctos moesti ac silentes efferunt, precatique propitium manibus deum, uti eorum clementer infirmitatibus ignoscat, terra cadauer obruunt.

Contra, quicunque alacriter ac pleni bona spe decesserint, hos nemo luget, sed cantu prosequuti funus, animas deo magno commendantes affectu, corpora tandem reuerenter magis quam dolenter concremant, columnamque loco insculptis defuncti titulis erigunt.

---

[1] That is, 'fore-feeling,' or anticipation.

[2] 'He would farther say unto them, that, upon his faith, if he might perceive his wife and children would encourage him to die in a good cause, it should so comfort him, that for very joy thereof it would make him merrily *run to death.*'—Roper's *Life of More,* ed. 1822, p. 54.

[3] That is, merrily. See the preceding note.

[4] It is noticeable that More assigns cremation to the good, and interment to the bad. This would have been contrary to the feeling of the early Christians. Burial they called the 'veterem et meliorem consuetudinem' (Minucius Felix, *Octav.* c. 39). Sulla is said to have been the first Roman of note who prescribed for himself the Greek custom of cremation. See the article 'Burial of the Dead' in the *Dict. of Christian Antiquities,* i. p. 251.

A merry death: celebrated

stone, with the deade mans titles therin graued. When they be comme home they reherse his vertuouse maners and his good dedes. But no parte of his liffe is soo oft or gladly talked of as his mery deathe. They thinke that this remembraunce of their vertue and goodnes[a] doth vehemently próuoke and enforce the quicke[b] to vertue; and that nothing can be more pleasaunt and acceptable to

spirits present

the dead; whom they suppose to be present emong them when they talke of them, though to the dull and feoble eye sight of mortall men they be inuisibly[c]. For it were

Spirits of

an vnconuenient thinge, that the blessed shoulde not be at libertye to goo whether they wold. And it were a poynte of greate vnkyndnes in them, to haue vtterly caste awaye the desyer of vysytynge and seynge their frindes[1], to whome they were in theyr lyfe tyme ioyned by mutuall loue and charytye[d]; whych in good men after theyre deathe they cownte to be rather encreasede then dymynyshede. They beleue therefore that the deade be presentlye conuersaunte emong the quicke, as beholders and witnesses of all their woordes and deedes. Therefore

[a] the vertue and goodnes of the dead.   [b] liuing.
[c] inuisible.   [d] amitie.

domum reuersi, mores actaque eius recensent, nec ulla uitae pars aut saepius aut libentius quam laetus tractatur interitus. Hanc probitatis memoriam et uiuis efficacissima rentur incitamenta uirtutum, et gratissimum defunctis cultum putant; quos interesse quoque de se sermonibus opinantur, quanquam (ut est hebes mortalium acies) inuisibiles. Nam neque felicium sorti conueniat libertate carere migrandi quo uelint, et ingratorum fuerit prorsus abiecisse desyderium amicos inuisendi suos, quibus eos, dum uiuerent, mutuus amor charitasque deuinxerat; quanquam[2] bonis uiris, ut caetera bona, auctam post fata potius quam imminutam coniectant. Mortuos ergo ucrsari | inter uiuentes credunt, dictorum factorumque spectatores; 147

---

[1] A dream of poets in all ages that
'. . . As ancient sages ween,
Departed spirits, half unseen,
Can mingle with the mortal throng.'

[2] In a copy of the edition of November, 1518, which I possess, this has been altered to *quam*; which must be the true reading.

of Spirits

they go more corragiously to their busines, as hauing a trust and affiaunce in such ouerseers. And this same belefe of the present conuersacion of their forefathers and auncetours emonge them fearethe them from all secrete dishonesty.

vs. Auguries divination

They vtterly despise and mocke sothe sayinges and diuinacions of thinges to come by the flighte or voyces of birdes[1], and all other diuinations of vayne superstition, which in other countreys be in great obseruation. But they highly esteame and worshippe miracles, that come by no helpe of nature, as workes and witnesses of the presente powre of God[2]. And such they saye doo chaunce there very often. And sumtimes in great and dowtefull matters, by commen intercession and prayers, they procure and obteyne them with a suer hoope and confidence and a stedfast beleffe.

miracles believed

prayers.

They thinke that the contemplacion of nature, and the

eoque res agendas fidentius aggrediuntur, talibus uelut freti praesidibus, et ab inhonesto secreto deterret eos credita maiorum praesentia.

Auguria caeterasque superstitionis uanae diuinationes, quarum apud alias gentes magna est obseruatio, negligunt prorsus atque irrident. Miracula uero, quae nullo naturae proueniunt adminiculo, uelut praesentis opera testesque numinis uenerantur; qualia et ibi frequenter extare ferunt : et magnis interdum ac dubiis in rebus publica supplicatione certa cum fiducia procurant impetrantque.

Gratum deo cultum putant naturae contemplationem, laudemque ab

---

[1] From 'sothe sayings' to 'birdes' is all an equivalent for the single word *auguria*.

[2] In the *Dialogue concernynge Heresyes and Matters of Religion*, a great part of the first Book (chs. iv-xvii) is taken up with a discussion of the subject of miracles. More elsewhere draws the same distinction as in the text between 'vayne superstition' and true miracles. The test is in their profitableness. 'For that is a good mark betwene Gods miracles and the dyuels wonders. For Christ and hys saintes haue their miracles alway tending to frute and profit. The dyuel and hys wiches and necromancers, al theyr wonderful workes draw to no fruteful end, but to a fruitelesse ostentacion and shew, as it were a jugler that woulde for a shew before the people plai masteries at a feast.' — *Works*, p. 1091 c.

Men of good works; religious men

prayse thereof cumminge, is to God a very acceptable honour. Yet there be many so earnestly bent and affectioned to religion, that they passe no thinge for learning, nor giue their mindes to no[a] knowledge of thinges. But ydelnes they vtterly forsake and eschue, thinkinge felicitie after this liffe to be gotten and obteined by busy labors and good exercises [1]. Some therfore of them attende vpon the sicke, some amend highe waies, clense ditches, repaire bridges, digge turfes, grauell, and stones, fell and cleaue woode, bring wood, corne, and other thinges into the cities in cartes, and serue not onlye in commen woorkes, but also in pryuate laboures, as seruantes, yea, more then bondmen. For what so euer vnplesaunte, harde, and vile worke is any where, from the which labour, lothsumnes, and desperation doth fraye other, all that they take vpon them willingly and gladly; procuring quyete and rest to other; remayning in continuall woorke and labour them-

[a] any.

ea[2]. sunt tamen, hiique haud sane pauci, qui religione ducti, literas negligunt, nulli rerum cognitioni student, neque ocio

Vita actiua.   prorsus ulli uacant; negociis tantum bonisque in caeteris officiis statuunt futuram post fata felicitatem promereri [a]. Itaque alii aegrotis inseruiunt, alii uias reficiunt, purgant fossas, pontes reparant, cespites, arenam, lapides effodiunt, arbores demoliuntur, ac dissecant, bigisque ligna, fruges, item alia in urbes important, nec in publicum modo sed priuatim quoque ministros ac plus quam seruos agunt. Nam quicquid usquam operis est asperum, difficile, sordidum, a quo plerosque labor, fastidium, desperatio deterreat, hoc illi sibi totum libentes hilaresque desumunt. caeteris ocium procurant, ipsi perpetuo in opere ac labore uer|santur, nec imputant 148

[a] promoueri, A.

---

[1] More may have been thinking, when he wrote this, of the 'Brethren of the Common Life,' at whose school in Deventer the early years of Erasmus were passed. They 'differed from the mendicant orders in the fact that they did not beg, but, on the contrary, maintained themselves by manual labour, having at least a partial community of goods, and distinguished generally by their strict lives and fervent devotion.'—Drummond: *Erasmus,* 1873, i. p. 8.

[2] *Partam,* or some similar word, seems wanting.

selfes; not embrayding others there wyth. They nother
reproue other mens liues, nor glorye in theire owne.
Thies men, the more seruiseable[1] they behaue them
selfes, the moore they be honoured of all men.   *Two Sects:*

Yet they be diuided into ii. sectes. The one is of them   *Celibates A.*
that liue single and chast, absteining not only from the   *& ascetics*
company of women, but al so from the[a] eating of flesh,
and some of them from al maner of beastes[2]. Which,
vtterly reiectynge the pleasures of this present lyffe as
hurtefull, be all hollye set vpon the dessire of the lyffe
to come; by watchynge and sweatynge hoping shortely
to obtaine it, beyng in the meane season meerye and
lustye. The other sect is no lesse desyerous of labour,   *B.*
but they embrace matrimony; not despising the solace   *married*
therof; thinking that they can not be discharged of theire

---

^a the *omitted*.

---

tamen, nec aliorum sugillant uitam, nec suam efferunt. Hii quo
magis sese seruos exhibent, eo maiore apud omnes in honore sunt.

Eorum tamen haereses duae sunt. Altera caelibum, qui non Venere
modo in totum abstinent, sed carnium esu quoque, quidam animalium
etiam omnium, reiectisque penitus tanquam noxiis uitae praesentis
uoluptatibus, futurae duntaxat per uigilias ac sudores inhiant, eius
propediem obtinendae spe alacres interim uegetique. Altera laboris
haud minus appetens coniugium praefert, ut cuius nec aspernantur
solatium, et opus naturae debere se et patriae liberos putant. Nullam

---

[1] Not serviceable, in our sense, but
'as servants,' or slaves. Burnet has:
'by their stooping to such servile
Employments, they are ... the more
esteemed,' &c.

[2] 'Beastes' here, as a rendering of
animalium, is a more extensive term
than 'flesh' (*carnium*); just as *bestia*
in Latin may include fowl or fish.
Hence the meaning is that, while some
abstained from all that we should call
butcher's meat, others abstained even
from 'white-meats' as well, and were
absolute vegetarians. As an example

of the former may be taken the rule of
the Carthusians of Shene: 'For your
diet, it is a perpetuall abstinence from
flesh, in so much that in the greatest
or most dangerous sicknes you can
expect no dispensation therein: also
a good parte of the yeare wee abstaine
from all whitmeates, as in Advent,
Lent, and all the Fridayes of the
yeare...' *Formulare Carthusianorum*,
Lansdowne MSS., No. 1201, leaf 2 b.
The practice of St. Benedict himself
was an example of the latter, and still
more austere, practice.

bounden duetyes towardes nature withoute labour and tiole, nor towardes their natiue countreye, wythowte procreacion of chyldren. They abstayne from no pleasure that dothe nothynge hynder them from laboure. They loue the fleshe of fourefoted beastes, bycause they beleue that by that meate they be made hardier and stronger to woorke[1]. The Vtopians count this secte the wiser, but the other the hollier. Which, in that they preferre single liffe before matrimony, and that sharpe liffe before an easier liffe, if herin they grounded vpon reason, they wold mock them; but now, forasmuch as they say they be ledde to it by religion, they honour and worship them[2]. And thies be they whome in their language by a peculyare name they call Buthrescas[3], the whyche woorde by interpretation signifieth to vs men of religion, or religious men. They haue pryestes of exceding hollines, and therefore

uoluptatem refugiunt, quae nihil eos ab labore demoretur. Carnes quadrupedum uel eo nomine diligunt, quod tali cibo se ualidiores ad opus quodque censeant. Hos Vtopiani prudentiores, at illos sanctiores reputant. Quos quod caelibatum anteferunt matrimonio, asperamque uitam placidae anteponunt, si rationibus niterentur, irriderent: nunc uero quum se fateantur religione duci, suspiciunt ac reuerentur. Nihil enim sollicitius obseruant, quam ne temere quicquam ulla de religione pronuncient. Huiusmodi ergo sunt, quos illi peculiari nomine sua lingua Buthrescas uocant, quod uerbum latine religiosos licet interpretari.

Sacerdotes habent eximia sanctitate, eoque admodum paucos. neque

---

[1] The language of right reason, and justified, with proper qualifications, by St. Paul: 1 Cor. vi. 12, 1 Tim. iv. 3, 4, 1 Cor. viii. 13. In the *De quatuor nouissimis*, towards the end, More has much on the text ' meats for the belly, and the belly for meats; but God will destroy both it and them.' In the present passage he gives due weight to the words that precede that text, ' all things are lawful for me.' Compare Luther's *Table Talk*, ed. 1872, § dvii.

[2] The next sentence in the Latin is omitted by Robynson. Burnet renders it: ' There is nothing in which they are more cautious, than in giving their Opinion positively concerning any Sort of Religion.'

[3] The word, as More himself explains its meaning just after, is evidently formed to express ' very devout,' as if βούθρησκος, on the analogy of βούπαις.

very few[1]. For there be but xiii.[2] in euery city, according
to the number of theire churches, sauynge when they go
furth to battell. For thān vii. of them goo furthe wyth
the armye: in whose steades so manye newe be made at
home. But the other, at theyre retourne home, agayn
reentre euery one into his own place. They that be
aboue the numbre, vntyll suche tyme as they succede
into the places of the other at theyre dyinge, be in the
meane season continuallye in companye wyth the bishoppe.
For he ys the chyeffe heade of them all. They be chosen
of the people as the other magistrates be, by secrete
voices for the/a—[3] ... they be consecrate of their owne
company. They be ouerseers of all deuyne matters, or-
derers of religions, and as it were jugers and maisters of
maners. And it is a great dishonestye and shame to be
rebuked or spoken to by anny of them for dissolate and
incontinent liuing.

13 priests per city

The Bishop

avoiding of strife.

overseers of manners:

enim plus quam tredecim in singulis habent urbibus, pari templorum
149 numero, nisi quum itur | ad bellum.   tunc enim septem ex illis cum
exercitu profectis totidem sufficiuntur interim. sed illi reuersi suum
quisque locum recuperat: qui supersunt, hii, quoad decedentibus
illis ordine succedant[a], comites interea sunt Pontificis. Nam unus
reliquis praeficitur. Eliguntur a populo; idque, caeterorum ritu
magistratuum, occultis ad studia uitanda suffragiis: electi a suo col-
legio consecrantur. Hii rebus diuinis praesunt, religiones curant, ac
morum ueluti censores sunt; magnoque pudori ducitur ab hiis quenquam, tanquam uitae parum probatae, accersi compellariue.

[a] succedunt, A.

---

[1] There is probably a touch of satire
in this, but not of necessity, since
those who are *eximii* in any qualifications will naturally be few. More
censures Dorp for making a similar
remark about the bishops of his time:
—'quorum, ut sunt certe nonnulli tanto
digni fastigio, ita *mira est paucitas.*'
Lucubrationes, p. 421.

[2] Perhaps with reference to the
thirteen apostles. See, for instances
of such choice of numbers, the Rev.
J. H. Blunt's Introduction to the
Myroure of oure Ladye, 1873, p. xx.

[3] A line is here omitted in the
edition of 1551 between the first
syllable of ' auoydinge ' and ' they '
be consecrate.' The ed. of 1556
supplies it : ' uoyding of strife. After
their election '.

Priests

But as it is their offyce to gyue good exhortations and cownsell, so it is the deuty of the prince and the other magistrates to correct and punnyshe offenders; sauynge that the priestes, whome[1] they find exceading vicious liuers, them they excommunicate from hauing any interest in diuine matters. And there is almoost no punnishment emonge them more feared. For they runne in verye great infamy, and be inwardly tormented with a secrete feare of religion, and shall not long scape free with their bodies. For onles they, by quycke repentaunce approue the amendement of their lyffes to the priestes, they be taken and punnished of the cownsell as wycked and irreligious[2].

Excomm. of the wicked

Both childhode and youth is instructed, and tought of them. Nor they be not more deligente to instructe them in learning then in vertue and good maners. For they vse with very greate endeuour and deligence to put into the heades of their children, whiles they be yet tender and pliaunt, good opinions and profitable for the conser-

as teachers

Caeterum ut hortari atque admonere illorum est, ita coercere atque in facinorosos animaduertere principis atque aliorum est magistratuum; nisi quod sacris interdicunt, quos improbe malos comperiunt: nec ullum fere supplicium est quod horreant magis. Nam et summa percelluntur infamia, et occulto religionis metu lacerantur, ne corporibus quidem diu futuris in tuto. quippe ni properam poenitentiam sacerdotibus approbent, comprehensi impietatis poenam Senatui persoluunt.

Pueritia iuuentusque ab illis eruditur, nec prior literarum cura quam morum ac uirtutis habetur. namque summam adhibent industriam, ut bonas protenus opiniones et conseruandae ipsorum reipub-

---

[1] Burnet brings out the sense more clearly: 'The severest thing that the Priest does, is the excluding those that are desperately wicked from joining in their worship.'

[2] Lat. *impietatis poenam persolvunt.* This was a being delivered over to the secular arm. But it does not touch the subject of punishment for religious opinions, as those only are spoken of here as being seized by the council, whom the priests have pronounced to be *improbe malos.*

uation of their weale publique. Which, when they be ones rooted in children, do remayne wyth them all their lyfe after, and be wonders profitable for the defence and maintenaunce of the state of the commen wealthe; which neuer decaieth, but through vicis risinge of euell opinyons.

The pryestes, onles they be women [1] (for that kynd is not excluded from pryesthode ; howebeit fewe be chosen, and none but widdowes and old women): the men priestes, I saye, take to their wifes [2] the chiefest women in all their countreye. For to no office emong the vtopians is more

lioao utileo teneris adhuc et sequacibus puerorum animis instillent ; quae ubi pueris penitus insederint, uiros per totam uitam comitantur, 150 *magnamque ad tuendum publicae rei | statum (qui non nisi uitiis dilabitur, quae ex peruersis nascuntur opinionibus) afferunt utilitatem.*

Sacerdotibus (ni foeminae sint, nam neque ille sexus excluditur, sed rarius, et non nisi uidua natuque grandis eligitur) uxores sunt popularium selectissimae. Neque enim ulli apud Vtopienses magistratui maior habetur

Foeminae sacerdotes.

---

[1] It would be hard to say whether this is a mere *jeu d'esprit,* or whether More had any more serious thought in making women eligible for the priesthood in Utopia. He may have had in his mind the greater natural devoutness of their sex, as Cicero had when he wrote to Terentia : ' Neque dii, quos tu castissime coluisti, neque homines, quibus ego semper servivi, nobis gratiam retulerunt.' (*Epp. ad Div.* xiv. 4). Or perhaps, with daughters educated as were his own, often discussing at home the homilies they heard in church, it may have been jestingly remarked that one of them would be better qualified to discharge the teaching office, at least, of the priesthood than some of the preachers on whom he is occasionally so severe. But when he thought that a playful suggestion was in danger of being advocated in earnest, More could become bitterly contemptuous. 'For hys heresye,' he writes, referring to

Tyndall, ' rekeneth euerye woman a prest, and as able to say masse as euer was saynte Peter. And in good faythe, as for suche masses as he woulde haue sayde . . . I wene a woman were in dede a more mete priest than saynt Peter.'—*Fifth Book of the Confutacion* : *Works,* p. 623.

[2] In the *Supplicacion of Soules* (*Works,* p. 308), when writing of the existing priesthood of the Church, bound to celibacy, More's language is in violent contrast to that used in the text. The marginal note : ' The mariage of priestes is incestuouse,' is a very mild summary of the passage. Elsewhere (*ib.* p. 485), speaking of the celibacy of priests as an abstract principle, he admits that ' the churche both knoweth and confesseth, that wedlocke and priesthod be not repugnant but compatible of their nature, and that wedded men haue been made priestes and kept styll theyr wiues.'

Priests
honoured
&
left
alone

man's
nature

honour and preeminence geuen. In so much that if they committ any offence, they be vnder no commen iudge-ment, but be left only to god and themselfes[1]. For they thinke it not lawfull to touch him with mannes hande, be he neuer so vityous, whiche after so singuler a sort was dedicate and consecrate to god as a holly offering. This maner may they easely obserue, bicause they haue so few priestes, and do chuse them with such circumspection. For it scasely euer[2] chaunceth that the most vertuous emong vertuous, which in respect only of his vertue is auaunced to so high a dignity, can fal to vice and wicked-nes. And if it should chaunce in dede (as mans nature is mutable and fraile), yet by reason they be so few[3] and

honos, usque adeo ut si quid etiam flagitii admiserint, nullo publico iudicio subsint : deo tantum ac sibi relinquuntur. Neque enim fas putant illum, quantumuis scelestum, mortali manu con-tingere, qui Deo tam singulari modo uelut anathema
Excommunicatio. dedicatus est. Qui mos illis facilior est obseruatu, quod sacerdotes et tam pauci et tanta cum cura deligun-tur. Nam neque temere accidit, ut qui ex bonis optimus ad tantam dignitatem, solius respectu uirtutis, euehitur, in corruptelam et uitium degeneret. et si iam maxime contingeret, ut est mortalium natura mutabilis, tamen qua sunt paucitate, nec ulla praeter

---

[1] We may infer from this, which side More would have been likely to take in the great controversy lately stirred between the two parties of which Standish and Kidderminster were the representatives. The text *noli tangere Christos meos* expressed the view of the Abbot of Winchcombe. See Brewer's *Reign of Henry VIII*, i. p. 250. Colet, in his Convocation Sermon, delivered in 1512, gives a guarded assent to the same view :— ' Ye wyll haue the churches liberte,' he says to the assembled clergy ' and nat be drawen afore secular iuges : and that also is ryght. For hit is in the psalmes : *Touch ye nat myne anoynted.* But if ye desire this liberte, first vnlouse your selfe frome the world-lye bondage, and from the seruices of men ; and lyfte vp your selfe in to the trewe lybertie, the spirituall lybertye of Christe, in to grace from synnes ; and serue you God, and raygne in hym. And than, beleue me, the people wyll nat touche the anoynted of theyr Lorde God.'

[2] Lat. *neque temere*, ' it does not lightly chance.'

[3] The sarcastic marginal note to the Latin, at this point, should be observed.

promoted to no might nor powre, but only honour ¹, it *few priests: few problems.*
were not to be feared that anye great dammage by them
should happen and ensue to the commen wealth. They
hauc so rare and few priestes, least, if the honour were
communicate to many, the dignity of the ordre, which
emong them now is so highly estemed, should runne in
contempt ; speciallye bicause they thinke it harde to find
many so good, as to be meet for that dignity, to the execution and discharge wherof it is not sufficiente to be endued
with mean vertues.

Furthermore, thies priestes be not more estemed of *in battle:*
their owne countrey men, then they be of forrein and
straunge countreis.   Which thing maye hereby plainly
appere.   And I think al so that this is the cause of it.
For whiles the armes be fighting together in open feld,
they a litle beside, not farre of, knele vpon their knees in
their hallowed vestimentes, holding vp theyr handes to
heauen ; praying first of all for peace, nexte for vyctory
of theyr owne parte, but to neyther part a bluddy vyctory ¹.   If their host gette the vpper hand, they runne in

ᴬ to honour.

honorem   potestate   praediti,   ad   publicam   certe   perniciem   nihil
magni ab his momenti pertimescendum sit.   Quos
ideo tam raros atque infrequentes habent, ne dignitas   At apud nos
ordinis, quem nunc tanta ueneratione prosequuntur,   quanta turba
                                                          est.
communicato cum multis honore, uilesceret ; praesertim
quum difficile putent frequentes inuenire tam bonos, ut ei sint
dignitati pares ; ad quam gerendam non sufficit mediocribus esse
uirtutibus.

   Nec eorum aestimatio apud suos magis quam apud exteras etiam
151 gen|tes habetur, quod inde facile patet unde etiam natum puto.
Nempe decernentibus praelio copiis, seorsum illi
non admodum procul considunt in genibus, sacras in-   O sacerdotes
duti uestes : tensis ad caelum palmis, primum omnium   nostris longe
                                                          sanctiores.
pacem, proxime suis uictoriam, sed neutri cruentam
parti, comprecantur.   uincentibus suis decurrunt in aciem, sae-

---

   ¹ The picture drawn is more sug-   during the battle against the Amalek-
gestive of Moses praying on the mount   ites (Exod. xvii. 12), than of the con-

Priests in battle

to the mayne battayle, and restrayne theyre owne men
from sleying and cruellye pursuynge theyre vanquyshed
ennemies. Whyche ennemyes, yf they do but see them
and speake to them, yt ys ynoughe for the sauegarde of
theyr lyues; and the towchynge of theire clothes defend-
eth and saueth al their gooddes from rauyne and spoyle.
Thys thing hath auaunced them to so greate wourshyp
and trew maiesty emong al natonis ᵃ, that many times they
haue aswel preserued theire own citizens from the cruel
force of their ennemies, as they haue their enemies from
the furyous rage of theyre owne men. For yt ys well
knowen that when their owne army hathe reculed, and in
dyspayre turned backe, and runne away, theyr ennemies
fyerslye pursuing with slaughter and spoyle, then the
priestes cumming betwene haue stayed the murder, and
parted bothe the hostes; so that peace hath bene made

ᵃ *i. e.* nations.

uientesque in profligatos inhibent. uidisse tantum atque appel-
lasse praesentes ad uitam satis; diffluentium contactus uestium
reliquas quoque fortunas ab omni bellorum iniuria defendit. Qua
ex re apud omnes undique gentes tanta illis ueneratio, tantum
uerae maiestatis accessit, ut saepe ab hostibus non minus salutis ad
ciues reportarint, quam ab ipsis ad hostes attulissent; siquidem
aliquando constat, inclinata suorum acie, desperatis rebus, quum
ipsi in fugam uerterentur, hostes in caedem ac praedam ruerent,
interuentu sacerdotum interpellatam stragem, ac diremptis inuicem

---

duct of great ecclesiastics in More's
own time. With his abhorrence of
war between Christian princes (one of
the three evils, to secure the abolition
of which he would gladly have been
'put in a sack and presently cast into
the Thames') More would not look
with a kindly eye on the martial
energy of Pope Julius II, 'more like
to that Caesar, whose Name hee bare,
then Peter, from whom he would faine
deriue his Succession,' or on the cam-
paigns directed by Ximenes, in whom

'the spirit of the soldier burned strong
and bright under his monastic weeds.'
Even to prelates like those who fell
at Flodden, fighting simply as brave
soldiers for their country—the Archbishop of St. Andrew's, the Bishops
of Caithness and of the Isles, the
Abbots of Inchaffray and Kilwinning,
and others—while his sympathy would
be with them as patriots, the description in the text would serve as a silent
reproach.—See Roper's *Life*, p. 24;
Godwyn's *Annales*, 1630, p. 9.

and concluded betwene bothe partes vpon equall and
indyfferent condytions. For there was neuer anny natyon
so fiers, so cruell and rude, but they hadde them in suche
reuerence, that they cownted theyr bodyes hallowed and
sanctyfyed, and therefore not to be violentlye and vnreuer-
entlye towched.

They kepe hollye daye[a] the fyrste and the laste day
of euerye moneth and yeare, deuydynge the yeare into
monethes; whyche they measure by the course of the
moone, as they doo the yeare by the course of the sonne.
The fyrste dayes they call in theyr language Lynemernes[1],
and the laste Trapemernes; the whyche woordes maye be
interpreted primifeste and finifest; or els, in our speache,
first feast and last feast.

Their churches be very gorgyous, and not onelye of

Calendar & holidays *Architecture gorgeous.*

[a] daye omitted.

copiis pacem aequis condicionibus esse compositam atque constitu-
tam. Neque enim unquam fuit ulla gens tam fera, crudelis ac barbara,
apud quos ipsorum corpus non sacrosanctum atque inuiolabile sit
habitum.

Festos celebrant initialem atque ultimum cuiusque mensis diem,
et anni item, quem in menses partiuntur, circuitu
lunae finitos, ut solis ambitus annum circinat[2].   Festorum dierum
Primos quosque dies Cynemernos, postremos ipso-   apud Vtopienses
rum lingua Trapemernos appellant; quae uocabula   obseruatio.
152 perinde sonant, ac si pri|mifesti et finifesti uocentur.

Delubra uisuntur egregia, utpote non operosa modo, sed, quod

---

[1] Why Robynson should give the
word in this form, when the Latin
texts have uniformly *Cynemernos*, is
not clear. Possibly he had a notion
that More must have been thinking of
Luna, as a suitable element in his
imaginary name for the first day of
the month, and that *Cynemernos* was
thus a misprint. It is more likely that
the word is meant to suggest κυν-
ημερινός, 'the dog's day of the month,'

strictly the night between the old
and new, when food was placed out
at the cross-roads, and the barking
of the dogs was taken as a sign
of the approach of Hecate. See
Theocr. *Idyll.* ii. 35, 36. So in like
manner τραπ-ημερινὸς would express
the turning or closing day of the
month.

[2] Comp. 'Anni tempora circinante
Phoebo,' Sidon. *Pan.* 3382.

U

Churches:

fyne and curious workemanship, but also (which in the
fewenes of them was necessary) very wyde and large, and
darkness able to receaue a great company of people. But they be
all sumwhat darke. Howbeit, that was not donne through
ignoraunce in buylding, but as they say by the cownsell of
the priestes. Bicause they thought that ouer much light
doth disperse mens cogitations; where as in dimme and
doutefull lighte [1] they be gathered together, and more
earnestly fixed vpon religion and deuocion. Which bicause it is not there of one sort emong all men; and yet all
the kindes and fassions of it, thoughe they be sondry and
generalized manifold, agree together in the honoure of the deuine
ceremony nature, as going diuers wayes to one ende; therfore nothing is sene nor hard in the churches, which [a] semeth
not to agre indifferently with them all. If there be a distinct kind of sacrifice, peculiare to any seuerall secte, that
they execute at home in their owne houses. The common
sacrifices be so ordered, that they be no derogatyon nor
preiudyce to annye of the pryuate sacryfyces and religions [2].

[a] but that.

erat in tanta ipsorum paucitate necessarium, immensi etiam populi
capacia. Sunt tamen omnia subobscura; nec id
Templa cuius- aedificandi inscitia factum, sed consilio sacerdotum
modi. ferunt, quod immodicam lucem cogitationes dispergere,
parciore ac uelut dubia colligi animos et intendi religionem putant.
quae quoniam non est ibi apud omnes eadem, et uniuersae tamen eius
formae, quanquam uariae ac multiplices, in diuinae naturae cultum
uelut in unum finem diuersa uia commigrant, idcirco nihil in templis
uisitur auditurue, quod non quadrare ad cunctas in commune uideatur.
Si quod proprium sit cuiusque sectae sacrum, id intra domesticos
quisque parietes curat; publica tali peragunt ordine, qui nulli prorsus
ex priuatis deroget.

---

[1] This will at once recall the 'dim religious light' of *Il Penseroso*. A little
less familiar may be the couplet from Pope's *Eloisa to Abelard*:—
'Where awful arches make a noon-day night,
And the dim windows shed a solemn light.'
[2] Compare what More says just afterwards about the public prayers.

Therefore no ymage of annye god is seene in the churche; to the intente it maye be free for euery man to conceyue god by their religion after what likenes and similitude they will. They call vpon no peculiar name of god, but only Mithra[1]. In the which word they all agree together in one nature of the deuine maiestye, whatsoeuer it be. No prayers be vsed, but such as euerye man maye boldelye pronownce wythowt the offending of anny secte.

They come therefore to the churche the laste day of euery moneth and yeare, in the euenynge, yet fastyng, there to gyue thanckes to God for that they haue pros perouslye passed ouer the yeare or monethe, wherof that hollye daye ys the laste daye. The next daye they come to the churche earlye in the mornyng, to praye to God that they maye haue good fortune and successe all the newe yeare or monethe, whyche they doo begynne of that same hollye daye. But in the holly dayes that be the laste dayes of the monethes and yeares, before they come to the churche, the wiffes fall downe prostrat before their husbandes feete at home; and the children before the feete of their parentes; confessing and acknowleginge that they

Itaque nulla deorum effigies in templo conspicitur, quo liberum cuique sit qua forma deum uelut e summa religione concipere. nullum peculiare dei nomen inuocant, sed Mythrae duntaxat, quo uocabulo cuncti in unam diuinae maiestatis naturam, quaecunque sit illa, conspirant. nullae concipiuntur preces, quas non pronunciare quiuis inoffensa sua secta possit.

Ad templum ergo in finifestis diebus uespere conueniunt, adhuc ieiuni, acturi deo de anno menseue cuius id festum postremus dies est, prospere acto gratias. Postero die, nam is primifestus est, mane 153 *ad templa confluitur, ut | insequentis anni mensisue, quem ab illo auspicaturi festo sint, faustum felicemque successum comprecentur. At in finifestis, antea quam templum petunt, uxores domi ad uirorum pedes, liberi ad parentum prouoluti, peccasse fatentur*

---

[1] The Persian name for the Sungod. See above, p. 267, and comp. Xen. *Cyr.* vii. 5, § 53. For the way in which More makes the old Utopian language to be connected with the Persian, see p. 148 *n.*

Preparation by Confession:

haue offended ^a other by some actuall dede, or by omission of their dewty, and desire pardon for their offence [1]. Thus yf anye cloude of preuy displeasure was risen at home, by this satisfaction it is ouer blowen; that they may be present at the sacrifices with pure and charitable mindes [2]. For they be aferd to come there with troubled consciences. Therefore, if they knowe themselfes to beare anye hatred or grudge towardes anye man [3], they presume not to come to the sacrifices before they haue reconcyled themselfes and purged theyre conscyences, for feare of greate vengeaunce and punyshemente for their offence.

Separation of sexes in church:

When they come thyther, the men goo into the ryghte syde of the churche, and the the ^b women into the left syde [4]. There they place themselfes in suche ordre that

    ^a [that . . . offended] themselfes offenders.   ^b *so repeated.*

sese aut admisso aliquo, aut officio indiligenter obito, ueniam-
           Confessio   que errati precantur. ita si qua se nubecula do-
     Vtopiensium.   mesticae simultatis offuderat, tali satisfactione discu-
     At apud nos,   titur, uti animo puro ac sereno sacrificiis intersint.
    qui sunt inquina-   nam interesse turbido, religio est. eoque odii iraeue
     tissimi, aris
     proximi esse   in quenquam sibi conscii, nisi reconciliati ac defecatis
     contendunt.   affectibus ad sacrificia non ingerunt sese, uindictae
celeris magnaeque metu.

     Eo quum ueniunt, uiri in dextram delubri partem, faeminae seorsum in sinistram commeant; tum ita se collocant, ut cuiusque domus

---

[1] The author of *Philomorus* sees in this a possible slight put upon the practice of confession to the priest alone (2nd ed., p. 128; cf. p. 238). But, as he justly says, 'the *Utopia* cannot be referred to as containing the writer's settled opinion upon the subjects which are introduced.'

[2] With the severe tone of the Latin marginal note here, compare the apostrophe into which Colet breaks out, in his *Treatises on the Hierarchies*, p. 90.

[3] The reader will note the similarity

between this and a passage in the rubric before the Communion Service in the Book of Common Prayer: 'The same order shall the Curate use with those betwixt whom he perceiveth malice and hatred to reign; not suffering them to be partakers of the Lord's Table, until he know them to be reconciled.'

[4] This custom of the separation of the sexes in Christian Churches is at least as old as the *Apostolical Constitutions*. Besides its being the com-

all they which be of the male kind in euery houshold sitte
before the goodman of the house ; and they of the female
kynde before the goodwyfe. Thus it is forsene [1] that all
their gestures and behauiours be marked and obserued
abrode of them, by whose aucthoritye and discipline they
be gouerned at home. This also they diligentlye see
vnto, that the yonger euermore be coupled with his elder ;
lest, if children be [a] ioyned together, they shold passe
ouer that time in childish wantonnes, wherin they ought
principallye to conceaue a religious and deuout feere
towardes god ; which is the chieffe and almost the only
incitation to vertue.

eyes watch

religious. feer of God

They kill no liuing beast in sacrifice, nor they thinke
not that the mercifull clemency of god hath delite in bloud
and slaughter ; which hath geuen liffe to beastes, to the
intent they should liue. They burne franckensence and
other sweet sauours [2], and light also a great numbre of

Ceremonies

<hr/>

[a] [if . . . he] children beinge.

<hr/>

masculi ante patremfamilias considerant [a], foeminarum materfamilias
agmen claudat. Ita prospicitur uti omnes omnium gestus foris ab iis
obseruentur, quorum autoritate domi ac disciplina reguntur. quin
hoc quoque sedulo cauent, uti iunior ibi passim cum seniore copuletur,
ne pueri pueris crediti id temporis puerilibus transigant ineptiis, in
quo deberent maxime religiosum erga superos metum, maximum ac
prope unicum uirtutibus incitamentum, concipere.

Nullum animal in sacrificiis mactant, nec sanguine rentur ac caedibus diuinam gaudere clementiam, qui uitam animantibus ideo est
elargitus, ut uiuerent. Thus incendunt et alia item odoramenta. ad

<hr/>

[a] *Leg.* considant.

<hr/>

mon practice in his own time, More
may have noticed the allusion to it in
St. Augustine, when lecturing on the
De Civitate (Lib. II. c. 28) :—'quia
populi confluunt ad ecclesias casta
celebritate, honesta utriusque sexus
discretione.'

[1] That is, *provided for.*

[2] Dionysius Pseudo-Areopagita is
said to be the earliest writer who
testifies to the ritual use of incense in
churches. Colet, in his abstract of
the *Hierarchies* (*Eccl. Hier.* iii. § 3),
draws out the symbolical meaning,
that the sweet odour of incense 'is
a sign of the Almighty's fragrant love.'
'This assuredly,' he says, 'the fuming
of incense, beginning from the altar,
and thence proceeding through the
whole temple, and returning to the

Ceremonies & Garments

waxe candelles and tapers [1]; nott supposinge this geere to be any thing auaylable to the diuine nature, as nother the prayers of men ; but this vnhurtfull and harmeles kind of worship pleaseth them. And by thies sweet sauoures, and lightes, and other such ceremonies, men feele themselfes secretly lifted vp, and encouraged to deuotion, with more willynge and feruent hartes. The people weareth in the churche white apparell : the priest is clothed in chaungeable coloures, whiche in workemanshyp be excellent, but in stuffe not verye pretious. For theire vestementes be nother embrodered with golde, nor set with precious stones ; but they be wrought so fynely and connyngly with diuers fetheres of fowles [2], that the estimacion of no costelye stuffe is able to counteruaile the price

white & colours

fethers

haec ce|reos numerosos praeferunt, non quod haec nesciant nihil ad 154 diuinam conferre naturam, quippe ut nec ipsas hominum preces, sed et innoxium colendi genus placet, et hiis odoribus luminibusque, ac caeteris etiam ceremoniis, nescio quomodo sese sentiunt homines erigi, atque in dei cultum animo alacriore consurgere. Candidis in templo uestibus amicitur populus ; sacerdos uersicolores induitur, et opere et forma mirabiles, materia non perinde preciosa. neque enim auro intextae, aut raris coagmentatae lapidibus, sed diuersis auium plumis tam scite tantoque artificio laboratae sunt, ut operis precium

---

place whence it set forth, signifies in sacred and solemn manner to the unlearned ; that herein, if they are able, they may perceive that sweet-smelling grace is diffused far and wide over all from the high place of God.'

[1] For the profusion of wax candles and tapers which would meet the eye in St. Paul's Cathedral, see Dr. W. S. Simpson's *Registrum Statutorum*, p. 74. Their plenty may have been in part a cause of Dean Colet's well-known ordinance for his newly-founded school.

[2] More's selection of this fanciful apparel for his priests may have been in pure whim, or in the endeavour to find something totally different from existing customs. But the thought may possibly have been suggested to him by the study of his favourite Plato. In the *Timaeus* the race of birds is created out of 'innocent, light-minded men, who thought to pursue the study of the heavens by sight : these were transformed into birds, and grew feathers instead of hair.'—See Professor Jowett's Introduction to the *Timaeus* (*Plato*, 1871, ii. p. 502). What Socrates says also in the *Phaedo*, § 85, about birds having a prophetic gift from Apollo, and singing for joy but never for sorrow, deserves to be compared.

of the worke.   Furthermore, in thies birdes fethers, and in
the dewe ordre of them, whiche is obserued in theire set-
tyng, they saye is conteyned certayn deuyne misteries ;
the interpretation wherof knowen, whiche is diligentlye
tawght by the priestes, they be put in remembraunce of
the bountyfull benefites of God towarde them, and of the
loue and honoure whiche of theire behalfe is dewe to God,
and also of theire dewties one towarde an other.

When the priest first commeth out of the vestrie, thus
apparelled, they fall downe incontinent euery one reuerently to the grounde, with so styll silence on euery part,
that the very fassion of the thinge striketh into them a
certayne feare of God, as though he were there personally
presente.   When they haue lien a little space on the
grounde, the priest giueth them a signe for to ryse.   Then
they sing prayses vnto God, whiche they intermixt with
instrumentes of musick, for the moste parte of other
fassions then thies that we vse in this parte of the worlde.
And like as some of owrs bee muche sweter then theirs,
so some of theirs doo farre passe owrs[1].   But in one

nullius aestimatio materiae fuerit aequatura. Ad hoc in illis uolucrum
pennis plumisque et certis earum ordinibus, quibus in sacerdotis ueste
discriminantur, arcana quaedam dicunt contineri mysteria, quorum
interpretatione cognita (quae per sacrificos diligenter traditur) diui-
norum in se beneficiorum, suaeque uicissim pietatis in deum, ac mutui
quoque inter se officii, admoneantur.

Quum primum sacerdos ita ornatus ex adyto sese offert, cuncti protinus in terram uenerabundi procumbunt, tam alto ab omni parte
silentio, ut ipsa rei facies terrorem quendam uelut praesentis cuiuspiam numinis incutiat. Tellure paulum morati, dato ab sacerdote
signo, erigunt sese. tum laudes deo canunt, quas musi-
cis instrumentis interstinguunt, aliis magna ex parte   Musica
formis quam quae nostro visuntur orbe.   Ex illis   Vtopiensium.
155 ple|raque sicuti quae nobis in usu sunt multum suaui-
tate uincunt, ita quaedam nostris ne conferenda quidem sint.   Verum

---

[1] More, who used often to don a   Chelsea, was well qualified to express
surplice, and sing in the choir at   an opinion on this subject. It seems

Skill in music

thynge dowteles they goo excedinge farre beyond vs. For all theire musicke, both that they playe vpon instrumentes, and that they singe with mans voyse, doth so resemble and expresse naturall affections ; the sownd and tune is so applied and made agreable to the thynge ; that whether it bee a prayer, or els a dytty of gladnes, of patience, of trouble, of mournynge, or of anger, the fassion of the melodye dothe so represente the meaning of the thing, that it doth wonderfullye moue, stire, pearce,

representational music.

and enflame the hearers myndes [1].

una in re haud dubie longo nos interuallo praecellunt; quod omnis eorum musica, siue quae personatur organis, siue quam uoce modulantur humana, ita naturales affectus imitatur et exprimit, ita sonus accommodatur ad rem ; seu deprecantis oratio sit, seu laeta, placabilis, turbida, lugubris, irata ; ita rei sensum quendam melodiae forma repraesentat, ut animos auditorum mirum in modum afficiat, penetret, incendat.

---

clear, from more than one contemporary account, that the church music of the day, at least in England, had become too elaborate and artificial, the sound leaving the sense far behind. Thus Polydore Vergil complains that 'our syngers cry out so loude, that we heare nothing saue a noyse, and those that be present cannot be edified with the word.' ' It were great furtherance to religion,' he adds, ' yf those singers, not far unlike to Jayes, wer ether banished out of the Temples, or els their singing wer so modified with more sobernesse, that the wordes might be understande, to thedifying of the laytie.' — Thomas Langley's *Abridgemente of the Notable Worke of Polidore Vergil*, s. a., leaf 114 b. Compare what Erasmus says in the *De sarcienda Ecclesiae concordia* : 'Si non placet in templis illud modulatae musicae genus, et organorum cantus, possunt citra pietatis jacturam omitti : Si placet, curandum est ut illa quoque

musica sit digna templo Dei ' ; and the striking passage which occurs in his note on 1 Cor. xiv. 19 in the *Annotationes* : — ' In sacram aedem uelut in theatrum concurritur, ad deliniendas aures . . . Haec adeo placent, ut monachi nihil aliud agant, praesertim apud Britannos ; et quorum cantus debuit esse luctus, hi lasciuis hinnitibus et mobili gutture Deum placari credunt.'

[1] Richard Pace, whose own skill in music had commended him as a boy to the notice of Thomas Langton, Bishop of Winchester, gives a high place in his *De Fructu* to that art, which teaches men ' et orare bene et concionari ' (ed. 1517, p. 32). But the best commentary on what More has written in the text is furnished by some sensible remarks of Erasmus towards the end of his *Christiani Matrimonii Institutum* (a treatise which he dedicated to Queen Katharine). After complaining of the licentious tone of much secular ballad-music, especially

At the laste the people and the priest together rehearse *Prayers¹*
solempne prayers in woordes, expresslye pronounced[1];
so made that euerye man may priuatelye applye to hymselfe that which is commonlye spoken of all[2]. In thies   *The Creed*
prayers euerye man recogniseth and knowledgeth God to
be hys maker, hys gouernoure, and the principal cause of
all other goodnes ; thankyng him for so many benefites
receaued at hys hande : but namelye, that through the
fauoure of God he hath chaunced into that publyque weale,   *of state*
whiche is moste happye and welthye, and hath chosen
that religion whyche he hopeth to be moste true. In the
whyche thynge yf he doo annye thynge erre, or yf there
bee annye other better then eyther of them is, beynge
moore acceptable to GOD, he desiereth hym that he wyll

Solennes ad ultimum conceptis uerbis preces sacerdos pariter
populusque percensent, ita compositas ut quae simul cuncti recitant,
priuatim quisque ad semet referat. In his deum et creationis et
gubernationis et caeterorum praeterea bonorum omnium quilibet
recognoscit autorem ; tot ob recepta beneficia gratias agit, nominatim
uero quod deo propitio in eam rempublicam inciderit quae sit felicissima, eam religionem sortitus sit, quam speret esse uerissimam. Qua
in re si quid erret, aut si quid[a] alterutra melius, et quod deus magis

a si quid sit, A.

in the Low Countries, he urges, in
words like those of More, the power
of music for good or evil: 'Numerosi
illi soni magnam uim habent ad affici-
endos hominum animos, in tantum ut
quidam hinc collegerint ipsam animam
esse harmoniam, aut certe habere harmoniam, nam simile simili delectari'
(ed. 1526, leaf C). He goes on to
censure the style of music introduced
into divine worship. 'Quid quod hoc
musices genus a choreis et comes-
sationibus inueximus in templa? Et,
quod est absurdius, magno condu-
cuntur, qui sacrorum maiestatem ineptis garritibus contaminent.   Non

excludo Musicam a sacris, sed harmo-
nias requiro sacris dignas.   Nunc sonis
nequissimis aptantur uerba sacra.'
[1] Burnet, more correctly, 'in a set
Form of Words.'
[2] See above, p. 290.   Erasmus
often pleads for the like simple and
comprehensive formulas. 'Adferamus
fidei professionem simplicem, vereque
Apostolicam,' he says, speaking of the
efforts to convert the Turks, '. . . in
paucis facilior erit consensus, et facilius
constabit concordia, si in plerisque liberum erit in suo cuique sensu abundare,
tantum ut absit contentio.'   *Adagia*,
ed. 1629, p. 301, col. b.

Conditional
creed-
prayer

of hys goodnes let hym haue knowledge thereof, as one
that is readye too followe what waye soeuer he wyll leade
hym.   But yf thys forme and fassion of a commen wealthe
be beste, and his owne religion moste true and perfecte,
then he desyreth God to gyue him a constaunte sted-
fastnes in the same, and to brynge all other people to
the same ordre of lyuyng, and to the same opinion of
God ; onles there be any thynge that in this dyuersitie of
religions doth delyte his vnsearcheable pleasure.   To be
shorte, he prayeth hym that after his deathe he may come
to hym[1] ; but how soone or late, that he dare not assygne
or determine.   Howebeit, if it myght stande with his

god-king

maiesties pleasure, he would be muche gladder to dye a
paynfull dethe and so to go to God, then by long lyuing in
worldlye prosperytie to bee awaye from hym.   Whan this
prayer is sayde, they fall downe to the ground agayne,
and a lytle after they ryse vp and go to dynner.   And the
resydewe of the daye they passe ouer in playes, and

playes &
chivalry.

exercise of cheualrye[2].

approbet, orare se eius bonitas efficiat hoc ut ipse cognoscat: paratum
enim sequi se qua qua uersus ab eo ducatur. sin et haec Reipublicae
forma sit optima, et sua religio rectissima, tum uti et ipsi constantiam
tribuat, et caeteros mortales omneis ad eadem instituta uiuendi, in
eandem de deo opinionem perducat, nisi inscrutabilem eius uolun-
tatem etiam sit quod in hac | religionum uarietate delectet.   Denique 156
precatur, ut facile defunctum exitu ad se recipiat ; quam cito seroue,
praefinire quidem non audere se.   Quanquam, quod inoffensa eius
maiestate fiat, multo magis ipsi futurum cordi sit, difficillima morte
obita ad deum peruadere, quam ab eo diutius prosperrimo uitae
cursu distineri.   Hac prece dicta rursus in terram proni, pauloque
post erecti, discedunt pransum ; et quod superest diei ludis et exercitio militaris disciplinae percurrunt.

---

[1] Robynson neglects the *facile* in the
Latin. Burnet is more correct. 'Then
they pray that God may give them an
easy Passage at last to himself.'
[2] It was one of the reforms peti-
tioned for by the Cardinal of Cambray
at the Council of Constance, that on
festivals, all but Sundays and the
majores feriae, the lay people might
be allowed, when divine service was
over, to return to work : 'liceret
operari post auditum officium ; cum

Raphael's peroration:

Nowe I haue declared and descrybyd vnto yowe, as
truely as I coulde, the fourme and ordre of that commen
wealth, which verely in my iudgement is not onlye the
beste, but also that whiche alone of good ryght may
clayme and take vpon it the name of a common wealthe
or publique weale. For in other places they speake stil
of the commen wealth ; but euerye man procureth hys
owne pryuate wealthe ᵃ. Here where nothynge is pryuate,
the commen affayres be earnestly loked vpon. And
truely on both partes they haue good cause so to do as
they do. For in other countreys who knowoth not that
he shall sterue for honger, onles he make some seuerall
prouision for hymself, though the commen wealthe
floryshe neuer so muche in ryches? And therefore he is
compelled, euen of verye necessitie, to haue regarde to
hym selfe rather then to the people, that is to saye, to
other. Contrarywyse, there where all thynges be commen
to euerye man, it is not to be dowted [1] that any man shal
lacke anye thynge necessarye for hys pryuate vses, so
that the commen store howses and barnes be sufficientlye

for Communism:

(cf. Elyot)

ᵃ gaine.

Descripsi uobis quam potui uerissime eius formam Reipublicae,
quam ego certe non optimam tantum, sed solam etiam censeo, quae
sibi suo iure possit Reipublicae uendicare uocabulum. Siquidem
alibi de publico loquentes ubique commodo priuatam curant; hic ubi
nihil priuati est, serio publicum negotium agunt, certe utrobique
merito. Nam alibi, quotus quisque est qui nesciat, nisi quid seorsum
prospiciat sibi, quantumuis florente Republica semet tamen fame
periturum ; eoque necessitas urget ut sui potius quam populi, id est
aliorum, habendam sibi rationem censeat. Contra hic, ubi omnia
omnium sunt, nemo dubitat (curetur modo ut plena sint horrea publica) nihil quicquam priuati cuiquam defuturum. Neque enim maligna

quia in festis saepe multiplicantur peccata, in tabernis, in choreis, et aliis
lasciviis quas docet otiositas, tum quia
dies operabiles vix sufficiunt pauperi-

bus ad vitae necessaria procuranda.'—
Fasciculus rerum expetend., &c., 1535,
fol. 206 B.

[1] That is, feared.

stored. For there nothynge is distrybuted after a nyggyshe
sorte, nother there is any poore man or begger. And
though no man haue any thynge, yet euerye man is ryche.
For what can be more ryche then to lyue ioyfullye and
merylye without all griefe and pensifenes ; not caryng for
hys owne lyuing, nor vexed or trowbled with hys wyfes
importunate complayntes, not ᵃ drydynge pouertie to his
sonne, nor sorrowyng for his dowghters dowrey? Yea,
they take no care at all for the lyuyng and wealthe of
themsefes ¹ and all theirs; of theire wyfes, theire chyldren, theire nephewes ², theire childrens chyldren, and all
the succession that euer shall followe in theire posteritie.
And yet, besydes thys, there is no lesse prouision for
them that were ones labourers, and be nowe weake and
impotent, then for them that do nowe laboure and take
payne.

Raphael

Heere nowe woulde (I) see yf anye man dare be so bolde,
as to compare with thys equytie the iustice of other nations.
Among whom, I forsake God ³, if I can fynde any signe

may I
despair,   ᵃ nor.

rerum distributio est, neque inops, neque mendicus ibi quisquam, et
quum nemo quicquam habeat, omnes tamen diuites sunt. Nam quid
ditius esse potest, quam, adempta prorsus omni solicitudine, laeto ac
tranquillo animo uiuere? non de suo uictu trepi|dum, non uxoris ¹57
querula flagitatione uexatum, non paupertatem filio metuentem, non
de filiae dote anxium ; sed de suo suorumque omnium, uxoris,
filiorum, nepotum, pronepotum, abnepotum, et quam longam poste-
rorum seriem suorum generosi praesumunt, uictu esse ac felicitate
securum. Quid quod nihilo minus his prospicitur, qui nunc impotes
olim laborauerunt, quam his qui nunc laborant?

Hic aliquis uelim cum hac aequitate audeat aliarum iustitiam gentium comparare, apud quas [dispeream] si ullum prorsus comperio

---

¹ The printing being indistinct, it is
not clear whether this or 'themseles'
is the word.
² In the old sense of ' nephews,' as
in 1 Tim. v. 4. The Latin terms used
are those for the successive stages in
lineal descent. Compare the language
of Budé, above, p. lxxxvi.
³ Lit. 'may I perish, if,' &c.

Raphael Hythloday

or token of equitie and iustice. For what iustice is this,
that a ryche goldsmythe [1] or an vsurer, or, to be shorte,   usurer:
any of them, whyche other doo nothyng at all ; or els that
whiche they do is suche, that it is not very necessary
to the commen wealthe ; should haue a pleasaunt and
a welthy lyuynge, other by Idilnes, or by vnnecessary
busynes ? when in the meane tyme poore labourers,
carters, yronsmythes, carpenters, and plowmen, by so
great and continual toyle, as drawynge and bearyng
beastes be skeant able to susteine ; and agayn so necessary toyle that with out it no commen wealth were able to
continewe and endure one yere ; do [a] yet get so harde
and poore a lyuing, and lyue so wretched and miserable
a lyfe, that the state and condition of the labouring beastes
maye seme muche better and welthier. For they be not
put to so contynuall laboure, nor theirc lyuynge is not
muche worse ; yea, to them much pleasaunter ; takynge
no thowghte in the meane season for the tyme to come.
But thies seilie poore wretches be presently tormented

[a] should.

iustitiae aequitatisque uestigium. Nam quae haec iustitia est, ut
nobilis quispiam, aut aurifex, aut foenerator, aut denique alius quisquam eorum, qui aut omnino nihil agunt, aut id quod agunt eius
generis est ut non sit Reipublicae magnopere necessarium, lautam
ac splendidam uitam, uel ex ocio uel superuacuo negotio, consequatur,
quum interim mediastinus, auriga, faber, agricola, tanto tamque
assiduo labore quam uix iumenta sustineant, tam necessario ut sine
eo ne unum quidem annum possit ulla durare Respublica, uictum
tamen adeo malignum parant, uitam adeo miseram ducunt, ut longe
potior uideri possit conditio iumentorum, quibus nec tam perpetuus
labor, nec uictus multo deterior est, et ipsis etiam suauior, nec ullus
interim de futuro timor. At hos et labor sterilis atque infructuosus in

---

[1] We should now rather say, a
banker. It was not till the Restora-
tion that banking became a distinct
occupation in England. And this new
branch of business, as Macaulay says,
'naturally fell into the hands of the
goldsmiths, who were accustomed to
traffic largely in the precious metals,
and who had vaults in which great
masses of bullion could be secure from
fire and from robbers.' *Hist. of England*, ed. 1858, iv. p. 492.

with barreyne and vnfrutefull labour. And the remembraunce of theire poore indigent and begerlye olde age
kylleth them vp. For theire dayly wages is so lytle that it
will not suffice for the same daye; muche lesse it yeldeth
any ouerplus, that may dayly be layde vp for the relyefe
of olde age.

Is not thys an vniust and an vnkynd publyque weale,
whyche gyueth great fees and rewardes to gentelmen, as
they call them, and to goldsmythes[1], and to suche other,
whiche be other ydell persones or els onlye flatterers, and
deuysers of vayne pleasures; and, of the contrary parte,
maketh no gentle prouision for poore plowmen, coliars,
laborers, carters, yronsmythes, and carpenters; without
whome no commen wealth can continewe? But when[a]
it hath abused the laboures off heire lusty and flowringe
age, at the laste, when they be oppressed with old age and
syckenes, being nedye, poore, and indigent of all thynges;
then, forgettynge theire so many paynfull watchynges,
not remembrynge theire so many and so great benefytes;
recompenseth and acquyteth them moste vnkyndly with
myserable death. And yet besides this the riche men not

[a] after.

---

praesenti stimulat, et inopis recordatio senectutis occidit; quippe
quibus parcior est | diurna merces, quam ut eidem possit diei suffi- 158
cere: tantum abest ut excrescat et supersit aliquid quod quotidie
queat in senectutis usum reponi.

An non haec iniqua est et ingrata respublica, quae generosis, ut
uocant, et aurificibus, et id genus reliquis, aut ociosis aut tantum
adulatoribus et inanium uoluptatum artificibus, tanta munera pro-
digit; agricolis contra, carbonariis, mediastinis, aurigis et fabris, sine
quibus nulla omnino Respublica esset, nihil benigne prospicit; sed
eorum florentis aetatis abusa laboribus, annis tandem ac morbo
graues, omnium rerum indigos, tot uigiliarum immemor, tot ac tan-
torum oblita beneficiorum, miserrima morte repensat ingratissima.
Quid quod ex diurno pauperum demenso diuites cotidie aliquid, non

---

[1] See the note above, p. 301.

only by priuate fraud, but also by commen lawes, do euery day plucke and snatche away from the poore some parte of their daily liuing. So, where as it semed before uniuste to recompense with vnkyndnes their paynes that haue bene beneficiall to the publique weale, nowe they haue to this their wrong and vniuste dealinge (whiche is yet a muche worse pointe), geuen the name of iustice[1], yea, and that by force of a law.

Therfore when I consider and way in my mind all thies commen wealthes which now a dayes any where do florish, so god helpe me, I can perceaue nothing but a certein conspiracy of riche men, procuringe theire owne commodities vnder the name and title of the commen wealth. They inuent and deuise all meanes and craftes, first how to kipe safely without feare of lesing that they haue vniustly gathered together; and next how to hire and abuse the woorke and labour of the poore for as litle

modo priuata fraude sed publicis etiam legibus abradunt: ita quod ante uidebatur iniustum, optime de Republica meritis pessimam referre gratiam, hoc isti deprauatum etiam fecerunt, tum prouulgata lege iustitiam.

Itaque omnes has quae hodie usquam florent Respublicas animo intuenti ac uersanti mihi, nihil, sic me amet deus, occurrit aliud quam quaedam conspiratio diuitum, de suis commodis Reipublicae nomine tituloque tractantium. comminiscun-turque et excogitant omnes modos atque artes quibus, quae malis artibus ipsi congesserunt, ea primum ut absque perdendi metu retineant, post hoc ut pauperum omnium opera 159 *ac laboribus[2] quam minimo sibi redimant, eisque[a] abutan|tur. Haec*

Haec annota, lector.

 [a] *eisque pro iumentis,* B.

---

[1] Burnet gives what must be the general sense of this passage : ' So that, though it is a Thing most unjust in it self, to give such small Rewards to those who deserve so well of the Publick, yet they have given those Hardships the Name and Colour of Justice, by procuring Laws to be made for regulating them.' But the Latin is obscure, at least if the *tum* before *prouulgata* be correct.

[2] The ablative is apparently due to attraction with *eisque* just afterwards. In this case *opera* must also be taken as ablative. But the proper construction would be *opera* (n. pl.) *ac labores.*

injustice made law:

money as may be. Thies deuyses when the riche men haue decreed to be kept and obserued for the commen wealthes sake[a], that is to saye, for the wealth[b] also of the poore people, then they be made lawes. But thies most wicked and vicious men, when they haue by their vnsatiable couetousnes deuided emong them selfes all those thinges which wold haue suffised all men, yet howe farre be they from the wealth and felicity of the vtopian commen wealth? owt of the which in that all the desire of moneye with the vse therof is vtterly secluded and bannisshed, howe great a heape of cares is cut away? How great an occasion of wickednes and mischiefe is plucked vp by the rotes? For who knoweth not that fraud, theft, rauine, brauling, quarelling, brabling, striffe, chiding, contention, murder, treason, poisoning; which by dayly punishmentes are rather reuenged then refrained; do dye when money dieth? And also that feare, griefe, care, laboures, and watchinges, do perishe, euen the very same moment that money perisseth? Yea, pouerty it selfe, which only semed to lacke money, if money were gone, it also wold decrease and vanishe away.

> [a] [for . . . sake] vnder coloure of the comminaltie.
> [b] [for . . . wealth] *omitted.*

machinamenta ubi semel diuites publico nomine, hoc est etiam pauperum, decreuerunt obseruari, iam leges fiunt. At homines deterrimi cum inexplebili cupiditate, quae fuerant omnibus suffectura, ea omnia inter se partiuerint, quam longe tamen ab Vtopiensium Reipublicae felicitate absunt? e qua cum ipso usu sublata penitus omni auiditate pecuniae, quanta moles molestiarum recisa, quanta scelerum seges radicitus euulsa est? Quis enim nescit fraudes, furta, rapinas, rixas, tumultus, iurgia, seditiones, caedes, proditiones, ueneficia, cotidianis uindicata potius quam refrenata suppliciis, interempta pecunia commori; ad haec metum, sollicitudinem, curas, labores, uigilias, eodem momento quo pecunia perituras? quin paupertas ipsa, quae sola pecuniis uisa est indigere, pecunia prorsus undique sublata, protinus etiam ipsa decresceret[a].

> [a] decesceret, A.; dicesceret, B.

And that you may perceaue this more plainly, consider with your selfes some barrein and vnfrutefull yeare,
wherin many thousandes of people haue starued for
honger. I dare be bolde to say, that in the end of that
penury so much corne or grain might haue bene found
in the riche mens barnes, if they had bene searched, as
being deuided emong them, whome famine and pestilence
hath killed[a], no man at all should haue felt that plage and
penury. So easely might men gett their liuinge, if that
same worthye princesse, lady money[1], did not alon stoppe
vp the way betwene vs and our liuing; whiche a goddes
name was very excellently deuised and inuented, that by
her the way therto should be opened. I am sewer the
ryche men perceaue thys, nor they be not ignoraunte how
much better yt werre to lacke noo necessarye thynge then
to abunde with ouermuch superfluyte; to be rydde owte
of innumerable cares and trowbles, then to be beseiged
wyth[b] greate ryches. And I dowte not that other the
respecte of euery mans priuate commoditie, or els the
aucthority of oure sauioure Christe (which for his great

---

[a] [hath killed] then consumed.   [b] and encombred wyth

Id quo fiat illustrius, reuolue in animo tecum annum aliquem steri-
lem atque infoecundum, in quo multa hominum millia fames abstulerit.
contendo plane in fine illius penuriae, excussis diuitum horreis, tantum
frugum potuisse reperiri, quantum si fuisset inter eos distributum,
quos macies ac tabes absumpsit, illam caeli solique parcitatem nemo
omnino sensisset. tam facile uictus parari posset, nisi beata illa
pecunia, quae praeclare scilicet inuenta est, ut aditus ad uictum per
eam patesceret, sola nobis ad uictum uiam intercluderet. Sentiunt
160 ista, non dubito, etiam diuites, nec ignorant quan|to potior esset illa
conditio nulla re necessaria carere, quam multis abundare superfluis;
tam numerosis eripi malis, quam magnis obsideri diuitiis. Neque
mihi quidem dubitare subit, quin uel sui cuiusque commodi ratio, uel
CHRISTI seruatoris autoritas (qui neque pro tanta sapientia potuit

---

[1] 'That blessed Thinge, called
Money' (Burnet). There is nothing
to show that More meant to personify
pecunia here; and *beata*, in the sense
of 'affluent,' is a common epithet of
ubertas, copia, and the like.

X

wisdom could not but know what were best, and for his
inestimable goodnes cold not but counsell to that which
he knew to be best) wold haue brought all the wordle
long agoo into the lawes of this weale publique, if it were
no that one only beast, the prince[a] and mother of all mischiefe, pride[1], doth withstonde and let it. She measureth
not wealth and prosperity by here own commodities, but
by the miseriies and incommodities of other. She wold
not by her good will be made a goddes, if there were no
wretches left, whom she might be lady ouer to mocke and
scorne[b]; ouer whose miseries her felicity might shine,
whose pouerty she might vexe, torment, and encrease by
gorgiously setting furthe her riches. This hell hound
crepeth in to mens hartes, and plucketh them backe from
entering the right pathe of liffe; and is so depely roted in
mens brestes, that she can not be plucked out.

This forme and fassion of a weale publique, which I
wold gladly wisshe vnto all nations, I am glad yet that it

[a] princesse.   [b] [whom ... scorne] ouer whom she might like a scorneful
ladie rule and triumph.

ignorare quid optimum esset, neque qua erat bonitate id consulere
                quod non optimum sciret) totum orbem facile in huius
    Mire dictum[a].   Reipublicae leges iamdudum traxisset, nisi una tantum
                belua, omnium princeps parensque pestium, superbia,
reluctaretur. haec non suis commodis prosperitatem, sed ex alienis
metitur incommodis. haec ne Dea quidem fieri uellet, nullis relictis
miseris, quibus imperare atque insultare possit; quorum miseriis
praefulgeat ipsius comparata felicitas ; quorum suis explicatis opibus
angat atque incendat inopiam. Haec auerni serpens, mortalium
pererrans pectora, ne meliorem uitae capessant uiam, uelut remora
retrahit ac remoratur.

Quae quoniam pressius hominibus infixa est, quam ut facile possit
euelli, hanc Reipublicae formam, quam omnibus libenter optarim,

         [a] *Haec adnotatio deest in* B.

---

[1] Dibdin here refers to the chapter
on Pride in More's treatise *De quatuor
nouissimis,* in evidence of the detesta-
tion in which this vice was held by
the author. See the *English Works,*
1577, pp. 82, 1270; and the extracts
given by Bridgett: *Wit and Wisdom,*
pp. 55-58.

hath chaunced to the Vtopians; which haue followed those
institutions of liffe, wherby they haue laid such fondations
of their common wealth, as shall continew and last, not
only wealthely, but also, as farre as mans wit maye iudge
and coniecture, shall endure for euer. For seinge the
chiefe causes of ambition and sedition with other vices be
plucked vp by the rootes and abandoned at home, there
can be no ieopardye of domesticall dissention; which
alone hathe caste vnder fote and broughte to noughte the
well fortefied and strongly defenced wealth and riches
of many cities. But for asmuch as perfect concord re-
maineth, and holsome lawes be executed at home, the
enuy of all forrein princes be not able to shake or moue
the empire, though they haue many tymes long ago gone
about to do it, beinge euermore dreuen backe.'

Thus when Raphaell hadde made an ende of his tale,
thoughe manye thinges came to my mind which in the
manners and lawes of that people semed to be instituted
and founded of no good reason[1], not only in the fassion of
their cheualry and in their sacrifices and religions, and in

More:

Vtopiensibus saltem contigisse gaudeo; qui ea uitae sunt instituta
sequuti, quibus Reipublicae fundamenta iecerunt non modo felicis-
sime, uerum etiam, quantum humana praesagiri coniectura contigit,
aeternum duratura. Extirpatis enim domi cum caeteris uitiis ambi-
tionis et factionum radicibus, nihil impendet periculi ne domestico
161 dissidio laboretur, quae | una multarum urbium egregie munitas opes
pessundedit. At salua domi concordia et salubribus institutis non
omnium finitimorum inuidia principum (quae saepius id iam olim
semper reuerberata tentauit) concutere illud imperium aut commo-
uere queat.

Haec ubi Raphael recensuit, quanquam haud pauca mihi succurre-
bant, quae in eius populi moribus legibusque perquam absurde
uidebantur instituta, non solum de belli gerendi ratione, et rebus
diuinis, ac religione, aliisque insuper eorum institutis, sed in eo

---

[1] This is weaker than the Latin, *perquam absurde,* 'very absurdly.'

other of their lawes, but also, yea and chieffely, in that
which is the principall fondacion of al their ordinaunces,
that is to saye, in the communitie of theire liffe and
liuinge, without anny occupieng of money; by the whyche
thynge onelye all nobilitie, magnificence, wourship, honour, and maiestie, the true ornamentes and honoures, as
the common opinion is, of a common wealth, vtterly be
ouerthrowen and destroyed; yet, bicause I knew that he
was wery of talkinge, and was not sure whether he coulde
abide that any thing shoulde be said againste hys minde;
speciallye bicause I remembred [a] that he had reprehended
this fault in other, which be aferd least they shoulde seme
not to be wise enough, onles they could find some fault
in other mens inuentions: therfore I, praising both their
institutions and his communication, toke him by the hand,
and led him into supper; saying that we wold chuse an
other time to way and examine the same matters, and to
talke wyth him more at lardge therin. Whiche wold to [b]
God it might ones come to passe. In the mean time as I
can not agree and consent to all thinges that he said;
being els without dowte a man singulerly well learned,
and also in all wordely [c] matters exactely and profoundely

[a] speciallye remembrynge.   [b] to *omitted*.   [c] worldely.

quoque ipso maxime, quod maximum totius institutionis fundamentum est, uita scilicet uictuque communi, sine ullo pecuniae commercio,
qua una re funditus euertitur omnis nobilitas, magnificentia, splendor,
maiestas, uera (ut publica est opinio) decora atque ornamenta Reipublicae; tamen, quoniam defessum narrando sciebam, neque mihi
satis exploratum erat, possetne ferre ut contra suam sententiam
sentiretur, praesertim quod recordabar eo nomine quosdam ab illo
reprehensos, quasi uererentur ne non satis putarentur sapere, nisi
aliquid inuenirent in quo uellicare aliorum inuenta possent, idcirco
et illorum institutione et ipsius oratione laudata, manu apprehendens
intro coenatum duco; praefatus tamen aliud nobis tempus iisdem de
rebus altius cogitandi atque uberius cum eo conferendi fore. Quod
utinam aliquando contingeret. interea, quemadmodum haud possum 162
omni|bus assentiri quae dicta sunt, alioqui ab homine citra controuer-

experienced; so must I nedes⌈confesse and graunt,⌉that *2 for 1*
many thinges be in the vtopian weal publique, which in *Latin*
our cities I may rather wisshe for then hoope after. *or for*
                                                        facile

Thus endeth the afternones talke
of Raphaell Hythlodaye concerning the lawes and in-
stitutions of the Iland
of Vtopia.

¶ Imprinted at London
by Abraham Vele, dwelling in Pauls
churcheyarde at the sygne of
the Lambe.   Anno.
1551.

siam eruditissimo simul et rerum humanarum peritissimo, ita facile
confiteor permulta esse in Vtopiensium republica, quae in nostris
ciuitatibus optarim uerius quam sperarim.

SECVNDI LIBRI FINIS.

SERMONIS POMERIDIANI RAPHAELIS HY

THLODAEI, DE LEGIDVS ET INSTITV-

TIS VTOPIENSIS INSVLAE PAVCIS

ADHVC COGNITAE, PER CLA-

RISSIMVM ET ERVDITISSI

MVM VIRVM D. THOMAM

MORVM CIVEM ET VI

CECOMITEM LON

DINENSEM,

FINIS.

APPENDIX

FROM THE ORIGINAL

JEROME BUSLEYDEN

TO THOMAS MORE
GREETING [1].

I T was not enough, my accomplished friend More, that you formerly spent all your care, labour and study upon the interests and advantage of individuals; but you must bestow them (such is your kindness and generosity) on the community at large. You thought that this benefit of yours, whatever it might be, deserved the greater indulgence, courted the greater favour, and aimed at the higher renown, on this very account, that it was likely to profit the more, the more widely it was diffused and the more there were to share it. To confer this benefit has always been your object on other occasions, and of late you have,

❧ HIERONYMVS

BVSLIDIVS THOMAE
MORO S.D.

N ON SAT FVIT ORNATISSIME More, olim omnem curam, operam, studium intulisse in rem et commodum singulorum, nisi uel ea (quae tua pietas et liberalitas est) conferres in uniuersum, ratus hoc tuum qualecumque foret beneficium eo maiorem hinc mereri [a] fauorem, uenari gratiam, aucupari gloriam, quanto illud et latius propagatum, et in plures distributum, pluribus esset profuturum. Quod et si alias semper praestare contenderis, tamen id

[a] morari, C.

---

[1] This letter, which was not translated by Robynson, came before the *Utopia*, in the edition of 1516, but in that of 1518 was placed after it, as here. For Busleyden see above, p. xcv.

with singular good fortune, been most successful in attain-
ing it : I mean, in that 'afternoon's talk,' which you have
reduced to writing and published, about the right and
good constitution, that all must long for, of the Utopian
commonwealth.

In your happy description of that fair institution, we
nowhere miss either the highest learning or consummate
knowledge of the world.   Both those qualities are blended
together in the work, meeting on such equal terms that
neither yields to the other, but both contend on an equality
for the palm.   The truth is, you are the able possessor of
such varied learning, and on the other hand of so wide and
exact a knowledge of the world, that, whatever you write,
you assert from full experience, and, whatever assertion
you have decided to make, you write most learnedly.
A felicity this as rare as it is admirable! What makes it
rarer is that it withholds itself from the many, and only
imparts itself to the few;—to such above all as have the
candour to wish, the knowledge to understand, the credit
which will qualify, and the influence which will enable
them to consult the common interest as dutifully, justly,
and providently as you now plainly do.   For, deeming
yourself born not for yourself alone, but for the whole

maxime es nuper mira felicitate adsecutus, scilicet pomeridiano illo
sermone abs te in literas relato, quem de recte et bene constituta, ab
omnibus expetenda, Vtopiensium republica aedidisti.

  In cuius pulcherrimi instituti felici descriptione nihil est in quo uel
summa eruditio, uel absoluta rerum humanarum peritia desyderari
possit ; quando ea quidem ambo in illo tanta paritate et aequabili
congressu concurrunt, ut, neutro alteri herbam porrigente [1], utrumque
aequo marte de gloria contendat. Tam siquidem multifaria polles
doctrina, rursum tam multa eaque certa rerum peritia, ut prorsus
expertus affir|mes quicquid scripseris, doctissime scribas quicquid 163 b
affirmandum destinaueris. Mira profecto raraque felicitas, ac plane
eo rarior, quo magis ipsa sese inuidens plurimis non praebet nisi
raris, maxime iis, qui, sicut candore uelint, ita eruditione sciant, fide
queant, autoritate possint, tam pie, recte, prouide in commune consulere, sicut tu iam facis probe, qui quod non solum tibi, uerum etiam

[1] Plin. *Hist. Nat.* xxii. 4.

world, you have thought fit by this fair service to make the whole world itself beholden to you.

And this result you would not have been able to effect so well and rightly by any other means, as by delineating for rational beings themselves an ideal commonwealth, a pattern and finished model of conduct, than which there has never been seen in the world one more wholesome in its institution, or more perfect, or to be thought more desirable. For it far surpasses and leaves a long way behind the many famous states, that we have heard so much about, of Sparta and Athens and Rome. Had these been inaugurated under the same favourable conditions, with the same institutions, laws, enactments and rules of life to control them as this commonwealth of yours, they would not, we may be sure, have by this time been lying in ruins, levelled with the ground, and now alas! obliterated beyond all hope of renewal. On the contrary, they would have been still unfallen, still fortunate and prosperous, leading a happy existence, mistresses of the world meanwhile, and dividing a widespread empire by land and sea.

Of these commonwealths you compassionated the un-

---

toti te genitum [a] orbi existimas, operae precium duxeris hoc tuo pulcherrimo merito uel totum ipsum orbem demereri.

Quod praestare alia ratione neque rectius neque melius potuisses, quam ipsis mortalibus ratione pollentibus eam reipublicae ideam, eam morum formulam absolutissimumque simulacrum praescribere ; quo nullo [b] unquam in orbe uisum sit uel salubrius institutum, uel magis absolutum, uel quod magis expetendum uideatur ; utpote multo quidem praestante, atque longo post se interuallo relinquente tot celebratissimas tantopere decantatas Lacedaemoniorum, Atheniensium, Romanorum respublicas. Quae si iisdem essent auspiciis auspicatae, iisdem quibus haec tua respublica institutis, legibus, decretis, moribus moderatae, profecto hae nondum labefactatae et solo aequatae iam pro dolor citra spem omnem instaurationis extinctae iacerent ; sed contra incolumes adhuc, beatae, felices, fortunatissime agerent ; interim rerum dominae, suum late imperium terra marique sortitae.

Quarum quidem rerum publicarum tu miserandum miseratus

[a] gentium, B.   [b] sic et A. Leg. nullum.

happy lot. And so you wished to save other states in like manner, which now hold the supreme power, from undergoing a like vicissitude, by your picture of a perfect state ; one which directed its chief energies not so much to framing laws as to appointing the most approved magistrates. (And with good reason : for otherwise, without them, even the best laws, if we take Plato's [1] word for it, would all be counted dead.) Magistrates these, above all, after whose likeness, pattern of uprightness, ensample of conduct, and mirror of justice, the whole state and right course of any perfect commonwealth whatever ought to be modelled ; wherein should unite, above all things, prudence in the rulers, courage in the soldiers, temperance in the private individuals, and justice in all [2].

And since the commonwealth you make so famous is manifestly formed, in fairest manner, of these principles, it is no wonder if on this account it comes not only as an object of fear to many, but also of reverence to all nations, and one for all generations to tell of ; the more so,

sortem, ne aliae itidem, quae | hodie rerum potitae summum tenent, 164 parem sustinerent uicem, prospicere uoluisti, scilicet hac tua absolutissima republica ; quae non tam in condendis legibus quam uel probatissimis magistratibus formandis maxime elaborauit. Nec id quidem ab re : quando alioqui sine illis omnes uel optimae leges, si Platoni credimus, mortuae censerentur ; praesertim ad quorum magistratuum simulacrum, probitatis specimen, exemplar morum, iusticiae imaginem, totus status et rectus tenor cuiusuis absolutae reipublicae sit effingendus ; in quo in primis concurrant prudentia in optimatibus, fortitudo in militibus, temperantia in singulis, iusticia in omnibus.

Quibus quum tua, quam tantopere celebras, respublica sit tam pulcherrime, ut liquet, composita, non mirum si hinc ueniat non solum multis timenda, sed et cunctis gentibus ueneranda, simul omnibus saeculis praedicanda ; idque eo magis quod in ea, omnis

---

[1] See the *De Legibus*, Lib. vi. (§ 751, B, C).

[2] This is a brief summary of the Fourth Book of the *Republic*, the object of which is to show that the *wisdom* of the ideal State will reside in the Guar-dians or Magistrates, the *courage* in the Soldiers or Auxiliaries, and the political *temperance* in the general body of citizens. *Justice*, like a common bond, keeps all classes in their place. See the Introduction, above, p. lii.

that in it all competition for ownership is taken away, and no one has any private property at all. For the rest, all men have all things in common, with a view to the commonwealth itself; so that every matter, every action, however unimportant, whether public or private, instead of being directed to the greed of many or the caprice of a few, has sole reference to the upholding of one uniform justice, equality and communion. When that is made the entire object of every action, there must needs be a clearance of all that serves as matter and fuel and feeder of intrigue, of luxury, envy, and wrong; to which mankind are hurried on, even at times against their will, either by the possession of private property, or by the burning thirst of gain, and that most pitiable of all things, ambition, to their own great and immeasurable loss. For it is from these things that there often suddenly arise divisions of feeling, taking up of arms, and wars worse than civil; whereby not only is the flourishing state of wealthy republics utterly overthrown, but the renown they won in other days, the triumphs celebrated, the splendid trophies, the rich spoils so often won from conquered enemies, are all utterly effaced.

If on these matters the words I write should chance to be less convincing than I desire, there will at any rate

proprietatis contentione sublata, nulli sit quippiam proprii. Caeterum in rem ipsam communem communia sunt omnibus omnia; adeo ut omnis res, quaeuis actio, seu publica seu priuata, non ad multorum cupiditatem, non ad paucorum libidinem, spectet; sed ad unam iusticiam, aequabilitatem, communionem sustinendam, quantulacunque sit, tota referatur. Quo illa integre relata, omnis materies, fax, et fomes ambitus, luxus, inuidentiae, iniuriae, facessat necesse est; in quae nonnunquam aut priuata rerum possessio, aut ardens habendi sitis, 164 b omniumque miserri|ma rerum ambitio, mortales uel reluctantes protrudit, maximo suo idque incomparabili malo; quando hinc saepenumero dissensiones animorum, motus armorum, et bella plus quam ciuilia derepente oriantur, quibus non solum florentissimus status beatissimarum rerumpublicarum funditus pessumdatur, uerum illarum olim parta gloria, acti triumphi, clara trophaea, totiesque opima spolia deuictis hostibus relata, penitus obliterantur.

Quod si in his haec nostra pagina minorem forte ac uelim fidem

be ready at hand the most sufficient witnesses for me to refer you to : I mean, the many great cities formerly laid waste, the states destroyed[1], the republics overthrown, the villages burnt and consumed. As scarce any relics or traces of their great calamity are to be seen at this day, so neither are their names preserved by any history, however ancient it be, and however far back its records extend.

These memorable disasters, devastations, overthrows, and other calamities of war our states, whatever they be, will easily succeed in escaping, if they only adapt themselves exactly to the one pattern of the Utopian commonwealth, and do not deviate a hair's-breadth from it. By so acting alone, they will at length most fully recognize by the result how greatly they have profited by this service you have rendered them ; especially since by its acquisition they have learnt to preserve their own state in safety, unharmed, and victorious. It follows that their debt to you, their present deliverer, will be no less than is the just due of those, who have saved—I do not say some one member of a state, but the whole state itself.

fecerit, certe in promptu aderunt testes ad quos te relegem locupletissimi, uidelicet, tot et tantae olim uastatae urbes, dirutae ciuitates, prostratae respublicae, incensi et consumpti uici ; quorum uti hodic uix ullae tantae calamitatis reliquiae aut uestigia uisuntur, ita nec nomina illorum ulla [a] quantumuis uetus et longe deducta historia sat probe tenet.

Quas quidem insignes clades, uastationes, euersiones, caeterasque belli calamitates, nostrae si quae sint respublicae facile euaserint, modo ad unam Vtopiensium reipublicae normam sese adamussim componentes ab ea ne transuersum quidem, ut aiunt, unguem recedant. Quod sic demum praestantes tandem re ipsa cumulatissime agnoscent, quantum hoc tuum in se collatum beneficium profuerit ; maxime quo accedente didicerint [b] suam rempublicam saluam, incolumem, triumphantem seruare ; proinde tantum tibi suo praesentissimo seruatori debiturae, quantum is haud iniuria promeretur, qui non tantum aliquem e republica ciuem, | sed uel ipsam totam rempublicam 165 seruarit.

[a] om. B.   [b] d dicerint, A ; id dicerint, B.

---

[1] This is a reiteration of what More had said about the Carthaginians and others, above, p. 49.

Meanwhile farewell. Go on and prosper, ever devising, carrying out and perfecting something, the bestowal of which on your country may give it long continuance and yourself immortality. Farewell, learned and courteous More, glory of your island, and ornament of this world of ours.

From my house at Mechlin [1], 1516.

Interea uale, ac feliciter perge nonnihil usque meditari, agere, elaborare, quod in rempublicam collatum illi perpetuitatem, tibi immortalitatem addat. Vale, doctissime et idem humanissime More, tuae Britanniae ac nostri huius orbis decus.

Ex aedibus nostris Mechliniae. M.D.XVI.

---

[1] The splendour of Busleyden's house at Mechlin seems to have impressed More. See his epigrams upon it, and on the collections of coins, and the like, to be found there (*Epigram-mata*, ed. 1638, pp. 131, 133). In his letter to Erasmus, written shortly after his return from Flanders, he dwells on the same subject.

ℭ Gerarde Nouiomage [1] of Utopia.

DOth pleasure please? then place the here, and well
the rest,
Most pleasaunt pleasures thou shalte finde here.
Doeth profit ease? then here arriue, this yle is best.
For passinge profettes do here appeare.

GERARDVS NOVIOMAGVS
DE VTOPIA.

Dulcia lector amas? sunt hic dulcissima quaeque.
Vtile si quaeris, nil legis utilius.

---

[1] Gerhard Geldenhaur, commonly called, from the place of his birth, Gerardus Noviomagus, was a native of Nimeguen in Guelderland. His father bore the same name. He studied at Deventer, and afterwards at Louvain, where he made such proficiency in philosophy that he became a teacher of that subject in the University. After passing some time at Antwerp, probably a few years before More's visit, he was called to the service of Charles of Austria as Court Chaplain. He then became secretary to Philip of Burgundy, Bishop of Utrecht (Horawitz, *Erasmus von Rotterdam und Martinus Lipsius*, 1882, p. 112). After a while he was sent, in 1526, to visit the schools of Wittenberg. What he there saw, strengthening, no doubt, some previous inclination that way, made him embrace the reformed faith. He removed to Worms, where, like Luther, he laid aside the cowl, and married. After teaching at Augsburg and Marburg, he died, Jan. 10, 1542, at the age of sixty. His change of religion lost him the friendship of Erasmus, who wrote bitterly of him in his letter *In Pseudevangelicos*. See Melchior Adam, *Vitae Germ. Theologorum*, 1653, p. 92; Bayle, *Dict.* ii. p. 1394; and the *Grosses vollständiges Lexikon*, 1735, s. v. I have been the more particular about this person, because of an opinion (see Dr. Lumby's *Utopia*, 2nd ed. p. 237 *bis*) that this Gerardus was no other than the Gerardus Listrius, who wrote the commentary on Erasmus's *Moriae Encomium*. As if to preclude the possibility of such a notion, the lives of the two are found side by side in Gesner's *Bibliotheca*, 1545, leaf 274.

Doeth bothe thee tempte, and woldest thou gripe both
　　gaine and pleasure?
This yle is fraight with both bounteously.
To still thy gredie intent, reape here incomparable
　　treasure
Bothe minde and tongue to garnishe richelie.
The hid welles and fountaines both of vice and vertue
Thou hast them here subiect vnto thine eye.
Be thankful now, and thankes where thankes be due
Geue to Thomas More Londons immortal glorye.

　　　Siue utrunque uoles, utroque haec insula abundat,
　　　　　Quo linguam ornes[a], quo doceas animum.
　　　Hic fontes aperit recti prauique disertus
　　　　　Morus, Londini gloria prima sui.

　　　　　　[a] exornes, B., *recte*.

Y

ⲦCornelius Graphey[1] to the Reader.

VVilt thou knowe what wonders straunge be in the
lande[2] that late was founde?
Wilte thou learne thy life to leade, by diuers wayes
that godly be?
Wilt thou of vertue and of vice vnderstande the very
grounde?
Wilt thou see this wretched world, how ful it is of
vanitie?
Then read, and marke, and beare in mind, for thy behoufe, as thou maie best
All thinges that in this present worke, that worthie
clerke sir Thomas More,
With witte diuine ful learnedly, vnto the worlde hath
plaine exprest,
In whom London well glory maye, for wisedome and
for godly lore.

CORNELIVS GRAPHEVS AD LECTOREM.

Vis noua monstra, nouo dudum nunc orbe reperto?
Viuendi uaria uis ratione modos?
Vis qui uirtutum fontes, uis unde malorum
Principia? et quantum rebus inane latet?
Haec lege, quae uario Morus dedit ille colore,
Morus Londinae nobilitatis honos.

BASILEAE APVD IOANNEM FROBE
NIVM MENSE MARTIO[3].
AN. M. D. XVIII.

---

[1] A full account of Cornelius Grapheus (Schreiber) of Alst is given in
the Appendix to vol. I. of Ullmann's
Reformers before the Reformation, tr.
by Menzies, 1855, pp. 397-416. Grapheus died Dec. 19, 1558, having
survived his friend Erasmus twenty-
two years. In 1521 he came under
the grasp of a severe penal law
enacted against heresy in the Netherlands by Charles V, and after being
imprisoned in Brussels for a considerable time, he recanted and was re-
leased, March 25, 1522. Erasmus
always retained a kindly feeling for
him, and left him a legacy in his will.

[2] The immediate reference is to
Utopia; but probably in the Latin,
nouo orbe, there is a suggestion of
the wider range of discoveries in the
New World.

[3] For the date, see the Introd. p. lxx.

GLOSSARY

——◆——

[The authorities chiefly relied on have been *The New English Dictionary*, now in progress ; Stratmann's *Middle-English Dictionary*, ed. by Bradley ; and Professor Skeat's *Etymological Dictionary*.]

A.

A (prep.), a worn form of 'on,' as in 'set a worke.' Comp. 'on liue' (p. 255)=alive.

A brode, abroad.

A goddes name, in God's name.

A pece, each. Comp. St. John ii. 6 ; 'two or three firkins apiece.'

Addict, devoted or inclined to.

Aduenture (at all), at all hazards, at any rate.

Aduisement, thought, consideration. Fr. *avis*. For the *d* inserted, comp. 'advantage.'

Aduoutrye, adultery. Old Fr. *avoutrie*, Lat. *adulterium*.

Aduoyded, avoided. For the inserted *d* see 'aduisement.'

Aford, afraid. So used in the *Homilies* of 1563.

Affection. See p. 237 *n*.

Aglettes, aglets. Fr. *aiguillettes*, tags of laces, pendants.

Allebencheis, ale-benches, seats in front of public-houses.

Alliaunce, alliance, used collectively (p. 257) for connexions.

Allyaunte to, akin to.

Alon, alone.

A lowe, to, to allow, approve. Old Fr. *alouer*, Lat. *allaudare*.

Ambre, amber. If 'or' be not a misprint for 'of' (p. 133), the word must be used for 'oil of amber.'

Amplyfycatyons, extensions or enlargements (logical term, p. 185).

An, and.

Anctientest, most ancient, oldest. Fr. *ancien*, Lat. *antianum*. For the added *t*, comp. 'peasant,' 'tyrant.'

Angerlye, angrily. So used in Shaksp., *Two Gentlemen of Verona*, i. 2. 62.

Appayred, impaired. So used in the *Paston Letters*.

Appoynte, to, to arrange, prepare. Old Fr. *apointer*, Lat. *appunctare*.

Archedoltes, arch dolts, great dullards.

Arrive, to, to come.

Assault, to, to assail (with reasoning). 'To assault him with a newer declaration' is quoted from Clarendon in the *New Engl. Dict.*

Assone, as soon.

Auale, to, to lower, or debase (pp. 240, 274) Old Fr. *avaler* 'to descend,' now 'to swallow.' Lat. *ad vallem* (of rivers flowing down to the valley).

Auaunce, to, to advance, move forward. For the *d*, comp. 'aduisement.'

Auauncement, furtherance, promotion. Comp. the title of Bacon's treatise : *The Aduancement of Learning.*

Auaylable, serviceable, efficacious.

Auctor, author, adviser.

Auenture, adventure, chance. 'At al auentures' (p. 274), all by chance.

Auncetours, ancestors. Old Fr. *ancestres*, Lat. *antecessores* ; with the Latin termination retained.

Auncient. See p. 271 *n.*

Auncyetnes, ancientness, antiquity ; also priority. In the *New Engl. Dict.* Coke *On Littleton* is quoted : 'And then all other Bishops of both Provinces after their ancientnesse.'

Aunters, in, in adventure (comp. 'peradventure'), in case that. Stratmann quotes Robert of Gloucester's *Chronicle*, ed. 1810, p. 65 : 'to do his lif an auntre' (in adventure).

A veyleable, available. See **Auaylable.**

Ayere, air. So spelt by Hawes, 1509.

B.

Bandes, bonds.

Basse, low, base. Fr. *bas*, *basse.*

Battayle, used sometimes for the army in battle array, as in 1 Sam. xvii. 21.

Be, by ; still common as a provincialism.

Behated, held in hatred. Comp. 'beloved.'

Behoufe, behoof, advantage.

Bende, band (of men), akin to *bind.*

Bestowe, to, to place, dispose of. So used in St. Luke xii. 17.

Bocher, butcher. Fr. *boucher*, properly one who kills *buck* goats.

Bolles, bowls.

Borderours, borderers, those living on the confines of a country.

Botys, boats.

Brabling, wrangling : the 'pribbles and prabbles' of Sir Hugh Evans.

Bredeth, breadth.

Bronte, brunt.

Bryde, Bryed, to, to breed.

Busily, eagerly, importunately. The *New Engl. Dict.* quotes the *Towneley Myst.* 26 : 'Pray for me besele.'

By and by, immediately. So in St. Luke xxi. 9.

Bycause that, in order that. Still often so used by uneducated people. The *New Engl. Dict.* quotes Burton, *Anat. of Melancholy*, ed. 1651, i. p. 525 : 'Anointing the doors and hinges with oyl, because they should not creak.'

By like, belike ('by what is like'), probably.

Bye, to, to buy.

Bygnes, bigness, magnitude.

C.

Cannellis, channels, canals.

Carfully, in a way full of care, anxiously.

Carke, to, to be anxious. Stratmann quotes 'carke and care' from *The Squyr of Lowe Degre*.

Cauillation, cavil, used to render *calumnia* (p. 239). Fr. *cavillation*, a quibble.

Cautell, caution, proviso. Lat. *cautela*.

Chaffayre, to, to chaffer, buy and sell: a contraction of cheapfare.

Charges, expense: the plural form used as a singular.

Cheualrye, chivalry, used co-extensively with *res militaris*.

Chouse, to, to choose. More uses both 'chese' and 'chuse' in his English Works.

Children. See p. 235 *n.*

Circumstaunce, surroundings; used (p. 235) for all that wraps up and obscures the truth.

Circumuertions, a word formed like 'perversions,' to express distortions of the truth (p. 235).

Cleped, called. 'Clepe' is used by Shakspere.

Cleyme, to, to claim. 'Cleimed theim quit of ther seruise' is quoted by Stratmann from Manning's *Hist. of England*.

Coliars, colliers.

Coloure, colour, as in 'colour of reason'; appearance or pretence.

Commen, to, to come.

Commen, to, to commune.

Commodytye, convenience.

Conceyt, opinion.

Conductyon, leading.

Condytyons, terms.

Conningly, cunningly, skilfully. Comp. the 'cunning work' of Exod. xxxi. 4.

Conueiaunce, conveyance, cunning management. The *New Engl. Dict.* quotes from Sir Thomas Elyot: 'If they be taken with any crafty conueiaunce.'

Conuersation, way of living, as in 2 Pet. iii. 11.

Coorpe, corpse. Lat. *corpus.* The form *corp* is quoted from Middleton.

Corragiously, with a good heart. See **Couraghe.**

Couch, to, to lie. Fr. *se coucher.*

Couett, to, to covet.

Coueyne, Couyne, covin, fraudulent action. Late Lat. *convenium.* The word occurs in Fabyan's *Chronicle.*

Couraghe, courage, in its original sense of 'heart.' Low Lat. *coraticum.* So used in Chaucer's *Prologue.*

Cowardysho, cowardly.

Coytes, quoits.

Cracke, to, to talk big, or vaunt. 'And Ethiops of their sweet complexion crack.'—*Love's Labour's Lost*, iv. 3.

Crafto, skill, as in 'handicraft.' 'Onely the crafte' (p. 253) = the only means.

Credence, credit. The *New Engl. Dict.* quotes from Strype: 'meat and drink .. had and obtained upon their credence.'

Cunnynge, (sub.) knowledge; (adj.) knowing, skilful.

Cure, care: still used in 'cure of souls.'

Customablye, as a matter of custom, usually.

Cyuyle, civil.

D.

Dasell, to, to dazzle, frequentative of to daze, or dase, to stupefy.

Daunger, danger. Originally in the sense of dominion or power.

Fr. *danger,* late Lat. *dominiarium.* See the note on p. 182.

Delycte, delight. The old spelling is nearer the Lat. *delectare.*

Deuydynge, dividing.

Deuyne, divine (adj.).

Deuyse, device.

Dew, due. Old Fr. *deut.*

Deyntye, dainty, exquisite. Old Fr. *daintié* (sub.), Lat. *dignitatem.*

Disbourdened, unburdened.

Discriue, to, to describe. Common in the form 'descriue.'

Diserdes, clowns, fools. A 'disar,' according to Halliwell, was an actor in a play, especially the clown; and hence a fool in general.

Dishonestie, dishonour, disgrace.

Displeasaunt, displeasing, offensive.

Dissidente (from), different from, at variance with.

Dissolate, dissolute. The *a* is probably a misprint.

Dissolue, to, to solve, settle (a doubt, or question).

Distaunces, intervals (in music), p. 209.

Domme, dumb. The form 'dom' is found in Rolle's *Pricke of Conscience.*

Dorres, drones. A 'dor' was a drone beetle, as in Ben Jonson's *Cynthia's Revels,* iii. 3 (quoted by Wright): 'What should I care what every dor doth buzz | In credulous ears?'

Dote, to, to be foolish. Comp. 'dotage.'

Dreuell, a drudge, bond-servant (Stratmann). According to Skeat, from 'drab,' a slut. Used as a word of contempt (p. 182) to translate *nebulo.*

Drydynge, dreading.

Dytty, song or poem. Old Fr. *dité* or *dicté,* Lat. *dictatum.* Comp. Ps. xlv. 1 : 'My heart is inditing a good matter."

E.

Easere, easier.

Edition, putting forth, publishing. The *New Engl. Dict.* quotes Bullinger's *Decades* (1592), 111 : 'Touching the proclamation or first edition of the ten Commaundements.'

Eftsones, soon, presently ; lit. 'soon after,' 'eft' being 'afterwards' in Gower and other early writers.

Egal, equal. Fr. *égal.* Chaucer uses 'egall.'

Elles, else.

Eloquence, not only 'eloquent language' (in the concrete), but the art of using such language.

Embrayding, upbraiding, bringing as a reproach against. According to Skeat, the simple verb, besides its meaning of 'to weave,' also signified to fasten on, or attack.

Emonge, among. Used in this form by Sir Thomas Malory.

Endaunger, to, to subject to control, bring under one's power or influence. See **Daunger.**

Endeauoure, to, used transitively. For the reflexive use, see p. 249 *n.*

Endeuoire, endeavour. Fr. *en devoir,* as in 'se mettre en devoir de faire quelque chose.'

Enfamed. See **Infamed.**

Ensure, to, to assure.

Enterteynement, occupation, way of spending (time). Shaksp., *Love's Labour's Lost,* v. 1. 126 :

'as concerning some entertainment of time.'

Equynoctyall, equinoctial. ' The line equynoctyall,' the equator.

Eschue, eschew. 1 Pet. iii. 11 : ' Let him eschew evil and do good.' Fr. *essuyer*, Lat. *exsuccare*.

Espiall, a spy.

Euel, evil, ill.

Existymatyon, estimation.

Exploited, managed, worked (esp. of land). Fr. *exploiter*, Lat. **explicitare* (*explicare*) ; lit. to develop.

Expresslyo, openly, aloud.

F.

False, wrong (p. 214), as in a ' false note.'

Falshed, falsehood. The Anglo-Saxon *hád* denoted state or quality.

Fanglenes, used in the phrase ' newe fanglenes ' (p. 57). We still use ' newfangled.' The root of ' fangle ' is the same as of ' fang,' so that the word means ' readiness to catch at (news).'

Fantasy, to, to fancy, imagine. The form ' phantasie ' is used by Foxe.

Fardell, a package. Fr. *fardeau*, said to be of Arabic origin.

Farfurth, far forth ; used in the phrase ' in so far forth as,' in so far as.

Fassyon, fashion. Fr. *façon*, Lat. *factionem*.

Fauour, look, countenance, as in ' well - favoured.' So used by Shakspere.

Fawt, fault.

Fealnige (p. 224), a misprint in the original for ' fealinge.'

Feare, to, to frighten, deter. Hence ' afeared,' afraid.

Feat, anything done. Fr. *fait*, Lat. *factum*. ' Feat of armes ' (p. 243), used to translate *disciplina militaris*, ' military training.'

Ferefull, formidable. See **to Feare.**

Ferfurth. See **Farfurth.**

Fermes, farms. Fr. *fermes*, lit. ' agreements ' (Lat. *firma*).

Filde, field.

Flowringe, flowering, in its prime.

Flowtynge, flouting, mocking. Acc. to Skeat, the root is the same as that of ' to flute,' Du. *fluyten*. The word occurs (p. 10) in the phrase ' lowtynge and flowtynge,' used to render the Lat. *capellicio uellicantes*, an unusual expression, apparently meant for ' plucking by the hair.'

Fond, foolish, as in ' When men were fond, I smiled.'—*Measure for Measure*, ii. 2.

Forby. See p. 128 *n*.

Forestalle, to, to buy up beforehand ; joined with ' ingrossing ' (p. 57). See Jacob's *Law Dictionary* for the nature of the offence implied in each term.

Forsothe, forsooth, in truth.

Fownde, found.

Foynes, foins, thrusts with the point of a sword or other weapon.

Fraight, freighted.

Fraye, to, to frighten, deter. Hence ' afraid.'

Frinde, friend.

Furth with, forthwith.

Fyerslye, fiercely.

Fyne, fine ; used (p. 42) of speech, refined, polished.

Fynesse, fineness.

G.

Gage, pledge. Fr. *gage*.

Gallawnte, fine, gay. Fr. *galant*, originally partic. of *galer*, to rejoice.

Gallous, gibbet. 'Gallous wretche,' Lat. *furcifer*, one who deserves hanging.

Gallymalfreye, used (p. 99) to express an incongruous medley. For its use to denote a dish of various meats mixed together, Halliwell quotes Cotgrave s. v. *Hachis*, and Lilly's *Six Court Comedies*, 1632, sig. T. *The French Schoolmaster*, 1636, gives 'a gallimaufrey, *une fricassée.*'

Garnishing, furnishing.

Gawl, gall. As used at p. 75, the word has no reference to gall in the sense of bile, but is the Old Fr. *galle*, Lat. *callus*, in the sense of a sore place.

Geanyng, gaining.

Geaste wyse, guestwise, as a guest, or visitor.

Geere, gear, business in hand. At p. 294 for 'stuff' or 'things.'

Geme, gem.

Gently men, gentlemen.

Gieste, to, to jest. The *g* recalls the Lat. *gesta*.

Giues, gyves.

Gorgious, gorgeous, with the notion of a certain pompousness. Lit. 'swelling out the *throat*' (Fr. *gorge*).

Gramercye, originally *grand merci*, 'many thanks.' Then used for the obtaining anything for mere thanks, gratuitously. Shakspere uses it in the former sense.

Greiffe, grief, in the sense of trouble; lit. 'burden' (Lat. *gravis*).

Greuously, grievously, with pain or reluctance.

Gripe, to, to grip, or seize.

Grislye, grisly, dreadful.

Grosse, strictly 'big' (Fr. *gros*), then plain, probable.

Ground, to (used intransitively, p. 282), to rest as on a basis.

Groundes, lands.

Guyse, guise.

Gyaunte, giant.

Gyell, Gyle, guile.

Gyues. See **Giues**.

H.

Hable, able. Fr. *habile*, Lat. *habilis*.

Handsome, handy, manageable. Skeat cites the Dutch *handzaam*, 'tractable.'

Hapt, wrapt. 'Happing' is used in the *York Mysteries* for wrapping.

Harboroughe, harbour, shelter. Fr. *auberge*, anciently *herberge*. The word is used by Chaucer.

Hard, heard.

Harmelesse, unharmed.

Haylsede. See p. 29 *n*.

Heard man, herdsman.

Heare, hair; spelt *heer* in the *Prompt. Parvulorum*.

Hether, hither.

Heuely, heavily.

Heuynes, heaviness.

Hole, whole.

Hollye, holy.

Holsom, wholesome, salutary.

Holy, Holye, wholly.

Honeste, honourable. Lat. *honestus*.

Howke, hook. Used (p. 53) in the phrase 'by howke or crooke,' 'by hook or by crook,' by one means or another.

Hurley-Burley, tumult. So used by Shaksp., *Macbeth*, i. 1. Shakspere also uses the simple word *hurly* in the same sense (Comp. Fr. *hurler*, to howl) : 'Amid this hurly.'—*Taming of the Shrew*, iv. 1. The 'burly' is merely a reduplication.

Hydeous, hideous, frightful. Fr. *hideux*, from Lat. *hispidosus*, shaggy. Hence the word has passed through stages of meaning similar to 'horrid.'

Hyere, to, to hire.

I.

Iauell, a vagabond, worthless person. Halliwell quotes from Lansdowne MSS., no. 1033 (in an account of Sir Thomas More's execution) : 'shall I count him a javel, who is to doe me so great a benefit?' *Avoines javelées* are oats spoilt by the rain, from lying on the ground.

Ieopardye, jeopardy. Old Fr. *jeu parti*, a game in which the hazard was equally divided.

Iette, to, to strut. Lat. *iactare* (comp. 'jetty'). Wright quotes from Rowlands, *Knave of Hearts*, 1613 : 'Along the streetes as he doth jetting passe | His outside showes him for an inward asse.'

Ight, eighth

Imbrayde, to. See **Embrayding.**

Impery. See p. 112 *n.*

Incomprehensible (p. 267), not to be confined within boundaries. Compare its use in the Athanasian Creed.

Incontinent, immediately. 'He says he will return incontinent.' —*Othello*, iv. 3.

Indyfferent, impartial. Comp. 'judge indifferent' in *Hen. VIII*, ii. 4.

Inestymable, too great to be measured.

Infamed, made infamous, degraded.

Informatyons, instructions. Comp. the use of Lat. *informator.*

Ingrosse, to. See **Forestall.**

Institute, trained.

Instructe (past partic., like the preceding).

Intentyons. See p. 185 *n.*

Interest, concern or share in. Comp. the use of the Lat. *interesse.*

Intreataunce, entreaty.

Intreate, to, to treat of.

Intyerlye, entirely.

Inuehing, inveighing. Lat. *invehere* (the *g* being an intrusion).

Inured, trained.

Ionckettes, sweetmeats, originally served upon rushes (Lat. *iuncus*) : hence the name.

Iugers, judgers, adjudicators.

Iust, equal.

K.

Kendle, to, to kindle. The old spelling is nearer to *candle*, which is given as the origin of the word.

Kinrede, kindred. The *d* in the modern form is an intrusion. Comp. 'hatred.'

Kipe, to, to keep.

Knowledge, to, to acknowledge. Wright quotes from Gascoigne : 'Mine owne deere nimphes, which knowledge me your queene.'

Kyeles, keels. Skeat compares the Dutch *Kiel.*

L.

Lauasse, lavish.

Laundes. See p. 52 *n.* Perhaps used there as the Fr. *landes,* waste lands.

Leage, league.

Lease, Leaste, lest.

Leese, Leise, Lese, to, to lose. Comp. Germ. *verlieren.*

Leffe, life.

Let, to, to hinder.

Letell, little.

Lette, to. See **Let.**

Lette (sub.), a hindrance.

Lewde, base, ignorant. Comp. Acts xvii. 5 : 'Certain lewd fellows of the baser sort.'

Lieuetenaunte, lieutenant.

Liqueresse, liquorice ; a corrupted form of Pliny's *glycyrrhiza,* 'sweet root.'

Liue (sub.), life.

Liue, to, to live.

Lores, teachings, systems. Used (p. 211) with 'ordinaunces' to render *instituta.*

Lothsumnes, loathsomeness, irksomeness.

Lowtynge, bowing (in mockery). See **Flowtynge.** Stratmann quotes from Robert of Gloucester : 'his hed loutede a doun'; and 'louting' for 'inclination.'

Lubbor, lubber, dolt.

Lumpyshe, stupid.

Lust, to, to desire.

Lycensed, left free.

M.

Madder, a plant from which a red dye is made.

Make, 'to make to' (p. 205), to contribute to.

Manfully, twice used (pp. 46, 247)

to translate *strennue* (*strenue*), 'resolutely,' 'courageously.'

Mansleers, manslayers, homicides.

Margent, margin. For the *t* comp. 'peasant,' 'tyrant.'

Marrish, marish, marsh.

Meane, moderate, ordinary.

Meate, meet.

Meese, a mess, a set (of four) at table (p. 164). Orig. a portion of food. Comp. Fr. *mets.*

Meruellyng, marvelling. Comp. Fr. *merveille.*

Mery, merry, cheerful. The word could formerly be applied to the weather, or to clean and cheerful towns, conveying the notion of quieter gladness than now. Hence even 'Glad homage pay with awful mirth,' in the *New Version* of the Hundredth Psalm.

Methe, mead. See p. 124 *n.*

Mo, Moo, more. 'Ne mo ne les' is found in the *Ayenbite of Inwyt.* 'More' is sometimes thought to be a comparative of 'mo'; but, as Professor Skeat shows, wrongly.

Modestie, moderation.

Mone, moon.

Moneth, month.

Mormosett, a marmoset, a monkey. Acc. to Littré, the word is from **marmoretum,* a little marble figure, such as the grotesque ones seen on fountains.

Morreyn, murrain.

Mortall, deadly, as in 'a mortal wound.'

Moughteaten, motheaten.

Moyle. See p. 86 *n.*

Musynge, meditating.

Myddes, the middle. Comp. 'midship,' 'mid-ocean.'

Myenes, mines.

Myke, meek.

Myte, mite.

N.

Namelye (p. 143), by name, specially.

Natiue, innate.

Necke (to lay in the, set in the). See p. 103 *n.*

Nemblenes, nimbleness. The *e* appears in the German *nehmen*, which is akin to it.

Next, nighest, nearest.

Nigeshe, niggardly, stingy. The adj. *nig* is quoted from old writers by Stratmann. Hence 'niggard' (with French termination).

Nother, neither. The spelling with *o* preserves the true form of the negative.

Noughtenes, naughtiness, as in St. James i. 21 : 'all superfluity of naughtiness.'

Nourceis, nurses. Fr. *nourrices,* Lat. *nutrices.*

Noyinge, injuring. We retain the compound, 'annoy.' The simple verb to 'noy' is quoted by Halliwell from North and Bacon.

Noyous, hurtful, injurious. See the preceding.

Noysome, noisome, troublesome.

Nyce, nice, fastidious. Old Fr. *nice,* Lat. *nescius* ; orig. ignorant, then indolent.

Nye, nigh.

Nyggyshe. See **Nigeshe.**

O.

Obseruation, respect, Lat. *observatio.*

Occupy, to, to do business. Ezek. xxvii. 9 : 'to occupy thy merchandise.' Lit. 'to take hold of,' Lat. *occupare.*

Oneles, unless.

Opteyne, to, to obtain.

Orels, or else.

Other, either. See **Nother.**

Ouerseen. See p. 138 *n.*

Ouerthwarte, cross, contradictory. We retain the compound 'athwart,' and the sub. 'thwarts,' cross-pieces.

P.

Parasite, a sycophant. Lit. 'one who dines beside another at his table' ; hence a hanger-on.

Parcell, part. Comp. our phrase 'part and parcel of.' The form is a diminutive.

Parloure, a room in a house. Fr. *parloir,* lit. 'a room to talk in.' Comp. 'boudoir.'

Parsons, persons.

Paseis, paces.

Pass for, to (also to *pass* alone), to care, to have regard for. ' These silken-coated slaves I pass not.' —2 *Hen. VI,* iv. 2.

Patient, to (used reflexively, 'to patient oneself '), to compose, calm. Comp. the Fr. *patienter.*

Peerles, pearls.

Pennyfathers, misers, penurious persons. Wright quotes from Harrington : 'Cosmus has ever been a penny-father.'

Pensifenes, (anxious) thought, solicitude. Fr. *pensif.*

Pensille, pencil, orig. a small brush for painting. Fr. *pinceau.*

Perfet, perfect.

Performed, completed. The word has nothing to do with *form,* but is from the same root as Fr. *fournir.*

Persecute, Persequute, to, to follow up.

Perseuer, to, to persevere.

Phisick (books), medical works.

Phrensie, frenzy, madness. Fr. *frénésie*.

Pike (a thank), to, to be a pickthank, a flatterer. Wright quotes from Fairfax : ' A flatterer, a pickthank, and a lyer.'

Plat, plot (of ground). 2 Kings ix. 26.

Platte fourme, platform, in its literal sense of ' ground plan.'

Plotte. See **Plat**.

Pluck away, to, to seize and take away, to remove. Comp. ' pluck up one's courage.'

Plucke backe, to. See the preceding. Used of setting back one who had been promoted.

Policie, device.

Polle, to, to shave (the head), hence to plunder.

Pour, power.

Praye, prey.

Preese, press.

Prescrypt, prescribed.

Presentlye, in one's presence; at the present time.

Pretended, Pretensed, intended, designed.

Preuented, anticipated, forestalled.

Preuy, Preuelye, privy, privily.

Pristynate, original, ancient.

Procure, to, to take means for, to manage.

Proffe, proof.

Propriety, property.

Prouoke, to, to challenge, invite.

Prouost, provost, the head of a college, and the like. Lat. *praepositus*. For the office of provost see *The Inmates of Beverley Minster*, by Arthur Leach, F.S.A., p. 11.

Pryestes, priests.

Puisaunce, power. Fr. *puissance*.

Pulleyne, poultry. Comp. ' pullet '

and Fr. *poule*. Wright quotes Beaumont and Fletcher's *Scornful Lady*, v. 2 : ' She .. knows how pullen should be cramm'd.'

Puppettes, dolls. Fr. *poupées*.

Pusyaunce. See **Puisaunce**.

Pylled, plundered. For *to pill*, sometimes confused with *peel*, comp. Fr. *piller*.

Q.

Quayled, quelled. ' Quell ' and ' quail ' are related to each other as active (or causal) and passive.

Quicke, living.

Quod, quoth, saith. One of More's Dialogues was popularly known as *Quod he and Quod I*, from the frequent recurrence in it of those two sentences. See Bridgett's *Life*, p. 283.

Quyte, quit, discharged.

Qweynes, queans, immodest women. Not necessarily in a bad sense by derivation, being the same word as ' queens.'

R.

Rampiere, to, to fortify. The forms ' rampire ' and ' ramper ' are closely akin to Fr. *remparer* (Lat. *re-em-parare*). Hence the modern ' rampart.'

Rauin, to, to devour, plunder. Comp. Gen. xlix. 27 : ' Benjamin shall ravin as a wolf.'

Rauyne, rapine. See the preceding.

Recule, to, to recoil, give ground. Fr. *reculer*.

Reherse, to, to repeat, declare. Said to mean originally to drag the ' herse ' (harrow) again over the same ground.

Rehersynge, repeating. Used (p. 59) to translate the Lat. *repetunt.*

Reken, to, to reckon.

Renowme, renown. The old spelling is more agreeable to the derivation. Fr. *renom.*

Repriued, reprieved.

Retaynoure, retainer.

Reuerende, used (p. 110) as a noun, ' reverence,' if the spelling be correct.

Rewle, rule.

Rides. See p. 219 *n.*

Rounding, used (p. 74) for the mode of cropping the hair of bondmen, ' rownded a lytle aboue the eeres' (p. 68).

Rowme, room, position. St. Luke xiv. 8.

Rubbers, robbers.

Russhe-bucklers. See p. 146 *n.*

Ryffe, rife.

S.

Sad, serious. Lit. sated ; and so heavy, oppressive.

Saffe, safe.

Saintuaries, sanctuaries.

Sauffe. See **Saffe.** Fr. *sauf.*

Scasely, scarcely. The *r* is wanting also in the cognate Spanish *escaso.*

Sciences, used (p. 140) in the sense of arts.

Sclaunderer, slanderer. Fr. *esclandre,* a scandal ; Lat. *scandalum.* The *l* is an interpolation.

Scoupe, scope. Joined (p. 63) with ' license.' The original idea of ' mark to aim at ' passes into that of space (as in ' scope-law,' a distance allowed to one

running a race), and so into that of liberty.

Seal, to, to assure by written contract.

Seilie, Sely, Seely, silly, simple, innocent. Germ. *selig,* 'blessed'; with which compare the history of the Fr. *benêt* and the Greek *euēthes.*

Seke (to be to), to be wanting in, to be at a loss.

Selfe (in common use not joined to its pronoun, as 'it selfe.' Sometimes used as a noun, as 'the owne selfe ').

Sene (to be well), in anything, is to be well prepared, skilful in it. Comp. *Taming of the Shrew,* i. 2 : 'A schoolmaster | well seen in music.'

Separrtion, separation.

Sethe, to, to boil.

Seuerall, separate. Lat. *separatus.* For the change of *pa* to *v* comp. *Sèvre* (the river), from *Separis.*

Sowere, sure.

Shamefastnes, a sense of what is becoming (p. 177), used to translate Lat. *pudor.* ' Shamefacedness ' is a modern corruption. Trench compares ' rootfast,' ' rockfast,' &c.

Sheathes (p. 179), apparently in the sense of 'outsides,' ' cases.' Comp. Daniel vii. 15, where ' body ' is an equivalent for ' sheath '

Sheffe, sheaf.

Shilter, shelter. The *i* preserves the connexion with ' shield.'

Shrewedlye, cursedly, maliciously, and so roughly. *Hen. VIII,* v. 2 : 'Do my lord of Canterbury a shrewd turn, and he is your friend for ever.'

Shyere, shire.

Sickerly, surely. Germ. *sicherlich.*

Sike, to, to seek.

Siriens, Syrians.

Skante, scarcely.

Skape, to, to escape.

Skarsenes, scarcity.

Skaselie. See **Scasely.**

Skeant. See **Skante.**

Skyrnyshe, skirmish.

Sleane, slain.

Sloughishnes, sluggishness.

Slowth, sloth, slowness.

Smacke, a taste.

Smugge, neat, trim, used disparagingly, p. 11, in the same collocation as by Davies, *Scourge of Folly* (1611) : ' And makes the same to look most smooth and smugge.' Comp. the German *schmuck.*

Socour, to, to succour.

Sodde, sodden. See **to Sethe.**

Sodeyne, sudden.

Softely, gently, quietly. Wright quotes from Palsgrave : ' Soft, softe, the chylde is aslepe.'

Solas, solace.

Solempne, solemn, customary. The form is found in Chaucer.

Sollicitour, suitor.

Som, Some, sum.

Soone, sun.

Sorte (a good), a good number or quantity. 'We were set upon | By a sort of country fellows.'— Ben Jonson, *Tale of a Tub,* ii. 2.

Speces, spices. Lat. *species.*

Spill, to, to spoil, ruin. Halliwell quotes from *MS. Cantab.* Ff. ii. 38 : ' Allas ! sche seyde, now am y spylte.'

States, men of high rank, like Estates. St. Mark vi. 21 : 'Herod made a supper to his chief estates.'

Stiele, to, to steal.

Stomackes, tempers, inclinations, *Hen. V,* iv. 3 : ' Which have no stomach to this fight.'

Stonde, to, to stand.

Stonyshe, stony, hard.

Storries, storeys.

Straung, strange.

Streken, stricken.

Stroke (to bear the). See p. 104 *n.*

Stuffe, matter. *The Tempest,* ii. 1 : 'What stuff is this ? How say you ?'

Sturre, to, to stir.

Stynte, to, to stint.

Subiect, placed under. Lat. *subiectus.*

Subleuation, elevation. Applied (p. xcix) to the latitude of a place measured from the equator.

Suete, suit.

Sueters, suitors.

Surmount, to, to mount up, to swell.

Swing (to bear the), to have the chief influence. Halliwell quotes from Hall : ' Whiche in those quarters bare great swynge.' Comp. also the expression ' to give full swing to '; and the note on ' bearing the stroke,' p. 104.

Sylie. See **Seilie.**

T.

Thadmynystratyon, the administration. The definite article is often blended thus with nouns beginning with vowels.

The (sometimes), thee.

The (p. 221), they.

Then, than.

There selfes, themselves. See **Self.**

Throng, crowded.

Throughly, thoroughly.

Tiole (p. 282), a misprint for toil.

To, too.

Toolynge, toiling.

Torues, turves, pl. of turf.

Trade, habit or custom. Lit. 'a beaten path,' from 'tread.' Skeat compares 'trade-wind,' a wind that blows habitually in one direction.

Traditions, rules delivered, or handed down.

Traine, Trayne, contrivance. Halliwell quotes from *MS. Cantab.* Ff. ii. 38 : 'Have slayne Syr Roger be some trayne.'

Trauayle, travail, labour.

Trime, to, to trim.

Trippe, trip, a fault.

Troughewyse, troughwise, like a trough.

Tuition, keeping, guardianship. Comp. Fr. *tuteur*.

V.

Valiaunt, strong. Fr. *vaillant*.

Vewere, viewer, contemplator.

Vielnes, vileness, worthlessness.

Vmpier, umpire, arbiter.

Vnconuenient, inconvenient, unfitting. Comp. Eph. v. 4 : 'Nor foolish talking, nor jesting, which are not convenient.'

Vndoynge, undoing, destruction.

Vnhonest, dishonourable.

Vnpleasaunt, displeasing, disagreeable.

Vnquiete, to, to disquiet, to disturb.

Vnthyfty (p. 149), a misprint in the original for 'vnthryfty.'

Vntyed, untied, set free.

Vnweldye, unwieldly, awkward, unmanageable. Used of impotent persons, and of armour.

Vplandishe, rustic, countryfied.

Wright quotes from *Tales and Quicke Answers*: 'an uplandisshe man nourysshed in the woodes.'

Vpryght, right. Comp. 'uprightness,' in the sense of 'rectitude.'

Vred, used. We retain the compound 'inured.' 'Ure' is not from the same root as 'use,' but is akin to the French *œuvre*, Lat. *opera*, as in *manœuvre*.

Vtter, to, to publish. We speak of 'uttering counterfeit coin.'

W.

Wageyn, waggon, or wain.

Wantonly, unrestrainedly.

Ware, merchandise ; then, like 'gear,' of other matters.

Wayde, weighed.

Wayinge, weighing.

Weale publyque, commonwealth.

Wealthely, well.

Weldynge, wielding.

Well, will.

Well a worthe. See p. 227 *n*.

Weydes, weeds.

Whether, whither.

Whiles, at times.

Whomewyth, with whom. Comp. Lat. *quibuscum*.

Wieles, wiles.

Wipe beside, to. See p. 245 *n*.

Woll, wool.

Wonders, used adverbially, as in 'wonders gladde.'

Wonte, accustomed. Originally past ptcp. of *won* 'to dwell' (Germ. *wohnen*), from which Chaucer uses *woning*.

Wordle, a variety, occurring several times (as at pp. 184, 306) for world. Stratmann gives the form 'wordle' from William de Shoreham, circ. 1315, and from various other early writers.

Wower, wooer.

Wrie, to, to twist, pervert. Comp.
'awry.'

Wrythen, twisted.

Wysefooles, an oxymoron, like
morosophi, for persons wise in
their own conceits.

Wyttelye, wisely.

Y.

Ydill, idle.

Yelde, to, to yield.

Yeopardye. See Ieopardye.

Yle, isle. The *s* is an intrusion

Ynowe, enough. Germ. *genug*.

Yocke, yoke.

INDEX

—◆—

A.

Abraxa, old name of Utopia, xliii, 118; meaning of name, 118 *n.*

Achoriens, the, 85.

Act of Parliament, on enclosures, xxxvi.

Adam, of St. Victor, hymn of, 76-7.

Adamus (Ademus), new name of the 'Prince' in Utopia, 148.

Adultery, 229, 231.

Advertising, abuse of, lxiv.

Aegidius, Petrus. *See* Giles, Peter.

Agnadello, battle of, xxxii.

Agriculture, carefully taught in Utopia, 139.

Alaopolitanes, the, 244.

Aldus, Manutius, books printed by, 216; death of, 218 *n.*

Alphabet, the Utopian, xciv *n.*; facsimile of, facing p. xciv.

Alsop, Bernard, lxxiv.

Alternation, of town and country life, beneficial, lxii, 121.

Amaurote, chief city of Utopia, xxx, xliv, xlv, 6, 119, 126, 177; origin of name, 126 *n.*; described, 127; council of, 169.

Ambuscades, 260.

Anaxagoras, saying of, 28 *n.*

Anemolians, the, 177.

Anemolius, poet laureate of Utopia, xciii.

Antwerp, description of, xxix; cathedral of, 25.

Anyder, river of Amaurote, 6; meaning of name, 127 *n.*; described, 127.

Aragon, king of, 83.

Arber, Professor, x, lxiv *n.*, lxxv, lxxvi *n.*

Archbold, W. A. J., xxv *n.*, 41 *n.*

Archery, practice of, 262 *n.*

Aristophanes, 216.

Aristotle, 215.

Armies, standing, evil of, 49.

Arms, of the English soldiers, 262 *n.*

Arnold, George, xviii *n.*

Arthur, Prince of Wales, xxxiii.

Asceticism, how far meritorious, 210.

Ascham, Roger, 25 *n.*, 27 *n.*

Astrology, More's contempt for, 186.

Augustine, St., the *De Civitate Dei* of, xx, xlix, 268 *n.*, 293 *n.*; More lectures on it, xlviii, lxxxix *n.*; outline of the work, xlix; its theory of bondage, l.

Augustus, story of, 177 *n.*

B.

Bacon, Sir Francis, liv; advises James I as to Sutton's endowment, lix; his *New Atlantis*, lx.

Bainham, James, case of, 273 *n.*

z

THE END.

𝔒𝔵𝔣𝔬𝔯𝔡

PRINTED AT THE CLARENDON PRESS

BY HORACE HART, PRINTER TO THE UNIVERSITY